# TACHEOMETRIC TABLES
# FOR THE METRIC USER

# TACHEOMETRIC
# TABLES
## FOR THE METRIC USER

By

D. T. F. MUNSEY, M.A., F.R.I.C.S.

*Principal Lecturer in Surveying, Royal Military College of Science,
Shrivenham, Berkshire*

TECHNICAL PRESS

LONDON

First Published 1971

SBN 291 39336 5

Table 1 calculated and film-set by
Computaprint Limited, London

Made and printed by offset in Great Britain by
William Clowes and Sons, Limited
London, Beccles and Colchester

# Preface

It is now nearly forty years since the well-known set of Tacheometric Tables devised by the late Professor F. A. Redmond were first published. Yet some words the Professor used in his Preface to those tables are as relevant today, when the United Kingdom is about to change over from the Imperial to the Metric system of mensuration, as they were when he wrote them in 1931. 'Tacheometric tables', he wrote, 'to be really satisfactory should possess the following qualities: they should be reasonably compact . . . conveniently arranged, accurate and, above all, capable of furnishing at sight the horizontal and vertical components represented by the terms $G \cos^2 V$ and $G \sin V \cos V$ not only for all staff-intercepts within the normal range of an ordinary tacheometer, but for all vertical angles which . . . we are compelled at one time or another to employ in the field.'

How well he succeeded in his aim to produce a satisfactory set of tables is shown by the fact that his original tables have been reprinted four times and are still, I am told, selling well at the time of writing.

Professor Redmond designed the layout of his tables for the reduction of staff-intercepts which have been recorded to 0·01 ft. His tables can themselves be used as they stand for the reduction of metric intercepts but, not having been arranged for that purpose, they are unnecessarily bulky. Since the metric system lends itself to a relatively simpler presentation of useful tacheometric tables, it has been thought better, while building on the foundations so ably laid by Professor Redmond, to present a somewhat differently arranged set of tables for the convenience of surveyors in countries where the metric system is employed.

Special points to be noted about the range and scope of the new tables are as follows:

## Main Tables (Table I)

(i) The range of vertical angles covered is from 0° 10' to 10° 00' at 10' intervals, and from 10° 20' to 20° 00' at 20' intervals. This is virtually identical with the range of the original Table I compiled by Redmond save that the smaller range now required in the integral values of G (see below) allows a 10' interval to be introduced up to 10° 00', instead of the 20' interval throughout which was necessary to keep the Redmond tables reasonably compact.

(ii) The range of G (the staff-intercept times the multiplying constant) covered in these metric Tables is from 10 to 210, as against Redmond's range of 50 to 850. Beyond 150–200 metres the accuracy of reading the staff falls off rapidly with increasing distance. In addition, at these distances observations become uneconomic because of difficulties of communication between observer and staff-holder, and of taking readings if the atmosphere is at all unsteady.

(iii) Limiting the maximum value of G to 210 allows the entries for each vertical angle to appear on a single page, instead of on four separate pages in the Redmond tables. This is an important benefit from the user's point of view, which also allows Table I to be restricted to 90 pages in place of Redmond's 240.

(iv) Integral intervals in G do, however, call for some interpolation if the metric intercepts are recorded to millimetres. If the multiplying constant is 100 (as is usually the case) and if the intercept is given to 0·001 m, then G is known to 0·1 m. It would clearly not be possible to produce a compact set of tables with a 0·1 interval in G, so some interpolation is inevitable. In the majority of cases, where the vertical angle is less than (say) 5°, this interpolation for the horizontal and vertical components involves no more than cursory inspection. With larger angles only the vertical component requires systematic interpolation, as will appear from examples given in the explanatory Introduction.

(v) Except for values of the horizontal component exceeding 100, both components are tabulated to two decimal places. This means that the vertical component cannot be abstracted to better than a centimetre (0·01 m) even when it has been possible at the shorter distances to estimate each staff reading to the millimetre. At first sight, a third decimal place might appear to be justified; but when all sources of error are taken into consideration, it is only at close range that the standard error of the computed difference in height between the instrument and staff stations is appreciably less than 10 mm. Indeed, tacheometric methods are rarely used to achieve millimetric accuracy in spot levels. It was therefore felt that the greater clarity of presentation resulting from the omission of the third decimal place outweighed the occasional need for greater accuracy in spot levels at short range.

Table I was calculated by computer, the typographically formatted data being transferred to a magnetic tape, which in turn was used to drive a photo-typesetter. This photo-typesetter itself incorporated a special-purpose computer which set the pages of data on to photographic film. From this film the table was printed by standard photo-litho offset methods.

## Auxiliary Tables (Table II)

These tables fulfil the same function as did Tables II and III in the Redmond tables, namely, to fill in gaps left in Table I, and to cover vertical angles from 20° to 30°. Table II reduces observations taken with vertical angles 10° 10', 10° 30', 10° 50', etc., up to 19° 50', and from 20° 10' to 30° 00' at 10' intervals. For each vertical angle the horizontal and vertical components are tabulated for values of G at intervals of 10 from 10 to 100.

Table II was computed on a hand calculating machine, carefully checked, and filmset in the ordinary way.

## Acknowledgement

The Author is grateful to his colleague Mr. K. T. Pugh, of the Royal Military College of Science, Shrivenham, for fruitful discussions on practical aspects of tacheometry, and for the fair drawing of the diagram in the Introduction. He wishes to thank also Mrs. F. A. Redmond for permitting this adaptation, for the convenience of those using the metric system, of her late husband's simple method of tabulating the horizontal and vertical components in terms of 'even' vertical angles.

*Royal Military College of Science*        D.T.F.M.
*Shrivenham*

# Introduction

The diagram opposite shows the situation when an inclined sight is being taken with a theodolite whose internal-focusing telescope is so designed that the additive constant is negligible. The staff is held vertically on the point Y; and the readings at points A, B and C on the staff are taken with the upper and lower stadia hairs and the middle horizontal hair respectively.

Let the multiplying constant = K (usually 100),
the vertical angle = V,
the intercept on the staff (AB) = s,
the middle-hair reading on the staff = m.

From the diagram,
the effective intercept perpendicular to MC = A'B'
= AB cos V
= s cos V.

Then the slant distance MC = **Ks cos V**,
the horizontal component MY' = **Ks cos² V**,
the vertical component CY' = **Ks cos V sin V**.

Redmond denoted the expression Ks as the generating number **G**, and this notation is followed in these new tables. Thus, the horizontal component **D** is calculated from the expression *G cos² V*, and the vertical component **H** from the expression *G cos V sin V*.

The difference of level between X and Y can be seen from the diagram to be MX + CY' − CY. In other words, it is **the height of the instrument above the ground-mark at X + H − m**. If the vertical angle is an angle of *depression* instead of the angle of elevation shown in the diagram, the sign of the vertical component in the expression above will become *negative*.

## Examples of the Use of the Tables
### Table I

1. For integral values of G from 10 to 210, D and H are extracted directly from the Tables.

2. If the metric intercept is recorded to the millimetre and the multiplying constant is 100, G will be known to 0·1 m. Then the values of D and H require interpolation. But D is wanted to only one decimal place and may so be obtained by simple inspection. H may be treated in a similar manner for the smaller vertical angles; otherwise its value is derived by addition, the decimal point being shifted two places to the left in order to obtain the value of H corresponding to the tenths in G.

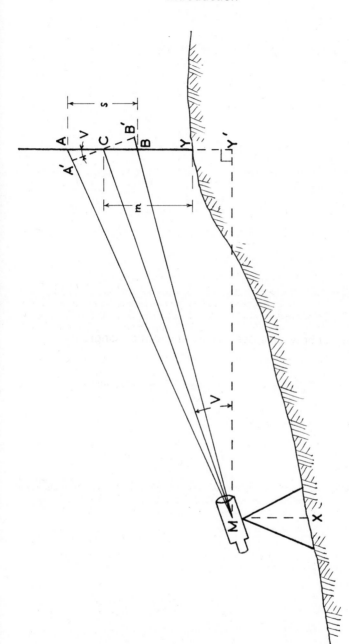

TAKING AN INCLINED SIGHT TO A VERTICAL STAFF

Three examples will make this clear:

(a) Let V = 4° 40′ and G = 89·4.
By inspection of the entries corresponding to G = 89 and G = 90, plainly D = 88·8 and H = 7·25.

(b) Let V = 9° 30′ and G = 71·8.
Clearly D = 69·8 by inspection, as in (a) above. H is obtained as follows:

|  | G | H |
|---|---|---|
| From the tables | 71 | 11·56 |
| From G = 80 | 0·8 | 0·13 |
| Adding | 71·8 | 11·69 |

(c) Let V = 17° 00′ and G = 117·4.
By inspection again, D = 107·4. H is obtained as follows:

|  | G | H |
|---|---|---|
| From the tables | 117 | 32·71 |
| From G = 40 | 0·4 | 0·11 |
| Adding | 117·4 | 32·82 |

3. At distances exceeding 210 m the intercept can only, under average conditions, be read to 0·01 m. Values of G are therefore integral if the multiplying constant is 100. The corresponding values of D and H are then found by simple addition. For instance:

Let V = 3° 10′ and G = 245.

|  | G | D | H |
|---|---|---|---|
| From the tables | 200 | 199·4 | 11·03 |
|  | 45 | 44·9 | 2·48 |
| Adding | 245 | 244 | 13·51 |

## Table II

For those occasional observations which cannot be reduced from Table I, D and H may be calculated from this table, either directly by means of a calculating machine or by addition. For example:

Let V = 22° 20′ and G = 196.

By machine, using the values of D and H for G = 100,
D = 85·56 × 1·96 = 167·7, and H = 35·149 × 1·96 = 68·89;
or from the tabular entries:

|  | G | D | H |
|---|---|---|---|
|  | 100 | 85·56 | 35·15 |
|  | 90 | 77·00 | 31·63 |
| From G = 60 | 6 | 5·13 | 2·11 |
| Adding | 196 | 167·7 | 68·89 |

# TABLE I

Giving the Values of D and H
at 10′ intervals of V
from 0° 10′ to 10° 00′
and at 20′ intervals of V
from 10° 20′ to 20° 00′

TABLE I     **0° 10′**

| G | D | H | G | D | H | G | D | H | G | D | H |
|---|---|---|---|---|---|---|---|---|---|---|---|
| 10 | 10·00 | 0·03 | 60 | 60·00 | 0·17 | 110 | 110·0 | 0·32 | 160 | 160·0 | 0·47 |
| 11 | 11·00 | 0·03 | 61 | 61·00 | 0·18 | 111 | 111·0 | 0·32 | 161 | 161·0 | 0·47 |
| 12 | 12·00 | 0·03 | 62 | 62·00 | 0·18 | 112 | 112·0 | 0·33 | 162 | 162·0 | 0·47 |
| 13 | 13·00 | 0·04 | 63 | 63·00 | 0·18 | 113 | 113·0 | 0·33 | 163 | 163·0 | 0·47 |
| 14 | 14·00 | 0·04 | 64 | 64·00 | 0·19 | 114 | 114·0 | 0·33 | 164 | 164·0 | 0·48 |
| 15 | 15·00 | 0·04 | 65 | 65·00 | 0·19 | 115 | 115·0 | 0·33 | 165 | 165·0 | 0·48 |
| 16 | 16·00 | 0·05 | 66 | 66·00 | 0·19 | 116 | 116·0 | 0·34 | 166 | 166·0 | 0·48 |
| 17 | 17·00 | 0·05 | 67 | 67·00 | 0·19 | 117 | 117·0 | 0·34 | 167 | 167·0 | 0·49 |
| 18 | 18·00 | 0·05 | 68 | 68·00 | 0·20 | 118 | 118·0 | 0·34 | 168 | 168·0 | 0·49 |
| 19 | 19·00 | 0·06 | 69 | 69·00 | 0·20 | 119 | 119·0 | 0·35 | 169 | 169·0 | 0·49 |
| 20 | 20·00 | 0·06 | 70 | 70·00 | 0·20 | 120 | 120·0 | 0·35 | 170 | 170·0 | 0·49 |
| 21 | 21·00 | 0·06 | 71 | 71·00 | 0·21 | 121 | 121·0 | 0·35 | 171 | 171·0 | 0·50 |
| 22 | 22·00 | 0·06 | 72 | 72·00 | 0·21 | 122 | 122·0 | 0·35 | 172 | 172·0 | 0·50 |
| 23 | 23·00 | 0·07 | 73 | 73·00 | 0·21 | 123 | 123·0 | 0·36 | 173 | 173·0 | 0·50 |
| 24 | 24·00 | 0·07 | 74 | 74·00 | 0·22 | 124 | 124·0 | 0·36 | 174 | 174·0 | 0·51 |
| 25 | 25·00 | 0·07 | 75 | 75·00 | 0·22 | 125 | 125·0 | 0·36 | 175 | 175·0 | 0·51 |
| 26 | 26·00 | 0·08 | 76 | 76·00 | 0·22 | 126 | 126·0 | 0·37 | 176 | 176·0 | 0·51 |
| 27 | 27·00 | 0·08 | 77 | 77·00 | 0·22 | 127 | 127·0 | 0·37 | 177 | 177·0 | 0·51 |
| 28 | 28·00 | 0·08 | 78 | 78·00 | 0·23 | 128 | 128·0 | 0·37 | 178 | 178·0 | 0·52 |
| 29 | 29·00 | 0·08 | 79 | 79·00 | 0·23 | 129 | 129·0 | 0·38 | 179 | 179·0 | 0·52 |
| 30 | 30·00 | 0·09 | 80 | 80·00 | 0·23 | 130 | 130·0 | 0·38 | 180 | 180·0 | 0·52 |
| 31 | 31·00 | 0·09 | 81 | 81·00 | 0·24 | 131 | 131·0 | 0·38 | 181 | 181·0 | 0·53 |
| 32 | 32·00 | 0·09 | 82 | 82·00 | 0·24 | 132 | 132·0 | 0·38 | 182 | 182·0 | 0·53 |
| 33 | 33·00 | 0·10 | 83 | 83·00 | 0·24 | 133 | 133·0 | 0·39 | 183 | 183·0 | 0·53 |
| 34 | 34·00 | 0·10 | 84 | 84·00 | 0·24 | 134 | 134·0 | 0·39 | 184 | 184·0 | 0·54 |
| 35 | 35·00 | 0·10 | 85 | 85·00 | 0·25 | 135 | 135·0 | 0·39 | 185 | 185·0 | 0·54 |
| 36 | 36·00 | 0·10 | 86 | 86·00 | 0·25 | 136 | 136·0 | 0·40 | 186 | 186·0 | 0·54 |
| 37 | 37·00 | 0·11 | 87 | 87·00 | 0·25 | 137 | 137·0 | 0·40 | 187 | 187·0 | 0·54 |
| 38 | 38·00 | 0·11 | 88 | 88·00 | 0·26 | 138 | 138·0 | 0·40 | 188 | 188·0 | 0·55 |
| 39 | 39·00 | 0·11 | 89 | 89·00 | 0·26 | 139 | 139·0 | 0·40 | 189 | 189·0 | 0·55 |
| 40 | 40·00 | 0·12 | 90 | 90·00 | 0·26 | 140 | 140·0 | 0·41 | 190 | 190·0 | 0·55 |
| 41 | 41·00 | 0·12 | 91 | 91·00 | 0·26 | 141 | 141·0 | 0·41 | 191 | 191·0 | 0·56 |
| 42 | 42·00 | 0·12 | 92 | 92·00 | 0·27 | 142 | 142·0 | 0·41 | 192 | 192·0 | 0·56 |
| 43 | 43·00 | 0·13 | 93 | 93·00 | 0·27 | 143 | 143·0 | 0·42 | 193 | 193·0 | 0·56 |
| 44 | 44·00 | 0·13 | 94 | 94·00 | 0·27 | 144 | 144·0 | 0·42 | 194 | 194·0 | 0·56 |
| 45 | 45·00 | 0·13 | 95 | 95·00 | 0·28 | 145 | 145·0 | 0·42 | 195 | 195·0 | 0·57 |
| 46 | 46·00 | 0·13 | 96 | 96·00 | 0·28 | 146 | 146·0 | 0·42 | 196 | 196·0 | 0·57 |
| 47 | 47·00 | 0·14 | 97 | 97·00 | 0·28 | 147 | 147·0 | 0·43 | 197 | 197·0 | 0·57 |
| 48 | 48·00 | 0·14 | 98 | 98·00 | 0·28 | 148 | 148·0 | 0·43 | 198 | 198·0 | 0·58 |
| 49 | 49·00 | 0·14 | 99 | 99·00 | 0·29 | 149 | 149·0 | 0·43 | 199 | 199·0 | 0·58 |
| 50 | 50·00 | 0·15 | 100 | 100·0 | 0·29 | 150 | 150·0 | 0·44 | 200 | 200·0 | 0·58 |
| 51 | 51·00 | 0·15 | 101 | 101·0 | 0·29 | 151 | 151·0 | 0·44 | 201 | 201·0 | 0·58 |
| 52 | 52·00 | 0·15 | 102 | 102·0 | 0·30 | 152 | 152·0 | 0·44 | 202 | 202·0 | 0·59 |
| 53 | 53·00 | 0·15 | 103 | 103·0 | 0·30 | 153 | 153·0 | 0·44 | 203 | 203·0 | 0·59 |
| 54 | 54·00 | 0·16 | 104 | 104·0 | 0·30 | 154 | 154·0 | 0·45 | 204 | 204·0 | 0·59 |
| 55 | 55·00 | 0·16 | 105 | 105·0 | 0·31 | 155 | 155·0 | 0·45 | 205 | 205·0 | 0·60 |
| 56 | 56·00 | 0·16 | 106 | 106·0 | 0·31 | 156 | 156·0 | 0·45 | 206 | 206·0 | 0·60 |
| 57 | 57·00 | 0·17 | 107 | 107·0 | 0·31 | 157 | 157·0 | 0·46 | 207 | 207·0 | 0·60 |
| 58 | 58·00 | 0·17 | 108 | 108·0 | 0·31 | 158 | 158·0 | 0·46 | 208 | 208·0 | 0·60 |
| 59 | 59·00 | 0·17 | 109 | 109·0 | 0·32 | 159 | 159·0 | 0·46 | 209 | 209·0 | 0·61 |
| 60 | 60·00 | 0·17 | 110 | 110·0 | 0·32 | 160 | 160·0 | 0·47 | 210 | 210·0 | 0·61 |

TABLE I

| G | D | H | G | D | H | G | D | H | G | D | H |
|---|---|---|---|---|---|---|---|---|---|---|---|
| 10 | 10·00 | 0·06 | 60 | 60·00 | 0·35 | 110 | 110·0 | 0·64 | 160 | 160·0 | 0·93 |
| 11 | 11·00 | 0·06 | 61 | 61·00 | 0·35 | 111 | 111·0 | 0·65 | 161 | 161·0 | 0·94 |
| 12 | 12·00 | 0·07 | 62 | 62·00 | 0·36 | 112 | 112·0 | 0·65 | 162 | 162·0 | 0·94 |
| 13 | 13·00 | 0·08 | 63 | 63·00 | 0·37 | 113 | 113·0 | 0·66 | 163 | 163·0 | 0·95 |
| 14 | 14·00 | 0·08 | 64 | 64·00 | 0·37 | 114 | 114·0 | 0·66 | 164 | 164·0 | 0·95 |
| 15 | 15·00 | 0·09 | 65 | 65·00 | 0·38 | 115 | 115·0 | 0·67 | 165 | 165·0 | 0·96 |
| 16 | 16·00 | 0·09 | 66 | 66·00 | 0·38 | 116 | 116·0 | 0·67 | 166 | 166·0 | 0·97 |
| 17 | 17·00 | 0·10 | 67 | 67·00 | 0·39 | 117 | 117·0 | 0·68 | 167 | 167·0 | 0·97 |
| 18 | 18·00 | 0·10 | 68 | 68·00 | 0·40 | 118 | 118·0 | 0·69 | 168 | 168·0 | 0·98 |
| 19 | 19·00 | 0·11 | 69 | 69·00 | 0·40 | 119 | 119·0 | 0·69 | 169 | 169·0 | 0·98 |
| 20 | 20·00 | 0·12 | 70 | 70·00 | 0·41 | 120 | 120·0 | 0·70 | 170 | 170·0 | 0·99 |
| 21 | 21·00 | 0·12 | 71 | 71·00 | 0·41 | 121 | 121·0 | 0·70 | 171 | 171·0 | 0·99 |
| 22 | 22·00 | 0·13 | 72 | 72·00 | 0·42 | 122 | 122·0 | 0·71 | 172 | 172·0 | 1·00 |
| 23 | 23·00 | 0·13 | 73 | 73·00 | 0·42 | 123 | 123·0 | 0·72 | 173 | 173·0 | 1·01 |
| 24 | 24·00 | 0·14 | 74 | 74·00 | 0·43 | 124 | 124·0 | 0·72 | 174 | 174·0 | 1·01 |
| 25 | 25·00 | 0·15 | 75 | 75·00 | 0·44 | 125 | 125·0 | 0·73 | 175 | 175·0 | 1·02 |
| 26 | 26·00 | 0·15 | 76 | 76·00 | 0·44 | 126 | 126·0 | 0·73 | 176 | 176·0 | 1·02 |
| 27 | 27·00 | 0·16 | 77 | 77·00 | 0·45 | 127 | 127·0 | 0·74 | 177 | 177·0 | 1·03 |
| 28 | 28·00 | 0·16 | 78 | 78·00 | 0·45 | 128 | 128·0 | 0·74 | 178 | 178·0 | 1·04 |
| 29 | 29·00 | 0·17 | 79 | 79·00 | 0·46 | 129 | 129·0 | 0·75 | 179 | 179·0 | 1·04 |
| 30 | 30·00 | 0·17 | 80 | 80·00 | 0·47 | 130 | 130·0 | 0·76 | 180 | 180·0 | 1·05 |
| 31 | 31·00 | 0·18 | 81 | 81·00 | 0·47 | 131 | 131·0 | 0·76 | 181 | 181·0 | 1·05 |
| 32 | 32·00 | 0·19 | 82 | 82·00 | 0·48 | 132 | 132·0 | 0·77 | 182 | 182·0 | 1·06 |
| 33 | 33·00 | 0·19 | 83 | 83·00 | 0·48 | 133 | 133·0 | 0·77 | 183 | 183·0 | 1·06 |
| 34 | 34·00 | 0·20 | 84 | 84·00 | 0·49 | 134 | 134·0 | 0·78 | 184 | 184·0 | 1·07 |
| 35 | 35·00 | 0·20 | 85 | 85·00 | 0·49 | 135 | 135·0 | 0·79 | 185 | 185·0 | 1·08 |
| 36 | 36·00 | 0·21 | 86 | 86·00 | 0·50 | 136 | 136·0 | 0·79 | 186 | 186·0 | 1·08 |
| 37 | 37·00 | 0·22 | 87 | 87·00 | 0·51 | 137 | 137·0 | 0·80 | 187 | 187·0 | 1·09 |
| 38 | 38·00 | 0·22 | 88 | 88·00 | 0·51 | 138 | 138·0 | 0·80 | 188 | 188·0 | 1·09 |
| 39 | 39·00 | 0·23 | 89 | 89·00 | 0·52 | 139 | 139·0 | 0·81 | 189 | 189·0 | 1·10 |
| 40 | 40·00 | 0·23 | 90 | 90·00 | 0·52 | 140 | 140·0 | 0·81 | 190 | 190·0 | 1·11 |
| 41 | 41·00 | 0·24 | 91 | 91·00 | 0·53 | 141 | 141·0 | 0·82 | 191 | 191·0 | 1·11 |
| 42 | 42·00 | 0·24 | 92 | 92·00 | 0·54 | 142 | 142·0 | 0·83 | 192 | 192·0 | 1·12 |
| 43 | 43·00 | 0·25 | 93 | 93·00 | 0·54 | 143 | 143·0 | 0·83 | 193 | 193·0 | 1·12 |
| 44 | 44·00 | 0·26 | 94 | 94·00 | 0·55 | 144 | 144·0 | 0·84 | 194 | 194·0 | 1·13 |
| 45 | 45·00 | 0·26 | 95 | 95·00 | 0·55 | 145 | 145·0 | 0·84 | 195 | 195·0 | 1·13 |
| 46 | 46·00 | 0·27 | 96 | 96·00 | 0·56 | 146 | 146·0 | 0·85 | 196 | 196·0 | 1·14 |
| 47 | 47·00 | 0·27 | 97 | 97·00 | 0·56 | 147 | 147·0 | 0·86 | 197 | 197·0 | 1·15 |
| 48 | 48·00 | 0·28 | 98 | 98·00 | 0·57 | 148 | 148·0 | 0·86 | 198 | 198·0 | 1·15 |
| 49 | 49·00 | 0·29 | 99 | 99·00 | 0·58 | 149 | 149·0 | 0·87 | 199 | 199·0 | 1·16 |
| 50 | 50·00 | 0·29 | 100 | 100·0 | 0·58 | 150 | 150·0 | 0·87 | 200 | 200·0 | 1·16 |
| 51 | 51·00 | 0·30 | 101 | 101·0 | 0·59 | 151 | 151·0 | 0·88 | 201 | 201·0 | 1·17 |
| 52 | 52·00 | 0·30 | 102 | 102·0 | 0·59 | 152 | 152·0 | 0·88 | 202 | 202·0 | 1·18 |
| 53 | 53·00 | 0·31 | 103 | 103·0 | 0·60 | 153 | 153·0 | 0·89 | 203 | 203·0 | 1·18 |
| 54 | 54·00 | 0·31 | 104 | 104·0 | 0·60 | 154 | 154·0 | 0·90 | 204 | 204·0 | 1·19 |
| 55 | 55·00 | 0·32 | 105 | 105·0 | 0·61 | 155 | 155·0 | 0·90 | 205 | 205·0 | 1·19 |
| 56 | 56·00 | 0·33 | 106 | 106·0 | 0·62 | 156 | 156·0 | 0·91 | 206 | 206·0 | 1·20 |
| 57 | 57·00 | 0·33 | 107 | 107·0 | 0·62 | 157 | 157·0 | 0·91 | 207 | 207·0 | 1·20 |
| 58 | 58·00 | 0·34 | 108 | 108·0 | 0·63 | 158 | 158·0 | 0·92 | 208 | 208·0 | 1·21 |
| 59 | 59·00 | 0·34 | 109 | 109·0 | 0·63 | 159 | 159·0 | 0·92 | 209 | 209·0 | 1·22 |
| 60 | 60·00 | 0·35 | 110 | 110·0 | 0·64 | 160 | 160·0 | 0·93 | 210 | 210·0 | 1·22 |

TABLE I

# 0° 30′

| G | D | H | G | D | H | G | D | H | G | D | H |
|---|---|---|---|---|---|---|---|---|---|---|---|
| 10 | 10·00 | 0·09 | 60 | 60·00 | 0·52 | 110 | 110·0 | 0·96 | 160 | 160·0 | 1·40 |
| 11 | 11·00 | 0·10 | 61 | 61·00 | 0·53 | 111 | 111·0 | 0·97 | 161 | 161·0 | 1·40 |
| 12 | 12·00 | 0·10 | 62 | 62·00 | 0·54 | 112 | 112·0 | 0·98 | 162 | 162·0 | 1·41 |
| 13 | 13·00 | 0·11 | 63 | 63·00 | 0·55 | 113 | 113·0 | 0·99 | 163 | 163·0 | 1·42 |
| 14 | 14·00 | 0·12 | 64 | 64·00 | 0·56 | 114 | 114·0 | 0·99 | 164 | 164·0 | 1·43 |
| 15 | 15·00 | 0·13 | 65 | 64·99 | 0·57 | 115 | 115·0 | 1·00 | 165 | 165·0 | 1·44 |
| 16 | 16·00 | 0·14 | 66 | 65·99 | 0·58 | 116 | 116·0 | 1·01 | 166 | 166·0 | 1·45 |
| 17 | 17·00 | 0·15 | 67 | 66·99 | 0·58 | 117 | 117·0 | 1·02 | 167 | 167·0 | 1·46 |
| 18 | 18·00 | 0·16 | 68 | 67·99 | 0·59 | 118 | 118·0 | 1·03 | 168 | 168·0 | 1·47 |
| 19 | 19·00 | 0·17 | 69 | 68·99 | 0·60 | 119 | 119·0 | 1·04 | 169 | 169·0 | 1·47 |
| 20 | 20·00 | 0·17 | 70 | 69·99 | 0·61 | 120 | 120·0 | 1·05 | 170 | 170·0 | 1·48 |
| 21 | 21·00 | 0·18 | 71 | 70·99 | 0·62 | 121 | 121·0 | 1·06 | 171 | 171·0 | 1·49 |
| 22 | 22·00 | 0·19 | 72 | 71·99 | 0·63 | 122 | 122·0 | 1·06 | 172 | 172·0 | 1·50 |
| 23 | 23·00 | 0·20 | 73 | 72·99 | 0·64 | 123 | 123·0 | 1·07 | 173 | 173·0 | 1·51 |
| 24 | 24·00 | 0·21 | 74 | 73·99 | 0·65 | 124 | 124·0 | 1·08 | 174 | 174·0 | 1·52 |
| 25 | 25·00 | 0·22 | 75 | 74·99 | 0·65 | 125 | 125·0 | 1·09 | 175 | 175·0 | 1·53 |
| 26 | 26·00 | 0·23 | 76 | 75·99 | 0·66 | 126 | 126·0 | 1·10 | 176 | 176·0 | 1·54 |
| 27 | 27·00 | 0·24 | 77 | 76·99 | 0·67 | 127 | 127·0 | 1·11 | 177 | 177·0 | 1·54 |
| 28 | 28·00 | 0·24 | 78 | 77·99 | 0·68 | 128 | 128·0 | 1·12 | 178 | 178·0 | 1·55 |
| 29 | 29·00 | 0·25 | 79 | 78·99 | 0·69 | 129 | 129·0 | 1·13 | 179 | 179·0 | 1·56 |
| 30 | 30·00 | 0·26 | 80 | 79·99 | 0·70 | 130 | 130·0 | 1·13 | 180 | 180·0 | 1·57 |
| 31 | 31·00 | 0·27 | 81 | 80·99 | 0·71 | 131 | 131·0 | 1·14 | 181 | 181·0 | 1·58 |
| 32 | 32·00 | 0·28 | 82 | 81·99 | 0·72 | 132 | 132·0 | 1·15 | 182 | 182·0 | 1·59 |
| 33 | 33·00 | 0·29 | 83 | 82·99 | 0·72 | 133 | 133·0 | 1·16 | 183 | 183·0 | 1·60 |
| 34 | 34·00 | 0·30 | 84 | 83·99 | 0·73 | 134 | 134·0 | 1·17 | 184 | 184·0 | 1·61 |
| 35 | 35·00 | 0·31 | 85 | 84·99 | 0·74 | 135 | 135·0 | 1·18 | 185 | 185·0 | 1·61 |
| 36 | 36·00 | 0·31 | 86 | 85·99 | 0·75 | 136 | 136·0 | 1·19 | 186 | 186·0 | 1·62 |
| 37 | 37·00 | 0·32 | 87 | 86·99 | 0·76 | 137 | 137·0 | 1·20 | 187 | 187·0 | 1·63 |
| 38 | 38·00 | 0·33 | 88 | 87·99 | 0·77 | 138 | 138·0 | 1·20 | 188 | 188·0 | 1·64 |
| 39 | 39·00 | 0·34 | 89 | 88·99 | 0·78 | 139 | 139·0 | 1·21 | 189 | 189·0 | 1·65 |
| 40 | 40·00 | 0·35 | 90 | 89·99 | 0·79 | 140 | 140·0 | 1·22 | 190 | 190·0 | 1·66 |
| 41 | 41·00 | 0·36 | 91 | 90·99 | 0·79 | 141 | 141·0 | 1·23 | 191 | 191·0 | 1·67 |
| 42 | 42·00 | 0·37 | 92 | 91·99 | 0·80 | 142 | 142·0 | 1·24 | 192 | 192·0 | 1·68 |
| 43 | 43·00 | 0·38 | 93 | 92·99 | 0·81 | 143 | 143·0 | 1·25 | 193 | 193·0 | 1·68 |
| 44 | 44·00 | 0·38 | 94 | 93·99 | 0·82 | 144 | 144·0 | 1·26 | 194 | 194·0 | 1·69 |
| 45 | 45·00 | 0·39 | 95 | 94·99 | 0·83 | 145 | 145·0 | 1·27 | 195 | 195·0 | 1·70 |
| 46 | 46·00 | 0·40 | 96 | 95·99 | 0·84 | 146 | 146·0 | 1·27 | 196 | 196·0 | 1·71 |
| 47 | 47·00 | 0·41 | 97 | 96·99 | 0·85 | 147 | 147·0 | 1·28 | 197 | 197·0 | 1·72 |
| 48 | 48·00 | 0·42 | 98 | 97·99 | 0·86 | 148 | 148·0 | 1·29 | 198 | 198·0 | 1·73 |
| 49 | 49·00 | 0·43 | 99 | 98·99 | 0·86 | 149 | 149·0 | 1·30 | 199 | 199·0 | 1·74 |
| 50 | 50·00 | 0·44 | 100 | 99·99 | 0·87 | 150 | 150·0 | 1·31 | 200 | 200·0 | 1·75 |
| 51 | 51·00 | 0·45 | 101 | 101·0 | 0·88 | 151 | 151·0 | 1·32 | 201 | 201·0 | 1·75 |
| 52 | 52·00 | 0·45 | 102 | 102·0 | 0·89 | 152 | 152·0 | 1·33 | 202 | 202·0 | 1·76 |
| 53 | 53·00 | 0·46 | 103 | 103·0 | 0·90 | 153 | 153·0 | 1·34 | 203 | 203·0 | 1·77 |
| 54 | 54·00 | 0·47 | 104 | 104·0 | 0·91 | 154 | 154·0 | 1·34 | 204 | 204·0 | 1·78 |
| 55 | 55·00 | 0·48 | 105 | 105·0 | 0·92 | 155 | 155·0 | 1·35 | 205 | 205·0 | 1·79 |
| 56 | 56·00 | 0·49 | 106 | 106·0 | 0·92 | 156 | 156·0 | 1·36 | 206 | 206·0 | 1·80 |
| 57 | 57·00 | 0·50 | 107 | 107·0 | 0·93 | 157 | 157·0 | 1·37 | 207 | 207·0 | 1·81 |
| 58 | 58·00 | 0·51 | 108 | 108·0 | 0·94 | 158 | 158·0 | 1·38 | 208 | 208·0 | 1·82 |
| 59 | 59·00 | 0·51 | 109 | 109·0 | 0·95 | 159 | 159·0 | 1·39 | 209 | 209·0 | 1·82 |
| 60 | 60·00 | 0·52 | 110 | 110·0 | 0·96 | 160 | 160·0 | 1·40 | 210 | 210·0 | 1·83 |

| G | D | H | G | D | H | G | D | H | G | D | H |
|---|---|---|---|---|---|---|---|---|---|---|---|
| 10 | 10·00 | 0·12 | 60 | 59·99 | 0·70 | 110 | 110·0 | 1·28 | 160 | 160·0 | 1·86 |
| 11 | 11·00 | 0·13 | 61 | 60·99 | 0·71 | 111 | 111·0 | 1·29 | 161 | 161·0 | 1·87 |
| 12 | 12·00 | 0·14 | 62 | 61·99 | 0·72 | 112 | 112·0 | 1·30 | 162 | 162·0 | 1·88 |
| 13 | 13·00 | 0·15 | 63 | 62·99 | 0·73 | 113 | 113·0 | 1·31 | 163 | 163·0 | 1·90 |
| 14 | 14·00 | 0·16 | 64 | 63·99 | 0·74 | 114 | 114·0 | 1·33 | 164 | 164·0 | 1·91 |
| 15 | 15·00 | 0·17 | 65 | 64·99 | 0·76 | 115 | 115·0 | 1·34 | 165 | 165·0 | 1·92 |
| 16 | 16·00 | 0·19 | 66 | 65·99 | 0·77 | 116 | 116·0 | 1·35 | 166 | 166·0 | 1·93 |
| 17 | 17·00 | 0·20 | 67 | 66·99 | 0·78 | 117 | 117·0 | 1·36 | 167 | 167·0 | 1·94 |
| 18 | 18·00 | 0·21 | 68 | 67·99 | 0·79 | 118 | 118·0 | 1·37 | 168 | 168·0 | 1·95 |
| 19 | 19·00 | 0·22 | 69 | 68·99 | 0·80 | 119 | 119·0 | 1·38 | 169 | 169·0 | 1·97 |
| 20 | 20·00 | 0·23 | 70 | 69·99 | 0·81 | 120 | 120·0 | 1·40 | 170 | 170·0 | 1·98 |
| 21 | 21·00 | 0·24 | 71 | 70·99 | 0·83 | 121 | 121·0 | 1·41 | 171 | 171·0 | 1·99 |
| 22 | 22·00 | 0·26 | 72 | 71·99 | 0·84 | 122 | 122·0 | 1·42 | 172 | 172·0 | 2·00 |
| 23 | 23·00 | 0·27 | 73 | 72·99 | 0·85 | 123 | 123·0 | 1·43 | 173 | 173·0 | 2·01 |
| 24 | 24·00 | 0·28 | 74 | 73·99 | 0·86 | 124 | 124·0 | 1·44 | 174 | 174·0 | 2·02 |
| 25 | 25·00 | 0·29 | 75 | 74·99 | 0·87 | 125 | 125·0 | 1·45 | 175 | 175·0 | 2·04 |
| 26 | 26·00 | 0·30 | 76 | 75·99 | 0·88 | 126 | 126·0 | 1·47 | 176 | 176·0 | 2·05 |
| 27 | 27·00 | 0·31 | 77 | 76·99 | 0·90 | 127 | 127·0 | 1·48 | 177 | 177·0 | 2·06 |
| 28 | 28·00 | 0·33 | 78 | 77·99 | 0·91 | 128 | 128·0 | 1·49 | 178 | 178·0 | 2·07 |
| 29 | 29·00 | 0·34 | 79 | 78·99 | 0·92 | 129 | 129·0 | 1·50 | 179 | 179·0 | 2·08 |
| 30 | 30·00 | 0·35 | 80 | 79·99 | 0·93 | 130 | 130·0 | 1·51 | 180 | 180·0 | 2·09 |
| 31 | 31·00 | 0·36 | 81 | 80·99 | 0·94 | 131 | 131·0 | 1·52 | 181 | 181·0 | 2·11 |
| 32 | 32·00 | 0·37 | 82 | 81·99 | 0·95 | 132 | 132·0 | 1·54 | 182 | 182·0 | 2·12 |
| 33 | 33·00 | 0·38 | 83 | 82·99 | 0·97 | 133 | 133·0 | 1·55 | 183 | 183·0 | 2·13 |
| 34 | 34·00 | 0·40 | 84 | 83·99 | 0·98 | 134 | 134·0 | 1·56 | 184 | 184·0 | 2·14 |
| 35 | 35·00 | 0·41 | 85 | 84·99 | 0·99 | 135 | 135·0 | 1·57 | 185 | 185·0 | 2·15 |
| 36 | 36·00 | 0·42 | 86 | 85·99 | 1·00 | 136 | 136·0 | 1·58 | 186 | 186·0 | 2·16 |
| 37 | 36·99 | 0·43 | 87 | 86·99 | 1·01 | 137 | 137·0 | 1·59 | 187 | 187·0 | 2·18 |
| 38 | 37·99 | 0·44 | 88 | 87·99 | 1·02 | 138 | 138·0 | 1·61 | 188 | 188·0 | 2·19 |
| 39 | 38·99 | 0·45 | 89 | 88·99 | 1·04 | 139 | 139·0 | 1·62 | 189 | 189·0 | 2·20 |
| 40 | 39·99 | 0·47 | 90 | 89·99 | 1·05 | 140 | 140·0 | 1·63 | 190 | 190·0 | 2·21 |
| 41 | 40·99 | 0·48 | 91 | 90·99 | 1·06 | 141 | 141·0 | 1·64 | 191 | 191·0 | 2·22 |
| 42 | 41·99 | 0·49 | 92 | 91·99 | 1·07 | 142 | 142·0 | 1·65 | 192 | 192·0 | 2·23 |
| 43 | 42·99 | 0·50 | 93 | 92·99 | 1·08 | 143 | 143·0 | 1·66 | 193 | 193·0 | 2·25 |
| 44 | 43·99 | 0·51 | 94 | 93·99 | 1·09 | 144 | 144·0 | 1·68 | 194 | 194·0 | 2·26 |
| 45 | 44·99 | 0·52 | 95 | 94·99 | 1·11 | 145 | 145·0 | 1·69 | 195 | 195·0 | 2·27 |
| 46 | 45·99 | 0·54 | 96 | 95·99 | 1·12 | 146 | 146·0 | 1·70 | 196 | 196·0 | 2·28 |
| 47 | 46·99 | 0·55 | 97 | 96·99 | 1·13 | 147 | 147·0 | 1·71 | 197 | 197·0 | 2·29 |
| 48 | 47·99 | 0·56 | 98 | 97·99 | 1·14 | 148 | 148·0 | 1·72 | 198 | 198·0 | 2·30 |
| 49 | 48·99 | 0·57 | 99 | 98·99 | 1·15 | 149 | 149·0 | 1·73 | 199 | 199·0 | 2·32 |
| 50 | 49·99 | 0·58 | 100 | 99·99 | 1·16 | 150 | 150·0 | 1·75 | 200 | 200·0 | 2·33 |
| 51 | 50·99 | 0·59 | 101 | 101·0 | 1·18 | 151 | 151·0 | 1·76 | 201 | 201·0 | 2·34 |
| 52 | 51·99 | 0·60 | 102 | 102·0 | 1·19 | 152 | 152·0 | 1·77 | 202 | 202·0 | 2·35 |
| 53 | 52·99 | 0·62 | 103 | 103·0 | 1·20 | 153 | 153·0 | 1·78 | 203 | 203·0 | 2·36 |
| 54 | 53·99 | 0·63 | 104 | 104·0 | 1·21 | 154 | 154·0 | 1·79 | 204 | 204·0 | 2·37 |
| 55 | 54·99 | 0·64 | 105 | 105·0 | 1·22 | 155 | 155·0 | 1·80 | 205 | 205·0 | 2·38 |
| 56 | 55·99 | 0·65 | 106 | 106·0 | 1·23 | 156 | 156·0 | 1·81 | 206 | 206·0 | 2·40 |
| 57 | 56·99 | 0·66 | 107 | 107·0 | 1·24 | 157 | 157·0 | 1·83 | 207 | 207·0 | 2·41 |
| 58 | 57·99 | 0·67 | 108 | 108·0 | 1·26 | 158 | 158·0 | 1·84 | 208 | 208·0 | 2·42 |
| 59 | 58·99 | 0·69 | 109 | 109·0 | 1·27 | 159 | 159·0 | 1·85 | 209 | 209·0 | 2·43 |
| 60 | 59·99 | 0·70 | 110 | 110·0 | 1·28 | 160 | 160·0 | 1·86 | 210 | 210·0 | 2·44 |

TABLE I

# 0° 50′

| G | D | H | G | D | H | G | D | H | G | D | H |
|---|---|---|---|---|---|---|---|---|---|---|---|
| 10 | 10·00 | 0·15 | 60 | 59·99 | 0·87 | 110 | 110·0 | 1·60 | 160 | 160·0 | 2·33 |
| 11 | 11·00 | 0·16 | 61 | 60·99 | 0·89 | 111 | 111·0 | 1·61 | 161 | 161·0 | 2·34 |
| 12 | 12·00 | 0·17 | 62 | 61·99 | 0·90 | 112 | 112·0 | 1·63 | 162 | 162·0 | 2·36 |
| 13 | 13·00 | 0·19 | 63 | 62·99 | 0·92 | 113 | 113·0 | 1·64 | 163 | 163·0 | 2·37 |
| 14 | 14·00 | 0·20 | 64 | 63·99 | 0·93 | 114 | 114·0 | 1·66 | 164 | 164·0 | 2·38 |
| 15 | 15·00 | 0·22 | 65 | 64·99 | 0·95 | 115 | 115·0 | 1·67 | 165 | 165·0 | 2·40 |
| 16 | 16·00 | 0·23 | 66 | 65·99 | 0·96 | 116 | 116·0 | 1·69 | 166 | 166·0 | 2·41 |
| 17 | 17·00 | 0·25 | 67 | 66·99 | 0·97 | 117 | 117·0 | 1·70 | 167 | 167·0 | 2·43 |
| 18 | 18·00 | 0·26 | 68 | 67·99 | 0·99 | 118 | 118·0 | 1·72 | 168 | 168·0 | 2·44 |
| 19 | 19·00 | 0·28 | 69 | 68·99 | 1·00 | 119 | 119·0 | 1·73 | 169 | 169·0 | 2·46 |
| 20 | 20·00 | 0·29 | 70 | 69·99 | 1·02 | 120 | 120·0 | 1·75 | 170 | 170·0 | 2·47 |
| 21 | 21·00 | 0·31 | 71 | 70·98 | 1·03 | 121 | 121·0 | 1·76 | 171 | 171·0 | 2·49 |
| 22 | 22·00 | 0·32 | 72 | 71·98 | 1·05 | 122 | 122·0 | 1·77 | 172 | 172·0 | 2·50 |
| 23 | 23·00 | 0·33 | 73 | 72·98 | 1·06 | 123 | 123·0 | 1·79 | 173 | 173·0 | 2·52 |
| 24 | 23·99 | 0·35 | 74 | 73·98 | 1·08 | 124 | 124·0 | 1·80 | 174 | 174·0 | 2·53 |
| 25 | 24·99 | 0·36 | 75 | 74·98 | 1·09 | 125 | 125·0 | 1·82 | 175 | 175·0 | 2·54 |
| 26 | 25·99 | 0·38 | 76 | 75·98 | 1·11 | 126 | 126·0 | 1·83 | 176 | 176·0 | 2·56 |
| 27 | 26·99 | 0·39 | 77 | 76·98 | 1·12 | 127 | 127·0 | 1·85 | 177 | 177·0 | 2·57 |
| 28 | 27·99 | 0·41 | 78 | 77·98 | 1·13 | 128 | 128·0 | 1·86 | 178 | 178·0 | 2·59 |
| 29 | 28·99 | 0·42 | 79 | 78·98 | 1·15 | 129 | 129·0 | 1·88 | 179 | 179·0 | 2·60 |
| 30 | 29·99 | 0·44 | 80 | 79·98 | 1·16 | 130 | 130·0 | 1·89 | 180 | 180·0 | 2·62 |
| 31 | 30·99 | 0·45 | 81 | 80·98 | 1·18 | 131 | 131·0 | 1·91 | 181 | 181·0 | 2·63 |
| 32 | 31·99 | 0·47 | 82 | 81·98 | 1·19 | 132 | 132·0 | 1·92 | 182 | 182·0 | 2·65 |
| 33 | 32·99 | 0·48 | 83 | 82·98 | 1·21 | 133 | 133·0 | 1·93 | 183 | 183·0 | 2·66 |
| 34 | 33·99 | 0·49 | 84 | 83·98 | 1·22 | 134 | 134·0 | 1·95 | 184 | 184·0 | 2·68 |
| 35 | 34·99 | 0·51 | 85 | 84·98 | 1·24 | 135 | 135·0 | 1·96 | 185 | 185·0 | 2·69 |
| 36 | 35·99 | 0·52 | 86 | 85·98 | 1·25 | 136 | 136·0 | 1·98 | 186 | 186·0 | 2·70 |
| 37 | 36·99 | 0·54 | 87 | 86·98 | 1·27 | 137 | 137·0 | 1·99 | 187 | 187·0 | 2·72 |
| 38 | 37·99 | 0·55 | 88 | 87·98 | 1·28 | 138 | 138·0 | 2·01 | 188 | 188·0 | 2·73 |
| 39 | 38·99 | 0·57 | 89 | 88·98 | 1·29 | 139 | 139·0 | 2·02 | 189 | 189·0 | 2·75 |
| 40 | 39·99 | 0·58 | 90 | 89·98 | 1·31 | 140 | 140·0 | 2·04 | 190 | 190·0 | 2·76 |
| 41 | 40·99 | 0·60 | 91 | 90·98 | 1·32 | 141 | 141·0 | 2·05 | 191 | 191·0 | 2·78 |
| 42 | 41·99 | 0·61 | 92 | 91·98 | 1·34 | 142 | 142·0 | 2·06 | 192 | 192·0 | 2·79 |
| 43 | 42·99 | 0·63 | 93 | 92·98 | 1·35 | 143 | 143·0 | 2·08 | 193 | 193·0 | 2·81 |
| 44 | 43·99 | 0·64 | 94 | 93·98 | 1·37 | 144 | 144·0 | 2·09 | 194 | 194·0 | 2·82 |
| 45 | 44·99 | 0·65 | 95 | 94·98 | 1·38 | 145 | 145·0 | 2·11 | 195 | 195·0 | 2·84 |
| 46 | 45·99 | 0·67 | 96 | 95·98 | 1·40 | 146 | 146·0 | 2·12 | 196 | 196·0 | 2·85 |
| 47 | 46·99 | 0·68 | 97 | 96·98 | 1·41 | 147 | 147·0 | 2·14 | 197 | 197·0 | 2·86 |
| 48 | 47·99 | 0·70 | 98 | 97·98 | 1·43 | 148 | 148·0 | 2·15 | 198 | 198·0 | 2·88 |
| 49 | 48·99 | 0·71 | 99 | 98·98 | 1·44 | 149 | 149·0 | 2·17 | 199 | 199·0 | 2·89 |
| 50 | 49·99 | 0·73 | 100 | 99·98 | 1·45 | 150 | 150·0 | 2·18 | 200 | 200·0 | 2·91 |
| 51 | 50·99 | 0·74 | 101 | 101·0 | 1·47 | 151 | 151·0 | 2·20 | 201 | 201·0 | 2·92 |
| 52 | 51·99 | 0·76 | 102 | 102·0 | 1·48 | 152 | 152·0 | 2·21 | 202 | 202·0 | 2·94 |
| 53 | 52·99 | 0·77 | 103 | 103·0 | 1·50 | 153 | 153·0 | 2·22 | 203 | 203·0 | 2·95 |
| 54 | 53·99 | 0·79 | 104 | 104·0 | 1·51 | 154 | 154·0 | 2·24 | 204 | 204·0 | 2·97 |
| 55 | 54·99 | 0·80 | 105 | 105·0 | 1·53 | 155 | 155·0 | 2·25 | 205 | 205·0 | 2·98 |
| 56 | 55·99 | 0·81 | 106 | 106·0 | 1·54 | 156 | 156·0 | 2·27 | 206 | 206·0 | 3·00 |
| 57 | 56·99 | 0·83 | 107 | 107·0 | 1·56 | 157 | 157·0 | 2·28 | 207 | 207·0 | 3·01 |
| 58 | 57·99 | 0·84 | 108 | 108·0 | 1·57 | 158 | 158·0 | 2·30 | 208 | 208·0 | 3·02 |
| 59 | 58·99 | 0·86 | 109 | 109·0 | 1·59 | 159 | 159·0 | 2·31 | 209 | 209·0 | 3·04 |
| 60 | 59·99 | 0·87 | 110 | 110·0 | 1·60 | 160 | 160·0 | 2·33 | 210 | 210·0 | 3·05 |

**2**

| G | D | H | G | D | H | G | D | H | G | D | H |
|---|---|---|---|---|---|---|---|---|---|---|---|
| 10 | 10·00 | 0·17 | 60 | 59·98 | 1·05 | 110 | 110·0 | 1·92 | 160 | 160·0 | 2·79 |
| 11 | 11·00 | 0·19 | 61 | 60·98 | 1·06 | 111 | 111·0 | 1·94 | 161 | 161·0 | 2·81 |
| 12 | 12·00 | 0·21 | 62 | 61·98 | 1·08 | 112 | 112·0 | 1·95 | 162 | 162·0 | 2·83 |
| 13 | 13·00 | 0·23 | 63 | 62·98 | 1·10 | 113 | 113·0 | 1·97 | 163 | 163·0 | 2·84 |
| 14 | 14·00 | 0·24 | 64 | 63·98 | 1·12 | 114 | 114·0 | 1·99 | 164 | 163·9 | 2·86 |
| 15 | 15·00 | 0·26 | 65 | 64·98 | 1·13 | 115 | 115·0 | 2·01 | 165 | 164·9 | 2·88 |
| 16 | 16·00 | 0·28 | 66 | 65·98 | 1·15 | 116 | 116·0 | 2·02 | 166 | 165·9 | 2·90 |
| 17 | 16·99 | 0·30 | 67 | 66·98 | 1·17 | 117 | 117·0 | 2·04 | 167 | 166·9 | 2·91 |
| 18 | 17·99 | 0·31 | 68 | 67·98 | 1·19 | 118 | 118·0 | 2·06 | 168 | 167·9 | 2·93 |
| 19 | 18·99 | 0·33 | 69 | 68·98 | 1·20 | 119 | 119·0 | 2·08 | 169 | 168·9 | 2·95 |
| 20 | 19·99 | 0·35 | 70 | 69·98 | 1·22 | 120 | 120·0 | 2·09 | 170 | 169·9 | 2·97 |
| 21 | 20·99 | 0·37 | 71 | 70·98 | 1·24 | 121 | 121·0 | 2·11 | 171 | 170·9 | 2·98 |
| 22 | 21·99 | 0·38 | 72 | 71·98 | 1·26 | 122 | 122·0 | 2·13 | 172 | 171·9 | 3·00 |
| 23 | 22·99 | 0·40 | 73 | 72·98 | 1·27 | 123 | 123·0 | 2·15 | 173 | 172·9 | 3·02 |
| 24 | 23·99 | 0·42 | 74 | 73·98 | 1·29 | 124 | 124·0 | 2·16 | 174 | 173·9 | 3·04 |
| 25 | 24·99 | 0·44 | 75 | 74·98 | 1·31 | 125 | 125·0 | 2·18 | 175 | 174·9 | 3·05 |
| 26 | 25·99 | 0·45 | 76 | 75·98 | 1·33 | 126 | 126·0 | 2·20 | 176 | 175·9 | 3·07 |
| 27 | 26·99 | 0·47 | 77 | 76·98 | 1·34 | 127 | 127·0 | 2·22 | 177 | 176·9 | 3·09 |
| 28 | 27·99 | 0·49 | 78 | 77·98 | 1·36 | 128 | 128·0 | 2·23 | 178 | 177·9 | 3·11 |
| 29 | 28·99 | 0·51 | 79 | 78·98 | 1·38 | 129 | 129·0 | 2·25 | 179 | 178·9 | 3·12 |
| 30 | 29·99 | 0·52 | 80 | 79·98 | 1·40 | 130 | 130·0 | 2·27 | 180 | 179·9 | 3·14 |
| 31 | 30·99 | 0·54 | 81 | 80·98 | 1·41 | 131 | 131·0 | 2·29 | 181 | 180·9 | 3·16 |
| 32 | 31·99 | 0·56 | 82 | 81·97 | 1·43 | 132 | 132·0 | 2·30 | 182 | 181·9 | 3·18 |
| 33 | 32·99 | 0·58 | 83 | 82·97 | 1·45 | 133 | 133·0 | 2·32 | 183 | 182·9 | 3·19 |
| 34 | 33·99 | 0·59 | 84 | 83·97 | 1·47 | 134 | 134·0 | 2·34 | 184 | 183·9 | 3·21 |
| 35 | 34·99 | 0·61 | 85 | 84·97 | 1·48 | 135 | 135·0 | 2·36 | 185 | 184·9 | 3·23 |
| 36 | 35·99 | 0·63 | 86 | 85·97 | 1·50 | 136 | 136·0 | 2·37 | 186 | 185·9 | 3·25 |
| 37 | 36·99 | 0·65 | 87 | 86·97 | 1·52 | 137 | 137·0 | 2·39 | 187 | 186·9 | 3·26 |
| 38 | 37·99 | 0·66 | 88 | 87·97 | 1·54 | 138 | 138·0 | 2·41 | 188 | 187·9 | 3·28 |
| 39 | 38·99 | 0·68 | 89 | 88·97 | 1·55 | 139 | 139·0 | 2·43 | 189 | 188·9 | 3·30 |
| 40 | 39·99 | 0·70 | 90 | 89·97 | 1·57 | 140 | 140·0 | 2·44 | 190 | 189·9 | 3·32 |
| 41 | 40·99 | 0·72 | 91 | 90·97 | 1·59 | 141 | 141·0 | 2·46 | 191 | 190·9 | 3·33 |
| 42 | 41·99 | 0·73 | 92 | 91·97 | 1·61 | 142 | 142·0 | 2·48 | 192 | 191·9 | 3·35 |
| 43 | 42·99 | 0·75 | 93 | 92·97 | 1·62 | 143 | 143·0 | 2·50 | 193 | 192·9 | 3·37 |
| 44 | 43·99 | 0·77 | 94 | 93·97 | 1·64 | 144 | 144·0 | 2·51 | 194 | 193·9 | 3·39 |
| 45 | 44·99 | 0·79 | 95 | 94·97 | 1·66 | 145 | 145·0 | 2·53 | 195 | 194·9 | 3·40 |
| 46 | 45·99 | 0·80 | 96 | 95·97 | 1·68 | 146 | 146·0 | 2·55 | 196 | 195·9 | 3·42 |
| 47 | 46·99 | 0·82 | 97 | 96·97 | 1·69 | 147 | 147·0 | 2·57 | 197 | 196·9 | 3·44 |
| 48 | 47·99 | 0·84 | 98 | 97·97 | 1·71 | 148 | 148·0 | 2·58 | 198 | 197·9 | 3·45 |
| 49 | 48·99 | 0·86 | 99 | 98·97 | 1·73 | 149 | 149·0 | 2·60 | 199 | 198·9 | 3·47 |
| 50 | 49·98 | 0·87 | 100 | 99·97 | 1·74 | 150 | 150·0 | 2·62 | 200 | 199·9 | 3·49 |
| 51 | 50·98 | 0·89 | 101 | 101·0 | 1·76 | 151 | 151·0 | 2·63 | 201 | 200·9 | 3·51 |
| 52 | 51·98 | 0·91 | 102 | 102·0 | 1·78 | 152 | 152·0 | 2·65 | 202 | 201·9 | 3·52 |
| 53 | 52·98 | 0·92 | 103 | 103·0 | 1·80 | 153 | 153·0 | 2·67 | 203 | 202·9 | 3·54 |
| 54 | 53·98 | 0·94 | 104 | 104·0 | 1·81 | 154 | 154·0 | 2·69 | 204 | 203·9 | 3·56 |
| 55 | 54·98 | 0·96 | 105 | 105·0 | 1·83 | 155 | 155·0 | 2·70 | 205 | 204·9 | 3·58 |
| 56 | 55·98 | 0·98 | 106 | 106·0 | 1·85 | 156 | 156·0 | 2·72 | 206 | 205·9 | 3·59 |
| 57 | 56·98 | 0·99 | 107 | 107·0 | 1·87 | 157 | 157·0 | 2·74 | 207 | 206·9 | 3·61 |
| 58 | 57·98 | 1·01 | 108 | 108·0 | 1·88 | 158 | 158·0 | 2·76 | 208 | 207·9 | 3·63 |
| 59 | 58·98 | 1·03 | 109 | 109·0 | 1·90 | 159 | 159·0 | 2·77 | 209 | 208·9 | 3·65 |
| 60 | 59·98 | 1·05 | 110 | 110·0 | 1·92 | 160 | 160·0 | 2·79 | 210 | 209·9 | 3·66 |

TABLE I **1° 10′**

| G | D | H | G | D | H | G | D | H | G | D | H |
|---|---|---|---|---|---|---|---|---|---|---|---|
| 10 | 10·00 | 0·20 | 60 | 59·98 | 1·22 | 110 | 110·0 | 2·24 | 160 | 159·9 | 3·26 |
| 11 | 11·00 | 0·22 | 61 | 60·97 | 1·24 | 111 | 111·0 | 2·26 | 161 | 160·9 | 3·28 |
| 12 | 12·00 | 0·24 | 62 | 61·97 | 1·26 | 112 | 112·0 | 2·28 | 162 | 161·9 | 3·30 |
| 13 | 12·99 | 0·26 | 63 | 62·97 | 1·28 | 113 | 113·0 | 2·30 | 163 | 162·9 | 3·32 |
| 14 | 13·99 | 0·28 | 64 | 63·97 | 1·30 | 114 | 114·0 | 2·32 | 164 | 163·9 | 3·34 |
| 15 | 14·99 | 0·31 | 65 | 64·97 | 1·32 | 115 | 115·0 | 2·34 | 165 | 164·9 | 3·36 |
| 16 | 15·99 | 0·33 | 66 | 65·97 | 1·34 | 116 | 116·0 | 2·36 | 166 | 165·9 | 3·38 |
| 17 | 16·99 | 0·35 | 67 | 66·97 | 1·36 | 117 | 117·0 | 2·38 | 167 | 166·9 | 3·40 |
| 18 | 17·99 | 0·37 | 68 | 67·97 | 1·38 | 118 | 118·0 | 2·40 | 168 | 167·9 | 3·42 |
| 19 | 18·99 | 0·39 | 69 | 68·97 | 1·40 | 119 | 119·0 | 2·42 | 169 | 168·9 | 3·44 |
| 20 | 19·99 | 0·41 | 70 | 69·97 | 1·42 | 120 | 120·0 | 2·44 | 170 | 169·9 | 3·46 |
| 21 | 20·99 | 0·43 | 71 | 70·97 | 1·45 | 121 | 120·9 | 2·46 | 171 | 170·9 | 3·48 |
| 22 | 21·99 | 0·45 | 72 | 71·97 | 1·47 | 122 | 121·9 | 2·48 | 172 | 171·9 | 3·50 |
| 23 | 22·99 | 0·47 | 73 | 72·97 | 1·49 | 123 | 122·9 | 2·50 | 173 | 172·9 | 3·52 |
| 24 | 23·99 | 0·49 | 74 | 73·97 | 1·51 | 124 | 123·9 | 2·52 | 174 | 173·9 | 3·54 |
| 25 | 24·99 | 0·51 | 75 | 74·97 | 1·53 | 125 | 124·9 | 2·54 | 175 | 174·9 | 3·56 |
| 26 | 25·99 | 0·53 | 76 | 75·97 | 1·55 | 126 | 125·9 | 2·56 | 176 | 175·9 | 3·58 |
| 27 | 26·99 | 0·55 | 77 | 76·97 | 1·57 | 127 | 126·9 | 2·59 | 177 | 176·9 | 3·60 |
| 28 | 27·99 | 0·57 | 78 | 77·97 | 1·59 | 128 | 127·9 | 2·61 | 178 | 177·9 | 3·62 |
| 29 | 28·99 | 0·59 | 79 | 78·97 | 1·61 | 129 | 128·9 | 2·63 | 179 | 178·9 | 3·64 |
| 30 | 29·99 | 0·61 | 80 | 79·97 | 1·63 | 130 | 129·9 | 2·65 | 180 | 179·9 | 3·66 |
| 31 | 30·99 | 0·63 | 81 | 80·97 | 1·65 | 131 | 130·9 | 2·67 | 181 | 180·9 | 3·68 |
| 32 | 31·99 | 0·65 | 82 | 81·97 | 1·67 | 132 | 131·9 | 2·69 | 182 | 181·9 | 3·70 |
| 33 | 32·99 | 0·67 | 83 | 82·97 | 1·69 | 133 | 132·9 | 2·71 | 183 | 182·9 | 3·73 |
| 34 | 33·99 | 0·69 | 84 | 83·97 | 1·71 | 134 | 133·9 | 2·73 | 184 | 183·9 | 3·75 |
| 35 | 34·99 | 0·71 | 85 | 84·96 | 1·73 | 135 | 134·9 | 2·75 | 185 | 184·9 | 3·77 |
| 36 | 35·99 | 0·73 | 86 | 85·96 | 1·75 | 136 | 135·9 | 2·77 | 186 | 185·9 | 3·79 |
| 37 | 36·98 | 0·75 | 87 | 86·96 | 1·77 | 137 | 136·9 | 2·79 | 187 | 186·9 | 3·81 |
| 38 | 37·98 | 0·77 | 88 | 87·96 | 1·79 | 138 | 137·9 | 2·81 | 188 | 187·9 | 3·83 |
| 39 | 38·98 | 0·79 | 89 | 88·96 | 1·81 | 139 | 138·9 | 2·83 | 189 | 188·9 | 3·85 |
| 40 | 39·98 | 0·81 | 90 | 89·96 | 1·83 | 140 | 139·9 | 2·85 | 190 | 189·9 | 3·87 |
| 41 | 40·98 | 0·83 | 91 | 90·96 | 1·85 | 141 | 140·9 | 2·87 | 191 | 190·9 | 3·89 |
| 42 | 41·98 | 0·85 | 92 | 91·96 | 1·87 | 142 | 141·9 | 2·89 | 192 | 191·9 | 3·91 |
| 43 | 42·98 | 0·88 | 93 | 92·96 | 1·89 | 143 | 142·9 | 2·91 | 193 | 192·9 | 3·93 |
| 44 | 43·98 | 0·90 | 94 | 93·96 | 1·91 | 144 | 143·9 | 2·93 | 194 | 193·9 | 3·95 |
| 45 | 44·98 | 0·92 | 95 | 94·96 | 1·93 | 145 | 144·9 | 2·95 | 195 | 194·9 | 3·97 |
| 46 | 45·98 | 0·94 | 96 | 95·96 | 1·95 | 146 | 145·9 | 2·97 | 196 | 195·9 | 3·99 |
| 47 | 46·98 | 0·96 | 97 | 96·96 | 1·97 | 147 | 146·9 | 2·99 | 197 | 196·9 | 4·01 |
| 48 | 47·98 | 0·98 | 98 | 97·96 | 1·99 | 148 | 147·9 | 3·01 | 198 | 197·9 | 4·03 |
| 49 | 48·98 | 1·00 | 99 | 98·96 | 2·02 | 149 | 148·9 | 3·03 | 199 | 198·9 | 4·05 |
| 50 | 49·98 | 1·02 | 100 | 99·96 | 2·04 | 150 | 149·9 | 3·05 | 200 | 199·9 | 4·07 |
| 51 | 50·98 | 1·04 | 101 | 101·0 | 2·06 | 151 | 150·9 | 3·07 | 201 | 200·9 | 4·09 |
| 52 | 51·98 | 1·06 | 102 | 102·0 | 2·08 | 152 | 151·9 | 3·09 | 202 | 201·9 | 4·11 |
| 53 | 52·98 | 1·08 | 103 | 103·0 | 2·10 | 153 | 152·9 | 3·11 | 203 | 202·9 | 4·13 |
| 54 | 53·98 | 1·10 | 104 | 104·0 | 2·12 | 154 | 153·9 | 3·13 | 204 | 203·9 | 4·15 |
| 55 | 54·98 | 1·12 | 105 | 105·0 | 2·14 | 155 | 154·9 | 3·16 | 205 | 204·9 | 4·17 |
| 56 | 55·98 | 1·14 | 106 | 106·0 | 2·16 | 156 | 155·9 | 3·18 | 206 | 205·9 | 4·19 |
| 57 | 56·98 | 1·16 | 107 | 107·0 | 2·18 | 157 | 156·9 | 3·20 | 207 | 206·9 | 4·21 |
| 58 | 57·98 | 1·18 | 108 | 108·0 | 2·20 | 158 | 157·9 | 3·22 | 208 | 207·9 | 4·23 |
| 59 | 58·98 | 1·20 | 109 | 109·0 | 2·22 | 159 | 158·9 | 3·24 | 209 | 208·9 | 4·25 |
| 60 | 59·98 | 1·22 | 110 | 110·0 | 2·24 | 160 | 159·9 | 3·26 | 210 | 209·9 | 4·27 |

TABLE I

| G | D | H | G | D | H | G | D | H | G | D | H |
|---|---|---|---|---|---|---|---|---|---|---|---|
| 10 | 9·99 | 0·23 | 60 | 59·97 | 1·40 | 110 | 109·9 | 2·56 | 160 | 159·9 | 3·72 |
| 11 | 10·99 | 0·26 | 61 | 60·97 | 1·42 | 111 | 110·9 | 2·58 | 161 | 160·9 | 3·75 |
| 12 | 11·99 | 0·28 | 62 | 61·97 | 1·44 | 112 | 111·9 | 2·61 | 162 | 161·9 | 3·77 |
| 13 | 12·99 | 0·30 | 63 | 62·97 | 1·47 | 113 | 112·9 | 2·63 | 163 | 162·9 | 3·79 |
| 14 | 13·99 | 0·33 | 64 | 63·97 | 1·49 | 114 | 113·9 | 2·65 | 164 | 163·9 | 3·81 |
| 15 | 14·99 | 0·35 | 65 | 64·96 | 1·51 | 115 | 114·9 | 2·68 | 165 | 164·9 | 3·84 |
| 16 | 15·99 | 0·37 | 66 | 65·96 | 1·54 | 116 | 115·9 | 2·70 | 166 | 165·9 | 3·86 |
| 17 | 16·99 | 0·40 | 67 | 66·96 | 1·56 | 117 | 116·9 | 2·72 | 167 | 166·9 | 3·88 |
| 18 | 17·99 | 0·42 | 68 | 67·96 | 1·58 | 118 | 117·9 | 2·74 | 168 | 167·9 | 3·91 |
| 19 | 18·99 | 0·44 | 69 | 68·96 | 1·61 | 119 | 118·9 | 2·77 | 169 | 168·9 | 3·93 |
| 20 | 19·99 | 0·47 | 70 | 69·96 | 1·63 | 120 | 119·9 | 2·79 | 170 | 169·9 | 3·95 |
| 21 | 20·99 | 0·49 | 71 | 70·96 | 1·65 | 121 | 120·9 | 2·81 | 171 | 170·9 | 3·98 |
| 22 | 21·99 | 0·51 | 72 | 71·96 | 1·67 | 122 | 121·9 | 2·84 | 172 | 171·9 | 4·00 |
| 23 | 22·99 | 0·54 | 73 | 72·96 | 1·70 | 123 | 122·9 | 2·86 | 173 | 172·9 | 4·02 |
| 24 | 23·99 | 0·56 | 74 | 73·96 | 1·72 | 124 | 123·9 | 2·88 | 174 | 173·9 | 4·05 |
| 25 | 24·99 | 0·58 | 75 | 74·96 | 1·74 | 125 | 124·9 | 2·91 | 175 | 174·9 | 4·07 |
| 26 | 25·99 | 0·60 | 76 | 75·96 | 1·77 | 126 | 125·9 | 2·93 | 176 | 175·9 | 4·09 |
| 27 | 26·99 | 0·63 | 77 | 76·96 | 1·79 | 127 | 126·9 | 2·95 | 177 | 176·9 | 4·12 |
| 28 | 27·98 | 0·65 | 78 | 77·96 | 1·81 | 128 | 127·9 | 2·98 | 178 | 177·9 | 4·14 |
| 29 | 28·98 | 0·67 | 79 | 78·96 | 1·84 | 129 | 128·9 | 3·00 | 179 | 178·9 | 4·16 |
| 30 | 29·98 | 0·70 | 80 | 79·96 | 1·86 | 130 | 129·9 | 3·02 | 180 | 179·9 | 4·19 |
| 31 | 30·98 | 0·72 | 81 | 80·96 | 1·88 | 131 | 130·9 | 3·05 | 181 | 180·9 | 4·21 |
| 32 | 31·98 | 0·74 | 82 | 81·96 | 1·91 | 132 | 131·9 | 3·07 | 182 | 181·9 | 4·23 |
| 33 | 32·98 | 0·77 | 83 | 82·96 | 1·93 | 133 | 132·9 | 3·09 | 183 | 182·9 | 4·26 |
| 34 | 33·98 | 0·79 | 84 | 83·95 | 1·95 | 134 | 133·9 | 3·12 | 184 | 183·9 | 4·28 |
| 35 | 34·98 | 0·81 | 85 | 84·95 | 1·98 | 135 | 134·9 | 3·14 | 185 | 184·9 | 4·30 |
| 36 | 35·98 | 0·84 | 86 | 85·95 | 2·00 | 136 | 135·9 | 3·16 | 186 | 185·9 | 4·33 |
| 37 | 36·98 | 0·86 | 87 | 86·95 | 2·02 | 137 | 136·9 | 3·19 | 187 | 186·9 | 4·35 |
| 38 | 37·98 | 0·88 | 88 | 87·95 | 2·05 | 138 | 137·9 | 3·21 | 188 | 187·9 | 4·37 |
| 39 | 38·98 | 0·91 | 89 | 88·95 | 2·07 | 139 | 138·9 | 3·23 | 189 | 188·9 | 4·40 |
| 40 | 39·98 | 0·93 | 90 | 89·95 | 2·09 | 140 | 139·9 | 3·26 | 190 | 189·9 | 4·42 |
| 41 | 40·98 | 0·95 | 91 | 90·95 | 2·12 | 141 | 140·9 | 3·28 | 191 | 190·9 | 4·44 |
| 42 | 41·98 | 0·98 | 92 | 91·95 | 2·14 | 142 | 141·9 | 3·30 | 192 | 191·9 | 4·47 |
| 43 | 42·98 | 1·00 | 93 | 92·95 | 2·16 | 143 | 142·9 | 3·33 | 193 | 192·9 | 4·49 |
| 44 | 43·98 | 1·02 | 94 | 93·95 | 2·19 | 144 | 143·9 | 3·35 | 194 | 193·9 | 4·51 |
| 45 | 44·98 | 1·05 | 95 | 94·95 | 2·21 | 145 | 144·9 | 3·37 | 195 | 194·9 | 4·54 |
| 46 | 45·98 | 1·07 | 96 | 95·95 | 2·23 | 146 | 145·9 | 3·40 | 196 | 195·9 | 4·56 |
| 47 | 46·97 | 1·09 | 97 | 96·95 | 2·26 | 147 | 146·9 | 3·42 | 197 | 196·9 | 4·58 |
| 48 | 47·97 | 1·12 | 98 | 97·95 | 2·28 | 148 | 147·9 | 3·44 | 198 | 197·9 | 4·61 |
| 49 | 48·97 | 1·14 | 99 | 98·95 | 2·30 | 149 | 148·9 | 3·47 | 199 | 198·9 | 4·63 |
| 50 | 49·97 | 1·16 | 100 | 99·95 | 2·33 | 150 | 149·9 | 3·49 | 200 | 199·9 | 4·65 |
| 51 | 50·97 | 1·19 | 101 | 100·9 | 2·35 | 151 | 150·9 | 3·51 | 201 | 200·9 | 4·68 |
| 52 | 51·97 | 1·21 | 102 | 101·9 | 2·37 | 152 | 151·9 | 3·54 | 202 | 201·9 | 4·70 |
| 53 | 52·97 | 1·23 | 103 | 102·9 | 2·40 | 153 | 152·9 | 3·56 | 203 | 202·9 | 4·72 |
| 54 | 53·97 | 1·26 | 104 | 103·9 | 2·42 | 154 | 153·9 | 3·58 | 204 | 203·9 | 4·75 |
| 55 | 54·97 | 1·28 | 105 | 104·9 | 2·44 | 155 | 154·9 | 3·61 | 205 | 204·9 | 4·77 |
| 56 | 55·97 | 1·30 | 106 | 105·9 | 2·47 | 156 | 155·9 | 3·63 | 206 | 205·9 | 4·79 |
| 57 | 56·97 | 1·33 | 107 | 106·9 | 2·49 | 157 | 156·9 | 3·65 | 207 | 206·9 | 4·82 |
| 58 | 57·97 | 1·35 | 108 | 107·9 | 2·51 | 158 | 157·9 | 3·68 | 208 | 207·9 | 4·84 |
| 59 | 58·97 | 1·37 | 109 | 108·9 | 2·54 | 159 | 158·9 | 3·70 | 209 | 208·9 | 4·86 |
| 60 | 59·97 | 1·40 | 110 | 109·9 | 2·56 | 160 | 159·9 | 3·72 | 210 | 209·9 | 4·89 |

TABLE I      **1° 30′**

| G | D | H | G | D | H | G | D | H | G | D | H |
|---|---|---|---|---|---|---|---|---|---|---|---|
| 10 | 9·99 | 0·26 | 60 | 59·96 | 1·57 | 110 | 109·9 | 2·88 | 160 | 159·9 | 4·19 |
| 11 | 10·99 | 0·29 | 61 | 60·96 | 1·60 | 111 | 110·9 | 2·90 | 161 | 160·9 | 4·21 |
| 12 | 11·99 | 0·31 | 62 | 61·96 | 1·62 | 112 | 111·9 | 2·93 | 162 | 161·9 | 4·24 |
| 13 | 12·99 | 0·34 | 63 | 62·96 | 1·65 | 113 | 112·9 | 2·96 | 163 | 162·9 | 4·27 |
| 14 | 13·99 | 0·37 | 64 | 63·96 | 1·67 | 114 | 113·9 | 2·98 | 164 | 163·9 | 4·29 |
| 15 | 14·99 | 0·39 | 65 | 64·96 | 1·70 | 115 | 114·9 | 3·01 | 165 | 164·9 | 4·32 |
| 16 | 15·99 | 0·42 | 66 | 65·95 | 1·73 | 116 | 115·9 | 3·04 | 166 | 165·9 | 4·34 |
| 17 | 16·99 | 0·44 | 67 | 66·95 | 1·75 | 117 | 116·9 | 3·06 | 167 | 166·9 | 4·37 |
| 18 | 17·99 | 0·47 | 68 | 67·95 | 1·78 | 118 | 117·9 | 3·09 | 168 | 167·9 | 4·40 |
| 19 | 18·99 | 0·50 | 69 | 68·95 | 1·81 | 119 | 118·9 | 3·11 | 169 | 168·9 | 4·42 |
| 20 | 19·99 | 0·52 | 70 | 69·95 | 1·83 | 120 | 119·9 | 3·14 | 170 | 169·9 | 4·45 |
| 21 | 20·99 | 0·55 | 71 | 70·95 | 1·86 | 121 | 120·9 | 3·17 | 171 | 170·9 | 4·47 |
| 22 | 21·98 | 0·58 | 72 | 71·95 | 1·88 | 122 | 121·9 | 3·19 | 172 | 171·9 | 4·50 |
| 23 | 22·98 | 0·60 | 73 | 72·95 | 1·91 | 123 | 122·9 | 3·22 | 173 | 172·9 | 4·53 |
| 24 | 23·98 | 0·63 | 74 | 73·95 | 1·94 | 124 | 123·9 | 3·24 | 174 | 173·9 | 4·55 |
| 25 | 24·98 | 0·65 | 75 | 74·95 | 1·96 | 125 | 124·9 | 3·27 | 175 | 174·9 | 4·58 |
| 26 | 25·98 | 0·68 | 76 | 75·95 | 1·99 | 126 | 125·9 | 3·30 | 176 | 175·9 | 4·61 |
| 27 | 26·98 | 0·71 | 77 | 76·95 | 2·01 | 127 | 126·9 | 3·32 | 177 | 176·9 | 4·63 |
| 28 | 27·98 | 0·73 | 78 | 77·95 | 2·04 | 128 | 127·9 | 3·35 | 178 | 177·9 | 4·66 |
| 29 | 28·98 | 0·76 | 79 | 78·95 | 2·07 | 129 | 128·9 | 3·38 | 179 | 178·9 | 4·68 |
| 30 | 29·98 | 0·79 | 80 | 79·95 | 2·09 | 130 | 129·9 | 3·40 | 180 | 179·9 | 4·71 |
| 31 | 30·98 | 0·81 | 81 | 80·94 | 2·12 | 131 | 130·9 | 3·43 | 181 | 180·9 | 4·74 |
| 32 | 31·98 | 0·84 | 82 | 81·94 | 2·15 | 132 | 131·9 | 3·45 | 182 | 181·9 | 4·76 |
| 33 | 32·98 | 0·86 | 83 | 82·94 | 2·17 | 133 | 132·9 | 3·48 | 183 | 182·9 | 4·79 |
| 34 | 33·98 | 0·89 | 84 | 83·94 | 2·20 | 134 | 133·9 | 3·51 | 184 | 183·9 | 4·81 |
| 35 | 34·98 | 0·92 | 85 | 84·94 | 2·22 | 135 | 134·9 | 3·53 | 185 | 184·9 | 4·84 |
| 36 | 35·98 | 0·94 | 86 | 85·94 | 2·25 | 136 | 135·9 | 3·56 | 186 | 185·9 | 4·87 |
| 37 | 36·97 | 0·97 | 87 | 86·94 | 2·28 | 137 | 136·9 | 3·58 | 187 | 186·9 | 4·89 |
| 38 | 37·97 | 0·99 | 88 | 87·94 | 2·30 | 138 | 137·9 | 3·61 | 188 | 187·9 | 4·92 |
| 39 | 38·97 | 1·02 | 89 | 88·94 | 2·33 | 139 | 138·9 | 3·64 | 189 | 188·9 | 4·95 |
| 40 | 39·97 | 1·05 | 90 | 89·94 | 2·36 | 140 | 139·9 | 3·66 | 190 | 189·9 | 4·97 |
| 41 | 40·97 | 1·07 | 91 | 90·94 | 2·38 | 141 | 140·9 | 3·69 | 191 | 190·9 | 5·00 |
| 42 | 41·97 | 1·10 | 92 | 91·94 | 2·41 | 142 | 141·9 | 3·72 | 192 | 191·9 | 5·02 |
| 43 | 42·97 | 1·13 | 93 | 92·94 | 2·43 | 143 | 142·9 | 3·74 | 193 | 192·9 | 5·05 |
| 44 | 43·97 | 1·15 | 94 | 93·94 | 2·46 | 144 | 143·9 | 3·77 | 194 | 193·9 | 5·08 |
| 45 | 44·97 | 1·18 | 95 | 94·93 | 2·49 | 145 | 144·9 | 3·79 | 195 | 194·9 | 5·10 |
| 46 | 45·97 | 1·20 | 96 | 95·93 | 2·51 | 146 | 145·9 | 3·82 | 196 | 195·9 | 5·13 |
| 47 | 46·97 | 1·23 | 97 | 96·93 | 2·54 | 147 | 146·9 | 3·85 | 197 | 196·9 | 5·15 |
| 48 | 47·97 | 1·26 | 98 | 97·93 | 2·56 | 148 | 147·9 | 3·87 | 198 | 197·9 | 5·18 |
| 49 | 48·97 | 1·28 | 99 | 98·93 | 2·59 | 149 | 148·9 | 3·90 | 199 | 198·9 | 5·21 |
| 50 | 49·97 | 1·31 | 100 | 99·93 | 2·62 | 150 | 149·9 | 3·93 | 200 | 199·9 | 5·23 |
| 51 | 50·97 | 1·33 | 101 | 100·9 | 2·64 | 151 | 150·9 | 3·95 | 201 | 200·9 | 5·26 |
| 52 | 51·96 | 1·36 | 102 | 101·9 | 2·67 | 152 | 151·9 | 3·98 | 202 | 201·9 | 5·29 |
| 53 | 52·96 | 1·39 | 103 | 102·9 | 2·70 | 153 | 152·9 | 4·00 | 203 | 202·9 | 5·31 |
| 54 | 53·96 | 1·41 | 104 | 103·9 | 2·72 | 154 | 153·9 | 4·03 | 204 | 203·9 | 5·34 |
| 55 | 54·96 | 1·44 | 105 | 104·9 | 2·75 | 155 | 154·9 | 4·06 | 205 | 204·9 | 5·36 |
| 56 | 55·96 | 1·47 | 106 | 105·9 | 2·77 | 156 | 155·9 | 4·08 | 206 | 205·9 | 5·39 |
| 57 | 56·96 | 1·49 | 107 | 106·9 | 2·80 | 157 | 156·9 | 4·11 | 207 | 206·9 | 5·42 |
| 58 | 57·96 | 1·52 | 108 | 107·9 | 2·83 | 158 | 157·9 | 4·13 | 208 | 207·9 | 5·44 |
| 59 | 58·96 | 1·54 | 109 | 108·9 | 2·85 | 159 | 158·9 | 4·16 | 209 | 208·9 | 5·47 |
| 60 | 59·96 | 1·57 | 110 | 109·9 | 2·88 | 160 | 159·9 | 4·19 | 210 | 209·9 | 5·50 |

| G | D | H | G | D | H | G | D | H | G | D | H |
|---|---|---|---|---|---|---|---|---|---|---|---|
| 10 | 9.99 | 0.29 | 60 | 59.95 | 1.74 | 110 | 109.9 | 3.20 | 160 | 159.9 | 4.65 |
| 11 | 10.99 | 0.32 | 61 | 60.95 | 1.77 | 111 | 110.9 | 3.23 | 161 | 160.9 | 4.68 |
| 12 | 11.99 | 0.35 | 62 | 61.95 | 1.80 | 112 | 111.9 | 3.26 | 162 | 161.9 | 4.71 |
| 13 | 12.99 | 0.38 | 63 | 62.95 | 1.83 | 113 | 112.9 | 3.29 | 163 | 162.9 | 4.74 |
| 14 | 13.99 | 0.41 | 64 | 63.95 | 1.86 | 114 | 113.9 | 3.31 | 164 | 163.9 | 4.77 |
| 15 | 14.99 | 0.44 | 65 | 64.94 | 1.89 | 115 | 114.9 | 3.34 | 165 | 164.9 | 4.80 |
| 16 | 15.99 | 0.47 | 66 | 65.94 | 1.92 | 116 | 115.9 | 3.37 | 166 | 165.9 | 4.83 |
| 17 | 16.99 | 0.49 | 67 | 66.94 | 1.95 | 117 | 116.9 | 3.40 | 167 | 166.9 | 4.86 |
| 18 | 17.98 | 0.52 | 68 | 67.94 | 1.98 | 118 | 117.9 | 3.43 | 168 | 167.9 | 4.88 |
| 19 | 18.98 | 0.55 | 69 | 68.94 | 2.01 | 119 | 118.9 | 3.46 | 169 | 168.9 | 4.91 |
| 20 | 19.98 | 0.58 | 70 | 69.94 | 2.04 | 120 | 119.9 | 3.49 | 170 | 169.9 | 4.94 |
| 21 | 20.98 | 0.61 | 71 | 70.94 | 2.06 | 121 | 120.9 | 3.52 | 171 | 170.9 | 4.97 |
| 22 | 21.98 | 0.64 | 72 | 71.94 | 2.09 | 122 | 121.9 | 3.55 | 172 | 171.9 | 5.00 |
| 23 | 22.98 | 0.67 | 73 | 72.94 | 2.12 | 123 | 122.9 | 3.58 | 173 | 172.9 | 5.03 |
| 24 | 23.98 | 0.70 | 74 | 73.94 | 2.15 | 124 | 123.9 | 3.60 | 174 | 173.9 | 5.06 |
| 25 | 24.98 | 0.73 | 75 | 74.94 | 2.18 | 125 | 124.9 | 3.63 | 175 | 174.9 | 5.09 |
| 26 | 25.98 | 0.76 | 76 | 75.94 | 2.21 | 126 | 125.9 | 3.66 | 176 | 175.9 | 5.12 |
| 27 | 26.98 | 0.78 | 77 | 76.93 | 2.24 | 127 | 126.9 | 3.69 | 177 | 176.8 | 5.15 |
| 28 | 27.98 | 0.81 | 78 | 77.93 | 2.27 | 128 | 127.9 | 3.72 | 178 | 177.8 | 5.17 |
| 29 | 28.98 | 0.84 | 79 | 78.93 | 2.30 | 129 | 128.9 | 3.75 | 179 | 178.8 | 5.20 |
| 30 | 29.97 | 0.87 | 80 | 79.93 | 2.33 | 130 | 129.9 | 3.78 | 180 | 179.8 | 5.23 |
| 31 | 30.97 | 0.90 | 81 | 80.93 | 2.35 | 131 | 130.9 | 3.81 | 181 | 180.8 | 5.26 |
| 32 | 31.97 | 0.93 | 82 | 81.93 | 2.38 | 132 | 131.9 | 3.84 | 182 | 181.8 | 5.29 |
| 33 | 32.97 | 0.96 | 83 | 82.93 | 2.41 | 133 | 132.9 | 3.87 | 183 | 182.8 | 5.32 |
| 34 | 33.97 | 0.99 | 84 | 83.93 | 2.44 | 134 | 133.9 | 3.90 | 184 | 183.8 | 5.35 |
| 35 | 34.97 | 1.02 | 85 | 84.93 | 2.47 | 135 | 134.9 | 3.92 | 185 | 184.8 | 5.38 |
| 36 | 35.97 | 1.05 | 86 | 85.93 | 2.50 | 136 | 135.9 | 3.95 | 186 | 185.8 | 5.41 |
| 37 | 36.97 | 1.08 | 87 | 86.93 | 2.53 | 137 | 136.9 | 3.98 | 187 | 186.8 | 5.44 |
| 38 | 37.97 | 1.10 | 88 | 87.93 | 2.56 | 138 | 137.9 | 4.01 | 188 | 187.8 | 5.47 |
| 39 | 38.97 | 1.13 | 89 | 88.92 | 2.59 | 139 | 138.9 | 4.04 | 189 | 188.8 | 5.49 |
| 40 | 39.97 | 1.16 | 90 | 89.92 | 2.62 | 140 | 139.9 | 4.07 | 190 | 189.8 | 5.52 |
| 41 | 40.97 | 1.19 | 91 | 90.92 | 2.65 | 141 | 140.9 | 4.10 | 191 | 190.8 | 5.55 |
| 42 | 41.96 | 1.22 | 92 | 91.92 | 2.67 | 142 | 141.9 | 4.13 | 192 | 191.8 | 5.58 |
| 43 | 42.96 | 1.25 | 93 | 92.92 | 2.70 | 143 | 142.9 | 4.16 | 193 | 192.8 | 5.61 |
| 44 | 43.96 | 1.28 | 94 | 93.92 | 2.73 | 144 | 143.9 | 4.19 | 194 | 193.8 | 5.64 |
| 45 | 44.96 | 1.31 | 95 | 94.92 | 2.76 | 145 | 144.9 | 4.22 | 195 | 194.8 | 5.67 |
| 46 | 45.96 | 1.34 | 96 | 95.92 | 2.79 | 146 | 145.9 | 4.24 | 196 | 195.8 | 5.70 |
| 47 | 46.96 | 1.37 | 97 | 96.92 | 2.82 | 147 | 146.9 | 4.27 | 197 | 196.8 | 5.73 |
| 48 | 47.96 | 1.40 | 98 | 97.92 | 2.85 | 148 | 147.9 | 4.30 | 198 | 197.8 | 5.76 |
| 49 | 48.96 | 1.42 | 99 | 98.92 | 2.88 | 149 | 148.9 | 4.33 | 199 | 198.8 | 5.79 |
| 50 | 49.96 | 1.45 | 100 | 99.92 | 2.91 | 150 | 149.9 | 4.36 | 200 | 199.8 | 5.81 |
| 51 | 50.96 | 1.48 | 101 | 100.9 | 2.94 | 151 | 150.9 | 4.39 | 201 | 200.8 | 5.84 |
| 52 | 51.96 | 1.51 | 102 | 101.9 | 2.97 | 152 | 151.9 | 4.42 | 202 | 201.8 | 5.87 |
| 53 | 52.96 | 1.54 | 103 | 102.9 | 2.99 | 153 | 152.9 | 4.45 | 203 | 202.8 | 5.90 |
| 54 | 53.96 | 1.57 | 104 | 103.9 | 3.02 | 154 | 153.9 | 4.48 | 204 | 203.8 | 5.93 |
| 55 | 54.95 | 1.60 | 105 | 104.9 | 3.05 | 155 | 154.9 | 4.51 | 205 | 204.8 | 5.96 |
| 56 | 55.95 | 1.63 | 106 | 105.9 | 3.08 | 156 | 155.9 | 4.54 | 206 | 205.8 | 5.99 |
| 57 | 56.95 | 1.66 | 107 | 106.9 | 3.11 | 157 | 156.9 | 4.56 | 207 | 206.8 | 6.02 |
| 58 | 57.95 | 1.69 | 108 | 107.9 | 3.14 | 158 | 157.9 | 4.59 | 208 | 207.8 | 6.05 |
| 59 | 58.95 | 1.72 | 109 | 108.9 | 3.17 | 159 | 158.9 | 4.62 | 209 | 208.8 | 6.08 |
| 60 | 59.95 | 1.74 | 110 | 109.9 | 3.20 | 160 | 159.9 | 4.65 | 210 | 209.8 | 6.11 |

TABLE I

| G | D | H | G | D | H | G | D | H | G | D | H |
|---|---|---|---|---|---|---|---|---|---|---|---|
| 10 | 9·99 | 0·32 | 60 | 59·94 | 1·92 | 110 | 109·9 | 3·52 | 160 | 159·8 | 5·12 |
| 11 | 10·99 | 0·35 | 61 | 60·94 | 1·95 | 111 | 110·9 | 3·55 | 161 | 160·8 | 5·15 |
| 12 | 11·99 | 0·38 | 62 | 61·94 | 1·98 | 112 | 111·9 | 3·58 | 162 | 161·8 | 5·18 |
| 13 | 12·99 | 0·42 | 63 | 62·94 | 2·01 | 113 | 112·9 | 3·61 | 163 | 162·8 | 5·21 |
| 14 | 13·99 | 0·45 | 64 | 63·93 | 2·05 | 114 | 113·9 | 3·65 | 164 | 163·8 | 5·24 |
| 15 | 14·98 | 0·48 | 65 | 64·93 | 2·08 | 115 | 114·9 | 3·68 | 165 | 164·8 | 5·28 |
| 16 | 15·98 | 0·51 | 66 | 65·93 | 2·11 | 116 | 115·9 | 3·71 | 166 | 165·8 | 5·31 |
| 17 | 16·98 | 0·54 | 67 | 66·93 | 2·14 | 117 | 116·9 | 3·74 | 167 | 166·8 | 5·34 |
| 18 | 17·98 | 0·58 | 68 | 67·93 | 2·17 | 118 | 117·9 | 3·77 | 168 | 167·8 | 5·37 |
| 19 | 18·98 | 0·61 | 69 | 68·93 | 2·21 | 119 | 118·9 | 3·81 | 169 | 168·8 | 5·40 |
| 20 | 19·98 | 0·64 | 70 | 69·93 | 2·24 | 120 | 119·9 | 3·84 | 170 | 169·8 | 5·44 |
| 21 | 20·98 | 0·67 | 71 | 70·93 | 2·27 | 121 | 120·9 | 3·87 | 171 | 170·8 | 5·47 |
| 22 | 21·98 | 0·70 | 72 | 71·93 | 2·30 | 122 | 121·9 | 3·90 | 172 | 171·8 | 5·50 |
| 23 | 22·98 | 0·74 | 73 | 72·93 | 2·33 | 123 | 122·9 | 3·93 | 173 | 172·8 | 5·53 |
| 24 | 23·98 | 0·77 | 74 | 73·92 | 2·37 | 124 | 123·9 | 3·96 | 174 | 173·8 | 5·56 |
| 25 | 24·97 | 0·80 | 75 | 74·92 | 2·40 | 125 | 124·9 | 4·00 | 175 | 174·8 | 5·60 |
| 26 | 25·97 | 0·83 | 76 | 75·92 | 2·43 | 126 | 125·9 | 4·03 | 176 | 175·8 | 5·63 |
| 27 | 26·97 | 0·86 | 77 | 76·92 | 2·46 | 127 | 126·9 | 4·06 | 177 | 176·8 | 5·66 |
| 28 | 27·97 | 0·90 | 78 | 77·92 | 2·49 | 128 | 127·9 | 4·09 | 178 | 177·8 | 5·69 |
| 29 | 28·97 | 0·93 | 79 | 78·92 | 2·53 | 129 | 128·9 | 4·12 | 179 | 178·8 | 5·72 |
| 30 | 29·97 | 0·96 | 80 | 79·92 | 2·56 | 130 | 129·9 | 4·16 | 180 | 179·8 | 5·76 |
| 31 | 30·97 | 0·99 | 81 | 80·92 | 2·59 | 131 | 130·9 | 4·19 | 181 | 180·8 | 5·79 |
| 32 | 31·97 | 1·02 | 82 | 81·92 | 2·62 | 132 | 131·9 | 4·22 | 182 | 181·8 | 5·82 |
| 33 | 32·97 | 1·06 | 83 | 82·92 | 2·65 | 133 | 132·9 | 4·25 | 183 | 182·8 | 5·85 |
| 34 | 33·97 | 1·09 | 84 | 83·91 | 2·69 | 134 | 133·9 | 4·28 | 184 | 183·8 | 5·88 |
| 35 | 34·96 | 1·12 | 85 | 84·91 | 2·72 | 135 | 134·9 | 4·32 | 185 | 184·8 | 5·92 |
| 36 | 35·96 | 1·15 | 86 | 85·91 | 2·75 | 136 | 135·9 | 4·35 | 186 | 185·8 | 5·95 |
| 37 | 36·96 | 1·18 | 87 | 86·91 | 2·78 | 137 | 136·9 | 4·38 | 187 | 186·8 | 5·98 |
| 38 | 37·96 | 1·22 | 88 | 87·91 | 2·81 | 138 | 137·9 | 4·41 | 188 | 187·8 | 6·01 |
| 39 | 38·96 | 1·25 | 89 | 88·91 | 2·85 | 139 | 138·9 | 4·44 | 189 | 188·8 | 6·04 |
| 40 | 39·96 | 1·28 | 90 | 89·91 | 2·88 | 140 | 139·9 | 4·48 | 190 | 189·8 | 6·08 |
| 41 | 40·96 | 1·31 | 91 | 90·91 | 2·91 | 141 | 140·9 | 4·51 | 191 | 190·8 | 6·11 |
| 42 | 41·96 | 1·34 | 92 | 91·91 | 2·94 | 142 | 141·9 | 4·54 | 192 | 191·8 | 6·14 |
| 43 | 42·96 | 1·37 | 93 | 92·90 | 2·97 | 143 | 142·9 | 4·57 | 193 | 192·8 | 6·17 |
| 44 | 43·95 | 1·41 | 94 | 93·90 | 3·01 | 144 | 143·9 | 4·60 | 194 | 193·8 | 6·20 |
| 45 | 44·95 | 1·44 | 95 | 94·90 | 3·04 | 145 | 144·9 | 4·64 | 195 | 194·8 | 6·24 |
| 46 | 45·95 | 1·47 | 96 | 95·90 | 3·07 | 146 | 145·9 | 4·67 | 196 | 195·8 | 6·27 |
| 47 | 46·95 | 1·50 | 97 | 96·90 | 3·10 | 147 | 146·8 | 4·70 | 197 | 196·8 | 6·30 |
| 48 | 47·95 | 1·53 | 98 | 97·90 | 3·13 | 148 | 147·8 | 4·73 | 198 | 197·8 | 6·33 |
| 49 | 48·95 | 1·57 | 99 | 98·90 | 3·17 | 149 | 148·8 | 4·76 | 199 | 198·8 | 6·36 |
| 50 | 49·95 | 1·60 | 100 | 99·90 | 3·20 | 150 | 149·8 | 4·80 | 200 | 199·8 | 6·40 |
| 51 | 50·95 | 1·63 | 101 | 100·9 | 3·23 | 151 | 150·8 | 4·83 | 201 | 200·8 | 6·43 |
| 52 | 51·95 | 1·66 | 102 | 101·9 | 3·26 | 152 | 151·8 | 4·86 | 202 | 201·8 | 6·46 |
| 53 | 52·95 | 1·69 | 103 | 102·9 | 3·29 | 153 | 152·8 | 4·89 | 203 | 202·8 | 6·49 |
| 54 | 53·94 | 1·73 | 104 | 103·9 | 3·33 | 154 | 153·8 | 4·92 | 204 | 203·8 | 6·52 |
| 55 | 54·94 | 1·76 | 105 | 104·9 | 3·36 | 155 | 154·8 | 4·96 | 205 | 204·8 | 6·55 |
| 56 | 55·94 | 1·79 | 106 | 105·9 | 3·39 | 156 | 155·8 | 4·99 | 206 | 205·8 | 6·59 |
| 57 | 56·94 | 1·82 | 107 | 106·9 | 3·42 | 157 | 156·8 | 5·02 | 207 | 206·8 | 6·62 |
| 58 | 57·94 | 1·85 | 108 | 107·9 | 3·45 | 158 | 157·8 | 5·05 | 208 | 207·8 | 6·65 |
| 59 | 58·94 | 1·89 | 109 | 108·9 | 3·49 | 159 | 158·8 | 5·08 | 209 | 208·8 | 6·68 |
| 60 | 59·94 | 1·92 | 110 | 109·9 | 3·52 | 160 | 159·8 | 5·12 | 210 | 209·8 | 6·71 |

| G | D | H | G | D | H | G | D | H | G | D | H |
|---|---|---|---|---|---|---|---|---|---|---|---|
| 10 | 9·99 | 0·35 | 60 | 59·93 | 2·09 | 110 | 109·9 | 3·84 | 160 | 159·8 | 5·58 |
| 11 | 10·99 | 0·38 | 61 | 60·93 | 2·13 | 111 | 110·9 | 3·87 | 161 | 160·8 | 5·62 |
| 12 | 11·99 | 0·42 | 62 | 61·92 | 2·16 | 112 | 111·9 | 3·91 | 162 | 161·8 | 5·65 |
| 13 | 12·98 | 0·45 | 63 | 62·92 | 2·20 | 113 | 112·9 | 3·94 | 163 | 162·8 | 5·69 |
| 14 | 13·98 | 0·49 | 64 | 63·92 | 2·23 | 114 | 113·9 | 3·98 | 164 | 163·8 | 5·72 |
| 15 | 14·98 | 0·52 | 65 | 64·92 | 2·27 | 115 | 114·9 | 4·01 | 165 | 164·8 | 5·75 |
| 16 | 15·98 | 0·56 | 66 | 65·92 | 2·30 | 116 | 115·9 | 4·05 | 166 | 165·8 | 5·79 |
| 17 | 16·98 | 0·59 | 67 | 66·92 | 2·34 | 117 | 116·9 | 4·08 | 167 | 166·8 | 5·82 |
| 18 | 17·98 | 0·63 | 68 | 67·92 | 2·37 | 118 | 117·9 | 4·12 | 168 | 167·8 | 5·86 |
| 19 | 18·98 | 0·66 | 69 | 68·92 | 2·41 | 119 | 118·9 | 4·15 | 169 | 168·8 | 5·89 |
| 20 | 19·98 | 0·70 | 70 | 69·91 | 2·44 | 120 | 119·9 | 4·19 | 170 | 169·8 | 5·93 |
| 21 | 20·97 | 0·73 | 71 | 70·91 | 2·48 | 121 | 120·9 | 4·22 | 171 | 170·8 | 5·96 |
| 22 | 21·97 | 0·77 | 72 | 71·91 | 2·51 | 122 | 121·9 | 4·26 | 172 | 171·8 | 6·00 |
| 23 | 22·97 | 0·80 | 73 | 72·91 | 2·55 | 123 | 122·8 | 4·29 | 173 | 172·8 | 6·03 |
| 24 | 23·97 | 0·84 | 74 | 73·91 | 2·58 | 124 | 123·8 | 4·32 | 174 | 173·8 | 6·07 |
| 25 | 24·97 | 0·87 | 75 | 74·91 | 2·62 | 125 | 124·8 | 4·36 | 175 | 174·8 | 6·10 |
| 26 | 25·97 | 0·91 | 76 | 75·91 | 2·65 | 126 | 125·8 | 4·39 | 176 | 175·8 | 6·14 |
| 27 | 26·97 | 0·94 | 77 | 76·91 | 2·69 | 127 | 126·8 | 4·43 | 177 | 176·8 | 6·17 |
| 28 | 27·97 | 0·98 | 78 | 77·90 | 2·72 | 128 | 127·8 | 4·46 | 178 | 177·8 | 6·21 |
| 29 | 28·96 | 1·01 | 79 | 78·90 | 2·76 | 129 | 128·8 | 4·50 | 179 | 178·8 | 6·24 |
| 30 | 29·96 | 1·05 | 80 | 79·90 | 2·79 | 130 | 129·8 | 4·53 | 180 | 179·8 | 6·28 |
| 31 | 30·96 | 1·08 | 81 | 80·90 | 2·83 | 131 | 130·8 | 4·57 | 181 | 180·8 | 6·31 |
| 32 | 31·96 | 1·12 | 82 | 81·90 | 2·86 | 132 | 131·8 | 4·60 | 182 | 181·8 | 6·35 |
| 33 | 32·96 | 1·15 | 83 | 82·90 | 2·89 | 133 | 132·8 | 4·64 | 183 | 182·8 | 6·38 |
| 34 | 33·96 | 1·19 | 84 | 83·90 | 2·93 | 134 | 133·8 | 4·67 | 184 | 183·8 | 6·42 |
| 35 | 34·96 | 1·22 | 85 | 84·90 | 2·96 | 135 | 134·8 | 4·71 | 185 | 184·8 | 6·45 |
| 36 | 35·96 | 1·26 | 86 | 85·90 | 3·00 | 136 | 135·8 | 4·74 | 186 | 185·8 | 6·49 |
| 37 | 36·95 | 1·29 | 87 | 86·89 | 3·03 | 137 | 136·8 | 4·78 | 187 | 186·8 | 6·52 |
| 38 | 37·95 | 1·33 | 88 | 87·89 | 3·07 | 138 | 137·8 | 4·81 | 188 | 187·8 | 6·56 |
| 39 | 38·95 | 1·36 | 89 | 88·89 | 3·10 | 139 | 138·8 | 4·85 | 189 | 188·8 | 6·59 |
| 40 | 39·95 | 1·40 | 90 | 89·89 | 3·14 | 140 | 139·8 | 4·88 | 190 | 189·8 | 6·63 |
| 41 | 40·95 | 1·43 | 91 | 90·89 | 3·17 | 141 | 140·8 | 4·92 | 191 | 190·8 | 6·66 |
| 42 | 41·95 | 1·46 | 92 | 91·89 | 3·21 | 142 | 141·8 | 4·95 | 192 | 191·8 | 6·70 |
| 43 | 42·95 | 1·50 | 93 | 92·89 | 3·24 | 143 | 142·8 | 4·99 | 193 | 192·8 | 6·73 |
| 44 | 43·95 | 1·53 | 94 | 93·89 | 3·28 | 144 | 143·8 | 5·02 | 194 | 193·8 | 6·77 |
| 45 | 44·95 | 1·57 | 95 | 94·88 | 3·31 | 145 | 144·8 | 5·06 | 195 | 194·8 | 6·80 |
| 46 | 45·94 | 1·60 | 96 | 95·88 | 3·35 | 146 | 145·8 | 5·09 | 196 | 195·8 | 6·84 |
| 47 | 46·94 | 1·64 | 97 | 96·88 | 3·38 | 147 | 146·8 | 5·13 | 197 | 196·8 | 6·87 |
| 48 | 47·94 | 1·67 | 98 | 97·88 | 3·42 | 148 | 147·8 | 5·16 | 198 | 197·8 | 6·91 |
| 49 | 48·94 | 1·71 | 99 | 98·88 | 3·45 | 149 | 148·8 | 5·20 | 199 | 198·8 | 6·94 |
| 50 | 49·94 | 1·74 | 100 | 99·88 | 3·49 | 150 | 149·8 | 5·23 | 200 | 199·8 | 6·98 |
| 51 | 50·94 | 1·78 | 101 | 100·9 | 3·52 | 151 | 150·8 | 5·27 | 201 | 200·8 | 7·01 |
| 52 | 51·94 | 1·81 | 102 | 101·9 | 3·56 | 152 | 151·8 | 5·30 | 202 | 201·8 | 7·05 |
| 53 | 52·94 | 1·85 | 103 | 102·9 | 3·59 | 153 | 152·8 | 5·34 | 203 | 202·8 | 7·08 |
| 54 | 53·93 | 1·88 | 104 | 103·9 | 3·63 | 154 | 153·8 | 5·37 | 204 | 203·8 | 7·12 |
| 55 | 54·93 | 1·92 | 105 | 104·9 | 3·66 | 155 | 154·8 | 5·41 | 205 | 204·7 | 7·15 |
| 56 | 55·93 | 1·95 | 106 | 105·9 | 3·70 | 156 | 155·8 | 5·44 | 206 | 205·7 | 7·18 |
| 57 | 56·93 | 1·99 | 107 | 106·9 | 3·73 | 157 | 156·8 | 5·48 | 207 | 206·7 | 7·22 |
| 58 | 57·93 | 2·02 | 108 | 107·9 | 3·77 | 158 | 157·8 | 5·51 | 208 | 207·7 | 7·25 |
| 59 | 58·93 | 2·06 | 109 | 108·9 | 3·80 | 159 | 158·8 | 5·55 | 209 | 208·7 | 7·29 |
| 60 | 59·93 | 2·09 | 110 | 109·9 | 3·84 | 160 | 159·8 | 5·58 | 210 | 209·7 | 7·32 |

TABLE I

# 2° 10′

| G | D | H | G | D | H | G | D | H | G | D | H |
|---|---|---|---|---|---|---|---|---|---|---|---|
| 10 | 9.99 | 0.38 | 60 | 59.91 | 2.27 | 110 | 109.8 | 4.16 | 160 | 159.8 | 6.04 |
| 11 | 10.98 | 0.42 | 61 | 60.91 | 2.30 | 111 | 110.8 | 4.19 | 161 | 160.8 | 6.08 |
| 12 | 11.98 | 0.45 | 62 | 61.91 | 2.34 | 112 | 111.8 | 4.23 | 162 | 161.8 | 6.12 |
| 13 | 12.98 | 0.49 | 63 | 62.91 | 2.38 | 113 | 112.8 | 4.27 | 163 | 162.8 | 6.16 |
| 14 | 13.98 | 0.53 | 64 | 63.91 | 2.42 | 114 | 113.8 | 4.31 | 164 | 163.8 | 6.20 |
| 15 | 14.98 | 0.57 | 65 | 64.91 | 2.46 | 115 | 114.8 | 4.34 | 165 | 164.8 | 6.23 |
| 16 | 15.98 | 0.60 | 66 | 65.91 | 2.49 | 116 | 115.8 | 4.38 | 166 | 165.8 | 6.27 |
| 17 | 16.98 | 0.64 | 67 | 66.90 | 2.53 | 117 | 116.8 | 4.42 | 167 | 166.8 | 6.31 |
| 18 | 17.97 | 0.68 | 68 | 67.90 | 2.57 | 118 | 117.8 | 4.46 | 168 | 167.8 | 6.35 |
| 19 | 18.97 | 0.72 | 69 | 68.90 | 2.61 | 119 | 118.8 | 4.50 | 169 | 168.8 | 6.38 |
| 20 | 19.97 | 0.76 | 70 | 69.90 | 2.64 | 120 | 119.8 | 4.53 | 170 | 169.8 | 6.42 |
| 21 | 20.97 | 0.79 | 71 | 70.90 | 2.68 | 121 | 120.8 | 4.57 | 171 | 170.8 | 6.46 |
| 22 | 21.97 | 0.83 | 72 | 71.90 | 2.72 | 122 | 121.8 | 4.61 | 172 | 171.8 | 6.50 |
| 23 | 22.97 | 0.87 | 73 | 72.90 | 2.76 | 123 | 122.8 | 4.65 | 173 | 172.8 | 6.54 |
| 24 | 23.97 | 0.91 | 74 | 73.89 | 2.80 | 124 | 123.8 | 4.68 | 174 | 173.8 | 6.57 |
| 25 | 24.96 | 0.94 | 75 | 74.89 | 2.83 | 125 | 124.8 | 4.72 | 175 | 174.7 | 6.61 |
| 26 | 25.96 | 0.98 | 76 | 75.89 | 2.87 | 126 | 125.8 | 4.76 | 176 | 175.7 | 6.65 |
| 27 | 26.96 | 1.02 | 77 | 76.89 | 2.91 | 127 | 126.8 | 4.80 | 177 | 176.7 | 6.69 |
| 28 | 27.96 | 1.06 | 78 | 77.89 | 2.95 | 128 | 127.8 | 4.84 | 178 | 177.7 | 6.72 |
| 29 | 28.96 | 1.10 | 79 | 78.89 | 2.98 | 129 | 128.8 | 4.87 | 179 | 178.7 | 6.76 |
| 30 | 29.96 | 1.13 | 80 | 79.89 | 3.02 | 130 | 129.8 | 4.91 | 180 | 179.7 | 6.80 |
| 31 | 30.96 | 1.17 | 81 | 80.88 | 3.06 | 131 | 130.8 | 4.95 | 181 | 180.7 | 6.84 |
| 32 | 31.95 | 1.21 | 82 | 81.88 | 3.10 | 132 | 131.8 | 4.99 | 182 | 181.7 | 6.88 |
| 33 | 32.95 | 1.25 | 83 | 82.88 | 3.14 | 133 | 132.8 | 5.02 | 183 | 182.7 | 6.91 |
| 34 | 33.95 | 1.28 | 84 | 83.88 | 3.17 | 134 | 133.8 | 5.06 | 184 | 183.7 | 6.95 |
| 35 | 34.95 | 1.32 | 85 | 84.88 | 3.21 | 135 | 134.8 | 5.10 | 185 | 184.7 | 6.99 |
| 36 | 35.95 | 1.36 | 86 | 85.88 | 3.25 | 136 | 135.8 | 5.14 | 186 | 185.7 | 7.03 |
| 37 | 36.95 | 1.40 | 87 | 86.88 | 3.29 | 137 | 136.8 | 5.18 | 187 | 186.7 | 7.06 |
| 38 | 37.95 | 1.44 | 88 | 87.87 | 3.32 | 138 | 137.8 | 5.21 | 188 | 187.7 | 7.10 |
| 39 | 38.94 | 1.47 | 89 | 88.87 | 3.36 | 139 | 138.8 | 5.25 | 189 | 188.7 | 7.14 |
| 40 | 39.94 | 1.51 | 90 | 89.87 | 3.40 | 140 | 139.8 | 5.29 | 190 | 189.7 | 7.18 |
| 41 | 40.94 | 1.55 | 91 | 90.87 | 3.44 | 141 | 140.8 | 5.33 | 191 | 190.7 | 7.22 |
| 42 | 41.94 | 1.59 | 92 | 91.87 | 3.48 | 142 | 141.8 | 5.36 | 192 | 191.7 | 7.25 |
| 43 | 42.94 | 1.62 | 93 | 92.87 | 3.51 | 143 | 142.8 | 5.40 | 193 | 192.7 | 7.29 |
| 44 | 43.94 | 1.66 | 94 | 93.87 | 3.55 | 144 | 143.8 | 5.44 | 194 | 193.7 | 7.33 |
| 45 | 44.94 | 1.70 | 95 | 94.86 | 3.59 | 145 | 144.8 | 5.48 | 195 | 194.7 | 7.37 |
| 46 | 45.93 | 1.74 | 96 | 95.86 | 3.63 | 146 | 145.8 | 5.52 | 196 | 195.7 | 7.40 |
| 47 | 46.93 | 1.78 | 97 | 96.86 | 3.66 | 147 | 146.8 | 5.55 | 197 | 196.7 | 7.44 |
| 48 | 47.93 | 1.81 | 98 | 97.86 | 3.70 | 148 | 147.8 | 5.59 | 198 | 197.7 | 7.48 |
| 49 | 48.93 | 1.85 | 99 | 98.86 | 3.74 | 149 | 148.8 | 5.63 | 199 | 198.7 | 7.52 |
| 50 | 49.93 | 1.89 | 100 | 99.86 | 3.78 | 150 | 149.8 | 5.67 | 200 | 199.7 | 7.56 |
| 51 | 50.93 | 1.93 | 101 | 100.9 | 3.82 | 151 | 150.8 | 5.70 | 201 | 200.7 | 7.59 |
| 52 | 51.93 | 1.96 | 102 | 101.9 | 3.85 | 152 | 151.8 | 5.74 | 202 | 201.7 | 7.63 |
| 53 | 52.92 | 2.00 | 103 | 102.9 | 3.89 | 153 | 152.8 | 5.78 | 203 | 202.7 | 7.67 |
| 54 | 53.92 | 2.04 | 104 | 103.9 | 3.93 | 154 | 153.8 | 5.82 | 204 | 203.7 | 7.71 |
| 55 | 54.92 | 2.08 | 105 | 104.8 | 3.97 | 155 | 154.8 | 5.86 | 205 | 204.7 | 7.74 |
| 56 | 55.92 | 2.12 | 106 | 105.8 | 4.00 | 156 | 155.8 | 5.89 | 206 | 205.7 | 7.78 |
| 57 | 56.92 | 2.15 | 107 | 106.8 | 4.04 | 157 | 156.8 | 5.93 | 207 | 206.7 | 7.82 |
| 58 | 57.92 | 2.19 | 108 | 107.8 | 4.08 | 158 | 157.8 | 5.97 | 208 | 207.7 | 7.86 |
| 59 | 58.92 | 2.23 | 109 | 108.8 | 4.12 | 159 | 158.8 | 6.01 | 209 | 208.7 | 7.90 |
| 60 | 59.91 | 2.27 | 110 | 109.8 | 4.16 | 160 | 159.8 | 6.04 | 210 | 209.7 | 7.93 |

| G | D | H | G | D | H | G | D | H | G | D | H |
|---|---|---|---|---|---|---|---|---|---|---|---|
| 10 | 9.98 | 0.41 | 60 | 59.90 | 2.44 | 110 | 109.8 | 4.47 | 160 | 159.7 | 6.51 |
| 11 | 10.98 | 0.45 | 61 | 60.90 | 2.48 | 111 | 110.8 | 4.52 | 161 | 160.7 | 6.55 |
| 12 | 11.98 | 0.49 | 62 | 61.90 | 2.52 | 112 | 111.8 | 4.56 | 162 | 161.7 | 6.59 |
| 13 | 12.98 | 0.53 | 63 | 62.90 | 2.56 | 113 | 112.8 | 4.60 | 163 | 162.7 | 6.63 |
| 14 | 13.98 | 0.57 | 64 | 63.89 | 2.60 | 114 | 113.8 | 4.64 | 164 | 163.7 | 6.67 |
| 15 | 14.98 | 0.61 | 65 | 64.89 | 2.64 | 115 | 114.8 | 4.68 | 165 | 164.7 | 6.71 |
| 16 | 15.97 | 0.65 | 66 | 65.89 | 2.68 | 116 | 115.8 | 4.72 | 166 | 165.7 | 6.75 |
| 17 | 16.97 | 0.69 | 67 | 66.89 | 2.73 | 117 | 116.8 | 4.76 | 167 | 166.7 | 6.79 |
| 18 | 17.97 | 0.73 | 68 | 67.89 | 2.77 | 118 | 117.8 | 4.80 | 168 | 167.7 | 6.83 |
| 19 | 18.97 | 0.77 | 69 | 68.89 | 2.81 | 119 | 118.8 | 4.84 | 169 | 168.7 | 6.87 |
| 20 | 19.97 | 0.81 | 70 | 69.88 | 2.85 | 120 | 119.8 | 4.88 | 170 | 169.7 | 6.92 |
| 21 | 20.97 | 0.85 | 71 | 70.88 | 2.89 | 121 | 120.8 | 4.92 | 171 | 170.7 | 6.96 |
| 22 | 21.96 | 0.89 | 72 | 71.88 | 2.93 | 122 | 121.8 | 4.96 | 172 | 171.7 | 7.00 |
| 23 | 22.96 | 0.94 | 73 | 72.88 | 2.97 | 123 | 122.8 | 5.00 | 173 | 172.7 | 7.04 |
| 24 | 23.96 | 0.98 | 74 | 73.88 | 3.01 | 124 | 123.8 | 5.04 | 174 | 173.7 | 7.08 |
| 25 | 24.96 | 1.02 | 75 | 74.88 | 3.05 | 125 | 124.8 | 5.08 | 175 | 174.7 | 7.12 |
| 26 | 25.96 | 1.06 | 76 | 75.87 | 3.09 | 126 | 125.8 | 5.13 | 176 | 175.7 | 7.16 |
| 27 | 26.96 | 1.10 | 77 | 76.87 | 3.13 | 127 | 126.8 | 5.17 | 177 | 176.7 | 7.20 |
| 28 | 27.95 | 1.14 | 78 | 77.87 | 3.17 | 128 | 127.8 | 5.21 | 178 | 177.7 | 7.24 |
| 29 | 28.95 | 1.18 | 79 | 78.87 | 3.21 | 129 | 128.8 | 5.25 | 179 | 178.7 | 7.28 |
| 30 | 29.95 | 1.22 | 80 | 79.87 | 3.25 | 130 | 129.8 | 5.29 | 180 | 179.7 | 7.32 |
| 31 | 30.95 | 1.26 | 81 | 80.87 | 3.29 | 131 | 130.8 | 5.33 | 181 | 180.7 | 7.36 |
| 32 | 31.95 | 1.30 | 82 | 81.86 | 3.34 | 132 | 131.8 | 5.37 | 182 | 181.7 | 7.40 |
| 33 | 32.95 | 1.34 | 83 | 82.86 | 3.38 | 133 | 132.8 | 5.41 | 183 | 182.7 | 7.44 |
| 34 | 33.94 | 1.38 | 84 | 83.86 | 3.42 | 134 | 133.8 | 5.45 | 184 | 183.7 | 7.48 |
| 35 | 34.94 | 1.42 | 85 | 84.86 | 3.46 | 135 | 134.8 | 5.49 | 185 | 184.7 | 7.53 |
| 36 | 35.94 | 1.46 | 86 | 85.86 | 3.50 | 136 | 135.8 | 5.53 | 186 | 185.7 | 7.57 |
| 37 | 36.94 | 1.51 | 87 | 86.86 | 3.54 | 137 | 136.8 | 5.57 | 187 | 186.7 | 7.61 |
| 38 | 37.94 | 1.55 | 88 | 87.85 | 3.58 | 138 | 137.8 | 5.61 | 188 | 187.7 | 7.65 |
| 39 | 38.94 | 1.59 | 89 | 88.85 | 3.62 | 139 | 138.8 | 5.65 | 189 | 188.7 | 7.69 |
| 40 | 39.93 | 1.63 | 90 | 89.85 | 3.66 | 140 | 139.8 | 5.70 | 190 | 189.7 | 7.73 |
| 41 | 40.93 | 1.67 | 91 | 90.85 | 3.70 | 141 | 140.8 | 5.74 | 191 | 190.7 | 7.77 |
| 42 | 41.93 | 1.71 | 92 | 91.85 | 3.74 | 142 | 141.8 | 5.78 | 192 | 191.7 | 7.81 |
| 43 | 42.93 | 1.75 | 93 | 92.85 | 3.78 | 143 | 142.8 | 5.82 | 193 | 192.7 | 7.85 |
| 44 | 43.93 | 1.79 | 94 | 93.84 | 3.82 | 144 | 143.8 | 5.86 | 194 | 193.7 | 7.89 |
| 45 | 44.93 | 1.83 | 95 | 94.84 | 3.86 | 145 | 144.8 | 5.90 | 195 | 194.7 | 7.93 |
| 46 | 45.92 | 1.87 | 96 | 95.84 | 3.91 | 146 | 145.8 | 5.94 | 196 | 195.7 | 7.97 |
| 47 | 46.92 | 1.91 | 97 | 96.84 | 3.95 | 147 | 146.8 | 5.98 | 197 | 196.7 | 8.01 |
| 48 | 47.92 | 1.95 | 98 | 97.84 | 3.99 | 148 | 147.8 | 6.02 | 198 | 197.7 | 8.05 |
| 49 | 48.92 | 1.99 | 99 | 98.84 | 4.03 | 149 | 148.8 | 6.06 | 199 | 198.7 | 8.10 |
| 50 | 49.92 | 2.03 | 100 | 99.83 | 4.07 | 150 | 149.8 | 6.10 | 200 | 199.7 | 8.14 |
| 51 | 50.92 | 2.07 | 101 | 100.8 | 4.11 | 151 | 150.7 | 6.14 | 201 | 200.7 | 8.18 |
| 52 | 51.91 | 2.12 | 102 | 101.8 | 4.15 | 152 | 151.7 | 6.18 | 202 | 201.7 | 8.22 |
| 53 | 52.91 | 2.16 | 103 | 102.8 | 4.19 | 153 | 152.7 | 6.22 | 203 | 202.7 | 8.26 |
| 54 | 53.91 | 2.20 | 104 | 103.8 | 4.23 | 154 | 153.7 | 6.26 | 204 | 203.7 | 8.30 |
| 55 | 54.91 | 2.24 | 105 | 104.8 | 4.27 | 155 | 154.7 | 6.31 | 205 | 204.7 | 8.34 |
| 56 | 55.91 | 2.28 | 106 | 105.8 | 4.31 | 156 | 155.7 | 6.35 | 206 | 205.7 | 8.38 |
| 57 | 56.91 | 2.32 | 107 | 106.8 | 4.35 | 157 | 156.7 | 6.39 | 207 | 206.7 | 8.42 |
| 58 | 57.90 | 2.36 | 108 | 107.8 | 4.39 | 158 | 157.7 | 6.43 | 208 | 207.7 | 8.46 |
| 59 | 58.90 | 2.40 | 109 | 108.8 | 4.43 | 159 | 158.7 | 6.47 | 209 | 208.7 | 8.50 |
| 60 | 59.90 | 2.44 | 110 | 109.8 | 4.47 | 160 | 159.7 | 6.51 | 210 | 209.7 | 8.54 |

TABLE I

# 2° 30′

| G | D | H | G | D | H | G | D | H | G | D | H |
|---|---|---|---|---|---|---|---|---|---|---|---|
| 10 | 9.98 | 0.44 | 60 | 59.89 | 2.61 | 110 | 109.8 | 4.79 | 160 | 159.7 | 6.97 |
| 11 | 10.98 | 0.48 | 61 | 60.88 | 2.66 | 111 | 110.8 | 4.84 | 161 | 160.7 | 7.02 |
| 12 | 11.98 | 0.52 | 62 | 61.88 | 2.70 | 112 | 111.8 | 4.88 | 162 | 161.7 | 7.06 |
| 13 | 12.98 | 0.57 | 63 | 62.88 | 2.75 | 113 | 112.8 | 4.92 | 163 | 162.7 | 7.10 |
| 14 | 13.97 | 0.61 | 64 | 63.88 | 2.79 | 114 | 113.8 | 4.97 | 164 | 163.7 | 7.15 |
| 15 | 14.97 | 0.65 | 65 | 64.88 | 2.83 | 115 | 114.8 | 5.01 | 165 | 164.7 | 7.19 |
| 16 | 15.97 | 0.70 | 66 | 65.87 | 2.88 | 116 | 115.8 | 5.05 | 166 | 165.7 | 7.23 |
| 17 | 16.97 | 0.74 | 67 | 66.87 | 2.92 | 117 | 116.8 | 5.10 | 167 | 166.7 | 7.28 |
| 18 | 17.97 | 0.78 | 68 | 67.87 | 2.96 | 118 | 117.8 | 5.14 | 168 | 167.7 | 7.32 |
| 19 | 18.96 | 0.83 | 69 | 68.87 | 3.01 | 119 | 118.8 | 5.19 | 169 | 168.7 | 7.36 |
| 20 | 19.96 | 0.87 | 70 | 69.87 | 3.05 | 120 | 119.8 | 5.23 | 170 | 169.7 | 7.41 |
| 21 | 20.96 | 0.92 | 71 | 70.86 | 3.09 | 121 | 120.8 | 5.27 | 171 | 170.7 | 7.45 |
| 22 | 21.96 | 0.96 | 72 | 71.86 | 3.14 | 122 | 121.8 | 5.32 | 172 | 171.7 | 7.50 |
| 23 | 22.96 | 1.00 | 73 | 72.86 | 3.18 | 123 | 122.8 | 5.36 | 173 | 172.7 | 7.54 |
| 24 | 23.95 | 1.05 | 74 | 73.86 | 3.22 | 124 | 123.8 | 5.40 | 174 | 173.7 | 7.58 |
| 25 | 24.95 | 1.09 | 75 | 74.86 | 3.27 | 125 | 124.8 | 5.45 | 175 | 174.7 | 7.63 |
| 26 | 25.95 | 1.13 | 76 | 75.86 | 3.31 | 126 | 125.8 | 5.49 | 176 | 175.7 | 7.67 |
| 27 | 26.95 | 1.18 | 77 | 76.85 | 3.36 | 127 | 126.8 | 5.53 | 177 | 176.7 | 7.71 |
| 28 | 27.95 | 1.22 | 78 | 77.85 | 3.40 | 128 | 127.8 | 5.58 | 178 | 177.7 | 7.76 |
| 29 | 28.94 | 1.26 | 79 | 78.85 | 3.44 | 129 | 128.8 | 5.62 | 179 | 178.7 | 7.80 |
| 30 | 29.94 | 1.31 | 80 | 79.85 | 3.49 | 130 | 129.8 | 5.67 | 180 | 179.7 | 7.84 |
| 31 | 30.94 | 1.35 | 81 | 80.85 | 3.53 | 131 | 130.8 | 5.71 | 181 | 180.7 | 7.89 |
| 32 | 31.94 | 1.39 | 82 | 81.84 | 3.57 | 132 | 131.7 | 5.75 | 182 | 181.7 | 7.93 |
| 33 | 32.94 | 1.44 | 83 | 82.84 | 3.62 | 133 | 132.7 | 5.80 | 183 | 182.7 | 7.97 |
| 34 | 33.94 | 1.48 | 84 | 83.84 | 3.66 | 134 | 133.7 | 5.84 | 184 | 183.6 | 8.02 |
| 35 | 34.93 | 1.53 | 85 | 84.84 | 3.70 | 135 | 134.7 | 5.88 | 185 | 184.6 | 8.06 |
| 36 | 35.93 | 1.57 | 86 | 85.84 | 3.75 | 136 | 135.7 | 5.93 | 186 | 185.6 | 8.11 |
| 37 | 36.93 | 1.61 | 87 | 86.83 | 3.79 | 137 | 136.7 | 5.97 | 187 | 186.6 | 8.15 |
| 38 | 37.93 | 1.66 | 88 | 87.83 | 3.83 | 138 | 137.7 | 6.01 | 188 | 187.6 | 8.19 |
| 39 | 38.93 | 1.70 | 89 | 88.83 | 3.88 | 139 | 138.7 | 6.06 | 189 | 188.6 | 8.24 |
| 40 | 39.92 | 1.74 | 90 | 89.83 | 3.92 | 140 | 139.7 | 6.10 | 190 | 189.6 | 8.28 |
| 41 | 40.92 | 1.79 | 91 | 90.83 | 3.97 | 141 | 140.7 | 6.14 | 191 | 190.6 | 8.32 |
| 42 | 41.92 | 1.83 | 92 | 91.82 | 4.01 | 142 | 141.7 | 6.19 | 192 | 191.6 | 8.37 |
| 43 | 42.92 | 1.87 | 93 | 92.82 | 4.05 | 143 | 142.7 | 6.23 | 193 | 192.6 | 8.41 |
| 44 | 43.92 | 1.92 | 94 | 93.82 | 4.10 | 144 | 143.7 | 6.28 | 194 | 193.6 | 8.45 |
| 45 | 44.91 | 1.96 | 95 | 94.82 | 4.14 | 145 | 144.7 | 6.32 | 195 | 194.6 | 8.50 |
| 46 | 45.91 | 2.00 | 96 | 95.82 | 4.18 | 146 | 145.7 | 6.36 | 196 | 195.6 | 8.54 |
| 47 | 46.91 | 2.05 | 97 | 96.82 | 4.23 | 147 | 146.7 | 6.41 | 197 | 196.6 | 8.58 |
| 48 | 47.91 | 2.09 | 98 | 97.81 | 4.27 | 148 | 147.7 | 6.45 | 198 | 197.6 | 8.63 |
| 49 | 48.91 | 2.14 | 99 | 98.81 | 4.31 | 149 | 148.7 | 6.49 | 199 | 198.6 | 8.67 |
| 50 | 49.90 | 2.18 | 100 | 99.81 | 4.36 | 150 | 149.7 | 6.54 | 200 | 199.6 | 8.72 |
| 51 | 50.90 | 2.22 | 101 | 100.8 | 4.40 | 151 | 150.7 | 6.58 | 201 | 200.6 | 8.76 |
| 52 | 51.90 | 2.27 | 102 | 101.8 | 4.44 | 152 | 151.7 | 6.62 | 202 | 201.6 | 8.80 |
| 53 | 52.90 | 2.31 | 103 | 102.8 | 4.49 | 153 | 152.7 | 6.67 | 203 | 202.6 | 8.85 |
| 54 | 53.90 | 2.35 | 104 | 103.8 | 4.53 | 154 | 153.7 | 6.71 | 204 | 203.6 | 8.89 |
| 55 | 54.90 | 2.40 | 105 | 104.8 | 4.58 | 155 | 154.7 | 6.75 | 205 | 204.6 | 8.93 |
| 56 | 55.89 | 2.44 | 106 | 105.8 | 4.62 | 156 | 155.7 | 6.80 | 206 | 205.6 | 8.98 |
| 57 | 56.89 | 2.48 | 107 | 106.8 | 4.66 | 157 | 156.7 | 6.84 | 207 | 206.6 | 9.02 |
| 58 | 57.89 | 2.53 | 108 | 107.8 | 4.71 | 158 | 157.7 | 6.89 | 208 | 207.6 | 9.06 |
| 59 | 58.89 | 2.57 | 109 | 108.8 | 4.75 | 159 | 158.7 | 6.93 | 209 | 208.6 | 9.11 |
| 60 | 59.89 | 2.61 | 110 | 109.8 | 4.79 | 160 | 159.7 | 6.97 | 210 | 209.6 | 9.15 |

| G | D | H | G | D | H | G | D | H | G | D | H |
|---|---|---|---|---|---|---|---|---|---|---|---|
| 10 | 9·98 | 0·46 | 60 | 59·87 | 2·79 | 110 | 109·8 | 5·11 | 160 | 159·7 | 7·44 |
| 11 | 10·98 | 0·51 | 61 | 60·87 | 2·83 | 111 | 110·8 | 5·16 | 161 | 160·7 | 7·48 |
| 12 | 11·97 | 0·56 | 62 | 61·87 | 2·88 | 112 | 111·8 | 5·21 | 162 | 161·6 | 7·53 |
| 13 | 12·97 | 0·60 | 63 | 62·86 | 2·93 | 113 | 112·8 | 5·25 | 163 | 162·6 | 7·58 |
| 14 | 13·97 | 0·65 | 64 | 63·86 | 2·97 | 114 | 113·8 | 5·30 | 164 | 163·6 | 7·62 |
| 15 | 14·97 | 0·70 | 65 | 64·86 | 3·02 | 115 | 114·8 | 5·34 | 165 | 164·6 | 7·67 |
| 16 | 15·97 | 0·74 | 66 | 65·86 | 3·07 | 116 | 115·7 | 5·39 | 166 | 165·6 | 7·71 |
| 17 | 16·96 | 0·79 | 67 | 66·85 | 3·11 | 117 | 116·7 | 5·44 | 167 | 166·6 | 7·76 |
| 18 | 17·96 | 0·84 | 68 | 67·85 | 3·16 | 118 | 117·7 | 5·48 | 168 | 167·6 | 7·81 |
| 19 | 18·96 | 0·88 | 69 | 68·85 | 3·21 | 119 | 118·7 | 5·53 | 169 | 168·6 | 7·85 |
| 20 | 19·96 | 0·93 | 70 | 69·85 | 3·25 | 120 | 119·7 | 5·58 | 170 | 169·6 | 7·90 |
| 21 | 20·95 | 0·98 | 71 | 70·85 | 3·30 | 121 | 120·7 | 5·62 | 171 | 170·6 | 7·95 |
| 22 | 21·95 | 1·02 | 72 | 71·84 | 3·35 | 122 | 121·7 | 5·67 | 172 | 171·6 | 7·99 |
| 23 | 22·95 | 1·07 | 73 | 72·84 | 3·39 | 123 | 122·7 | 5·72 | 173 | 172·6 | 8·04 |
| 24 | 23·95 | 1·12 | 74 | 73·84 | 3·44 | 124 | 123·7 | 5·76 | 174 | 173·6 | 8·09 |
| 25 | 24·95 | 1·16 | 75 | 74·84 | 3·49 | 125 | 124·7 | 5·81 | 175 | 174·6 | 8·13 |
| 26 | 25·94 | 1·21 | 76 | 75·84 | 3·53 | 126 | 125·7 | 5·86 | 176 | 175·6 | 8·18 |
| 27 | 26·94 | 1·25 | 77 | 76·83 | 3·58 | 127 | 126·7 | 5·90 | 177 | 176·6 | 8·23 |
| 28 | 27·94 | 1·30 | 78 | 77·83 | 3·62 | 128 | 127·7 | 5·95 | 178 | 177·6 | 8·27 |
| 29 | 28·94 | 1·35 | 79 | 78·83 | 3·67 | 129 | 128·7 | 6·00 | 179 | 178·6 | 8·32 |
| 30 | 29·94 | 1·39 | 80 | 79·83 | 3·72 | 130 | 129·7 | 6·04 | 180 | 179·6 | 8·37 |
| 31 | 30·93 | 1·44 | 81 | 80·82 | 3·76 | 131 | 130·7 | 6·09 | 181 | 180·6 | 8·41 |
| 32 | 31·93 | 1·49 | 82 | 81·82 | 3·81 | 132 | 131·7 | 6·13 | 182 | 181·6 | 8·46 |
| 33 | 32·93 | 1·53 | 83 | 82·82 | 3·86 | 133 | 132·7 | 6·18 | 183 | 182·6 | 8·50 |
| 34 | 33·93 | 1·58 | 84 | 83·82 | 3·90 | 134 | 133·7 | 6·23 | 184 | 183·6 | 8·55 |
| 35 | 34·92 | 1·63 | 85 | 84·82 | 3·95 | 135 | 134·7 | 6·27 | 185 | 184·6 | 8·60 |
| 36 | 35·92 | 1·67 | 86 | 85·81 | 4·00 | 136 | 135·7 | 6·32 | 186 | 185·6 | 8·64 |
| 37 | 36·92 | 1·72 | 87 | 86·81 | 4·04 | 137 | 136·7 | 6·37 | 187 | 186·6 | 8·69 |
| 38 | 37·92 | 1·77 | 88 | 87·81 | 4·09 | 138 | 137·7 | 6·41 | 188 | 187·6 | 8·74 |
| 39 | 38·92 | 1·81 | 89 | 88·81 | 4·14 | 139 | 138·7 | 6·46 | 189 | 188·6 | 8·78 |
| 40 | 39·91 | 1·86 | 90 | 89·81 | 4·18 | 140 | 139·7 | 6·51 | 190 | 189·6 | 8·83 |
| 41 | 40·91 | 1·91 | 91 | 90·80 | 4·23 | 141 | 140·7 | 6·55 | 191 | 190·6 | 8·88 |
| 42 | 41·91 | 1·95 | 92 | 91·80 | 4·28 | 142 | 141·7 | 6·60 | 192 | 191·6 | 8·92 |
| 43 | 42·91 | 2·00 | 93 | 92·80 | 4·32 | 143 | 142·7 | 6·65 | 193 | 192·6 | 8·97 |
| 44 | 43·90 | 2·04 | 94 | 93·80 | 4·37 | 144 | 143·7 | 6·69 | 194 | 193·6 | 9·02 |
| 45 | 44·90 | 2·09 | 95 | 94·79 | 4·42 | 145 | 144·7 | 6·74 | 195 | 194·6 | 9·06 |
| 46 | 45·90 | 2·14 | 96 | 95·79 | 4·46 | 146 | 145·7 | 6·79 | 196 | 195·6 | 9·11 |
| 47 | 46·90 | 2·18 | 97 | 96·79 | 4·51 | 147 | 146·7 | 6·83 | 197 | 196·6 | 9·16 |
| 48 | 47·90 | 2·23 | 98 | 97·79 | 4·55 | 148 | 147·7 | 6·88 | 198 | 197·6 | 9·20 |
| 49 | 48·89 | 2·28 | 99 | 98·79 | 4·60 | 149 | 148·7 | 6·92 | 199 | 198·6 | 9·25 |
| 50 | 49·89 | 2·32 | 100 | 99·78 | 4·65 | 150 | 149·7 | 6·97 | 200 | 199·6 | 9·29 |
| 51 | 50·89 | 2·37 | 101 | 100·8 | 4·69 | 151 | 150·7 | 7·02 | 201 | 200·6 | 9·34 |
| 52 | 51·89 | 2·42 | 102 | 101·8 | 4·74 | 152 | 151·7 | 7·06 | 202 | 201·6 | 9·39 |
| 53 | 52·89 | 2·46 | 103 | 102·8 | 4·79 | 153 | 152·7 | 7·11 | 203 | 202·6 | 9·43 |
| 54 | 53·88 | 2·51 | 104 | 103·8 | 4·83 | 154 | 153·7 | 7·16 | 204 | 203·6 | 9·48 |
| 55 | 54·88 | 2·56 | 105 | 104·8 | 4·88 | 155 | 154·7 | 7·20 | 205 | 204·6 | 9·53 |
| 56 | 55·88 | 2·60 | 106 | 105·8 | 4·93 | 156 | 155·7 | 7·25 | 206 | 205·6 | 9·57 |
| 57 | 56·88 | 2·65 | 107 | 106·8 | 4·97 | 157 | 156·7 | 7·30 | 207 | 206·6 | 9·62 |
| 58 | 57·87 | 2·70 | 108 | 107·8 | 5·02 | 158 | 157·7 | 7·34 | 208 | 207·5 | 9·67 |
| 59 | 58·87 | 2·74 | 109 | 108·8 | 5·07 | 159 | 158·7 | 7·39 | 209 | 208·5 | 9·71 |
| 60 | 59·87 | 2·79 | 110 | 109·8 | 5·11 | 160 | 159·7 | 7·44 | 210 | 209·5 | 9·76 |

TABLE I     **2° 50'**

| G | D | H | G | D | H | G | D | H | G | D | H |
|---|---|---|---|---|---|---|---|---|---|---|---|
| 10 | 9·98 | 0·49 | 60 | 59·85 | 2·96 | 110 | 109·7 | 5·43 | 160 | 159·6 | 7·90 |
| 11 | 10·97 | 0·54 | 61 | 60·85 | 3·01 | 111 | 110·7 | 5·48 | 161 | 160·6 | 7·95 |
| 12 | 11·97 | 0·59 | 62 | 61·85 | 3·06 | 112 | 111·7 | 5·53 | 162 | 161·6 | 8·00 |
| 13 | 12·97 | 0·64 | 63 | 62·85 | 3·11 | 113 | 112·7 | 5·58 | 163 | 162·6 | 8·05 |
| 14 | 13·97 | 0·69 | 64 | 63·84 | 3·16 | 114 | 113·7 | 5·63 | 164 | 163·6 | 8·10 |
| 15 | 14·96 | 0·74 | 65 | 64·84 | 3·21 | 115 | 114·7 | 5·68 | 165 | 164·6 | 8·15 |
| 16 | 15·96 | 0·79 | 66 | 65·84 | 3·26 | 116 | 115·7 | 5·73 | 166 | 165·6 | 8·20 |
| 17 | 16·96 | 0·84 | 67 | 66·84 | 3·31 | 117 | 116·7 | 5·78 | 167 | 166·6 | 8·24 |
| 18 | 17·96 | 0·89 | 68 | 67·83 | 3·36 | 118 | 117·7 | 5·83 | 168 | 167·6 | 8·29 |
| 19 | 18·95 | 0·94 | 69 | 68·83 | 3·41 | 119 | 118·7 | 5·88 | 169 | 168·6 | 8·34 |
| 20 | 19·95 | 0·99 | 70 | 69·83 | 3·46 | 120 | 119·7 | 5·92 | 170 | 169·6 | 8·39 |
| 21 | 20·95 | 1·04 | 71 | 70·83 | 3·51 | 121 | 120·7 | 5·97 | 171 | 170·6 | 8·44 |
| 22 | 21·95 | 1·09 | 72 | 71·82 | 3·55 | 122 | 121·7 | 6·02 | 172 | 171·6 | 8·49 |
| 23 | 22·94 | 1·14 | 73 | 72·82 | 3·60 | 123 | 122·7 | 6·07 | 173 | 172·6 | 8·54 |
| 24 | 23·94 | 1·18 | 74 | 73·82 | 3·65 | 124 | 123·7 | 6·12 | 174 | 173·6 | 8·59 |
| 25 | 24·94 | 1·23 | 75 | 74·82 | 3·70 | 125 | 124·7 | 6·17 | 175 | 174·6 | 8·64 |
| 26 | 25·94 | 1·28 | 76 | 75·81 | 3·75 | 126 | 125·7 | 6·22 | 176 | 175·6 | 8·69 |
| 27 | 26·93 | 1·33 | 77 | 76·81 | 3·80 | 127 | 126·7 | 6·27 | 177 | 176·6 | 8·74 |
| 28 | 27·93 | 1·38 | 78 | 77·81 | 3·85 | 128 | 127·7 | 6·32 | 178 | 177·6 | 8·79 |
| 29 | 28·93 | 1·43 | 79 | 78·81 | 3·90 | 129 | 128·7 | 6·37 | 179 | 178·6 | 8·84 |
| 30 | 29·93 | 1·48 | 80 | 79·80 | 3·95 | 130 | 129·7 | 6·42 | 180 | 179·6 | 8·89 |
| 31 | 30·92 | 1·53 | 81 | 80·80 | 4·00 | 131 | 130·7 | 6·47 | 181 | 180·6 | 8·94 |
| 32 | 31·92 | 1·58 | 82 | 81·80 | 4·05 | 132 | 131·7 | 6·52 | 182 | 181·6 | 8·99 |
| 33 | 32·92 | 1·63 | 83 | 82·80 | 4·10 | 133 | 132·7 | 6·57 | 183 | 182·6 | 9·03 |
| 34 | 33·92 | 1·68 | 84 | 83·79 | 4·15 | 134 | 133·7 | 6·62 | 184 | 183·6 | 9·08 |
| 35 | 34·91 | 1·73 | 85 | 84·79 | 4·20 | 135 | 134·7 | 6·66 | 185 | 184·5 | 9·13 |
| 36 | 35·91 | 1·78 | 86 | 85·79 | 4·25 | 136 | 135·7 | 6·71 | 186 | 185·5 | 9·18 |
| 37 | 36·91 | 1·83 | 87 | 86·79 | 4·30 | 137 | 136·7 | 6·76 | 187 | 186·5 | 9·23 |
| 38 | 37·91 | 1·88 | 88 | 87·78 | 4·34 | 138 | 137·7 | 6·81 | 188 | 187·5 | 9·28 |
| 39 | 38·90 | 1·93 | 89 | 88·78 | 4·39 | 139 | 138·7 | 6·86 | 189 | 188·5 | 9·33 |
| 40 | 39·90 | 1·97 | 90 | 89·78 | 4·44 | 140 | 139·7 | 6·91 | 190 | 189·5 | 9·38 |
| 41 | 40·90 | 2·02 | 91 | 90·78 | 4·49 | 141 | 140·7 | 6·96 | 191 | 190·5 | 9·43 |
| 42 | 41·90 | 2·07 | 92 | 91·78 | 4·54 | 142 | 141·7 | 7·01 | 192 | 191·5 | 9·48 |
| 43 | 42·89 | 2·12 | 93 | 92·77 | 4·59 | 143 | 142·7 | 7·06 | 193 | 192·5 | 9·53 |
| 44 | 43·89 | 2·17 | 94 | 93·77 | 4·64 | 144 | 143·6 | 7·11 | 194 | 193·5 | 9·58 |
| 45 | 44·89 | 2·22 | 95 | 94·77 | 4·69 | 145 | 144·6 | 7·16 | 195 | 194·5 | 9·63 |
| 46 | 45·89 | 2·27 | 96 | 95·77 | 4·74 | 146 | 145·6 | 7·21 | 196 | 195·5 | 9·68 |
| 47 | 46·89 | 2·32 | 97 | 96·76 | 4·79 | 147 | 146·6 | 7·26 | 197 | 196·5 | 9·73 |
| 48 | 47·88 | 2·37 | 98 | 97·76 | 4·84 | 148 | 147·6 | 7·31 | 198 | 197·5 | 9·78 |
| 49 | 48·88 | 2·42 | 99 | 98·76 | 4·89 | 149 | 148·6 | 7·36 | 199 | 198·5 | 9·82 |
| 50 | 49·88 | 2·47 | 100 | 99·76 | 4·94 | 150 | 149·6 | 7·41 | 200 | 199·5 | 9·87 |
| 51 | 50·88 | 2·52 | 101 | 100·8 | 4·99 | 151 | 150·6 | 7·45 | 201 | 200·5 | 9·92 |
| 52 | 51·87 | 2·57 | 102 | 101·8 | 5·04 | 152 | 151·6 | 7·50 | 202 | 201·5 | 9·97 |
| 53 | 52·87 | 2·62 | 103 | 102·7 | 5·09 | 153 | 152·6 | 7·55 | 203 | 202·5 | 10·02 |
| 54 | 53·87 | 2·67 | 104 | 103·7 | 5·13 | 154 | 153·6 | 7·60 | 204 | 203·5 | 10·07 |
| 55 | 54·87 | 2·72 | 105 | 104·7 | 5·18 | 155 | 154·6 | 7·65 | 205 | 204·5 | 10·12 |
| 56 | 55·86 | 2·76 | 106 | 105·7 | 5·23 | 156 | 155·6 | 7·70 | 206 | 205·5 | 10·17 |
| 57 | 56·86 | 2·81 | 107 | 106·7 | 5·28 | 157 | 156·6 | 7·75 | 207 | 206·5 | 10·22 |
| 58 | 57·86 | 2·86 | 108 | 107·7 | 5·33 | 158 | 157·6 | 7·80 | 208 | 207·5 | 10·27 |
| 59 | 58·86 | 2·91 | 109 | 108·7 | 5·38 | 159 | 158·6 | 7·85 | 209 | 208·5 | 10·32 |
| 60 | 59·85 | 2·96 | 110 | 109·7 | 5·43 | 160 | 159·6 | 7·90 | 210 | 209·5 | 10·37 |

| G | D | H | G | D | H | G | D | H | G | D | H |
|---|---|---|---|---|---|---|---|---|---|---|---|
| 10 | 9·97 | 0·52 | 60 | 59·84 | 3·14 | 110 | 109·7 | 5·75 | 160 | 159·6 | 8·36 |
| 11 | 10·97 | 0·57 | 61 | 60·83 | 3·19 | 111 | 110·7 | 5·80 | 161 | 160·6 | 8·41 |
| 12 | 11·97 | 0·63 | 62 | 61·83 | 3·24 | 112 | 111·7 | 5·85 | 162 | 161·6 | 8·47 |
| 13 | 12·96 | 0·68 | 63 | 62·83 | 3·29 | 113 | 112·7 | 5·91 | 163 | 162·6 | 8·52 |
| 14 | 13·96 | 0·73 | 64 | 63·82 | 3·34 | 114 | 113·7 | 5·96 | 164 | 163·6 | 8·57 |
| 15 | 14·96 | 0·78 | 65 | 64·82 | 3·40 | 115 | 114·7 | 6·01 | 165 | 164·5 | 8·62 |
| 16 | 15·96 | 0·84 | 66 | 65·82 | 3·45 | 116 | 115·7 | 6·06 | 166 | 165·5 | 8·68 |
| 17 | 16·95 | 0·89 | 67 | 66·82 | 3·50 | 117 | 116·7 | 6·11 | 167 | 166·5 | 8·73 |
| 18 | 17·95 | 0·94 | 68 | 67·81 | 3·55 | 118 | 117·7 | 6·17 | 168 | 167·5 | 8·78 |
| 19 | 18·95 | 0·99 | 69 | 68·81 | 3·61 | 119 | 118·7 | 6·22 | 169 | 168·5 | 8·83 |
| 20 | 19·95 | 1·05 | 70 | 69·81 | 3·66 | 120 | 119·7 | 6·27 | 170 | 169·5 | 8·88 |
| 21 | 20·94 | 1·10 | 71 | 70·81 | 3·71 | 121 | 120·7 | 6·32 | 171 | 170·5 | 8·94 |
| 22 | 21·94 | 1·15 | 72 | 71·80 | 3·76 | 122 | 121·7 | 6·38 | 172 | 171·5 | 8·99 |
| 23 | 22·94 | 1·20 | 73 | 72·80 | 3·82 | 123 | 122·7 | 6·43 | 173 | 172·5 | 9·04 |
| 24 | 23·93 | 1·25 | 74 | 73·80 | 3·87 | 124 | 123·7 | 6·48 | 174 | 173·5 | 9·09 |
| 25 | 24·93 | 1·31 | 75 | 74·79 | 3·92 | 125 | 124·7 | 6·53 | 175 | 174·5 | 9·15 |
| 26 | 25·93 | 1·36 | 76 | 75·79 | 3·97 | 126 | 125·7 | 6·59 | 176 | 175·5 | 9·20 |
| 27 | 26·93 | 1·41 | 77 | 76·79 | 4·02 | 127 | 126·7 | 6·64 | 177 | 176·5 | 9·25 |
| 28 | 27·92 | 1·46 | 78 | 77·79 | 4·08 | 128 | 127·6 | 6·69 | 178 | 177·5 | 9·30 |
| 29 | 28·92 | 1·52 | 79 | 78·78 | 4·13 | 129 | 128·6 | 6·74 | 179 | 178·5 | 9·36 |
| 30 | 29·92 | 1·57 | 80 | 79·78 | 4·18 | 130 | 129·6 | 6·79 | 180 | 179·5 | 9·41 |
| 31 | 30·92 | 1·62 | 81 | 80·78 | 4·23 | 131 | 130·6 | 6·85 | 181 | 180·5 | 9·46 |
| 32 | 31·91 | 1·67 | 82 | 81·78 | 4·29 | 132 | 131·6 | 6·90 | 182 | 181·5 | 9·51 |
| 33 | 32·91 | 1·72 | 83 | 82·77 | 4·34 | 133 | 132·6 | 6·95 | 183 | 182·5 | 9·56 |
| 34 | 33·91 | 1·78 | 84 | 83·77 | 4·39 | 134 | 133·6 | 7·00 | 184 | 183·5 | 9·62 |
| 35 | 34·90 | 1·83 | 85 | 84·77 | 4·44 | 135 | 134·6 | 7·06 | 185 | 184·5 | 9·67 |
| 36 | 35·90 | 1·88 | 86 | 85·76 | 4·49 | 136 | 135·6 | 7·11 | 186 | 185·5 | 9·72 |
| 37 | 36·90 | 1·93 | 87 | 86·76 | 4·55 | 137 | 136·6 | 7·16 | 187 | 186·5 | 9·77 |
| 38 | 37·90 | 1·99 | 88 | 87·76 | 4·60 | 138 | 137·6 | 7·21 | 188 | 187·5 | 9·83 |
| 39 | 38·89 | 2·04 | 89 | 88·76 | 4·65 | 139 | 138·6 | 7·26 | 189 | 188·5 | 9·88 |
| 40 | 39·89 | 2·09 | 90 | 89·75 | 4·70 | 140 | 139·6 | 7·32 | 190 | 189·5 | 9·93 |
| 41 | 40·89 | 2·14 | 91 | 90·75 | 4·76 | 141 | 140·6 | 7·37 | 191 | 190·5 | 9·98 |
| 42 | 41·88 | 2·20 | 92 | 91·75 | 4·81 | 142 | 141·6 | 7·42 | 192 | 191·5 | 10·03 |
| 43 | 42·88 | 2·25 | 93 | 92·75 | 4·86 | 143 | 142·6 | 7·47 | 193 | 192·5 | 10·09 |
| 44 | 43·88 | 2·30 | 94 | 93·74 | 4·91 | 144 | 143·6 | 7·53 | 194 | 193·5 | 10·14 |
| 45 | 44·88 | 2·35 | 95 | 94·74 | 4·97 | 145 | 144·6 | 7·58 | 195 | 194·5 | 10·19 |
| 46 | 45·87 | 2·40 | 96 | 95·74 | 5·02 | 146 | 145·6 | 7·63 | 196 | 195·5 | 10·24 |
| 47 | 46·87 | 2·46 | 97 | 96·73 | 5·07 | 147 | 146·6 | 7·68 | 197 | 196·5 | 10·30 |
| 48 | 47·87 | 2·51 | 98 | 97·73 | 5·12 | 148 | 147·6 | 7·74 | 198 | 197·5 | 10·35 |
| 49 | 48·87 | 2·56 | 99 | 98·73 | 5·17 | 149 | 148·6 | 7·79 | 199 | 198·5 | 10·40 |
| 50 | 49·86 | 2·61 | 100 | 99·73 | 5·23 | 150 | 149·6 | 7·84 | 200 | 199·5 | 10·45 |
| 51 | 50·86 | 2·67 | 101 | 100·7 | 5·28 | 151 | 150·6 | 7·89 | 201 | 200·4 | 10·51 |
| 52 | 51·86 | 2·72 | 102 | 101·7 | 5·33 | 152 | 151·6 | 7·94 | 202 | 201·4 | 10·56 |
| 53 | 52·85 | 2·77 | 103 | 102·7 | 5·38 | 153 | 152·6 | 8·00 | 203 | 202·4 | 10·61 |
| 54 | 53·85 | 2·82 | 104 | 103·7 | 5·44 | 154 | 153·6 | 8·05 | 204 | 203·4 | 10·66 |
| 55 | 54·85 | 2·87 | 105 | 104·7 | 5·49 | 155 | 154·6 | 8·10 | 205 | 204·4 | 10·71 |
| 56 | 55·85 | 2·93 | 106 | 105·7 | 5·54 | 156 | 155·6 | 8·15 | 206 | 205·4 | 10·77 |
| 57 | 56·84 | 2·98 | 107 | 106·7 | 5·59 | 157 | 156·6 | 8·21 | 207 | 206·4 | 10·82 |
| 58 | 57·84 | 3·03 | 108 | 107·7 | 5·64 | 158 | 157·6 | 8·26 | 208 | 207·4 | 10·87 |
| 59 | 58·84 | 3·08 | 109 | 108·7 | 5·70 | 159 | 158·6 | 8·31 | 209 | 208·4 | 10·92 |
| 60 | 59·84 | 3·14 | 110 | 109·7 | 5·75 | 160 | 159·6 | 8·36 | 210 | 209·4 | 10·98 |

| G | D | H | G | D | H | G | D | H | G | D | H |
|---|---|---|---|---|---|---|---|---|---|---|---|
| 10 | 9.97 | 0.55 | 60 | 59.82 | 3.31 | 110 | 109.7 | 6.07 | 160 | 159.5 | 8.82 |
| 11 | 10.97 | 0.61 | 61 | 60.81 | 3.36 | 111 | 110.7 | 6.12 | 161 | 160.5 | 8.88 |
| 12 | 11.96 | 0.66 | 62 | 61.81 | 3.42 | 112 | 111.7 | 6.18 | 162 | 161.5 | 8.94 |
| 13 | 12.96 | 0.72 | 63 | 62.81 | 3.47 | 113 | 112.7 | 6.23 | 163 | 162.5 | 8.99 |
| 14 | 13.96 | 0.77 | 64 | 63.80 | 3.53 | 114 | 113.7 | 6.29 | 164 | 163.5 | 9.05 |
| 15 | 14.95 | 0.83 | 65 | 64.80 | 3.59 | 115 | 114.6 | 6.34 | 165 | 164.5 | 9.10 |
| 16 | 15.95 | 0.88 | 66 | 65.80 | 3.64 | 116 | 115.6 | 6.40 | 166 | 165.5 | 9.16 |
| 17 | 16.95 | 0.94 | 67 | 66.80 | 3.70 | 117 | 116.6 | 6.45 | 167 | 166.5 | 9.21 |
| 18 | 17.95 | 0.99 | 68 | 67.79 | 3.75 | 118 | 117.6 | 6.51 | 168 | 167.5 | 9.27 |
| 19 | 18.94 | 1.05 | 69 | 68.79 | 3.81 | 119 | 118.6 | 6.56 | 169 | 168.5 | 9.32 |
| 20 | 19.94 | 1.10 | 70 | 69.79 | 3.86 | 120 | 119.6 | 6.62 | 170 | 169.5 | 9.38 |
| 21 | 20.94 | 1.16 | 71 | 70.78 | 3.92 | 121 | 120.6 | 6.67 | 171 | 170.5 | 9.43 |
| 22 | 21.93 | 1.21 | 72 | 71.78 | 3.97 | 122 | 121.6 | 6.73 | 172 | 171.5 | 9.49 |
| 23 | 22.93 | 1.27 | 73 | 72.78 | 4.03 | 123 | 122.6 | 6.78 | 173 | 172.5 | 9.54 |
| 24 | 23.93 | 1.32 | 74 | 73.77 | 4.08 | 124 | 123.6 | 6.84 | 174 | 173.5 | 9.60 |
| 25 | 24.92 | 1.38 | 75 | 74.77 | 4.14 | 125 | 124.6 | 6.89 | 175 | 174.5 | 9.65 |
| 26 | 25.92 | 1.43 | 76 | 75.77 | 4.19 | 126 | 125.6 | 6.95 | 176 | 175.5 | 9.71 |
| 27 | 26.92 | 1.49 | 77 | 76.76 | 4.25 | 127 | 126.6 | 7.00 | 177 | 176.5 | 9.76 |
| 28 | 27.91 | 1.54 | 78 | 77.76 | 4.30 | 128 | 127.6 | 7.06 | 178 | 177.5 | 9.82 |
| 29 | 28.91 | 1.60 | 79 | 78.76 | 4.36 | 129 | 128.6 | 7.12 | 179 | 178.5 | 9.87 |
| 30 | 29.91 | 1.65 | 80 | 79.76 | 4.41 | 130 | 129.6 | 7.17 | 180 | 179.5 | 9.93 |
| 31 | 30.91 | 1.71 | 81 | 80.75 | 4.47 | 131 | 130.6 | 7.23 | 181 | 180.4 | 9.98 |
| 32 | 31.90 | 1.76 | 82 | 81.75 | 4.52 | 132 | 131.6 | 7.28 | 182 | 181.4 | 10.04 |
| 33 | 32.90 | 1.82 | 83 | 82.75 | 4.58 | 133 | 132.6 | 7.34 | 183 | 182.4 | 10.09 |
| 34 | 33.90 | 1.88 | 84 | 83.74 | 4.63 | 134 | 133.6 | 7.39 | 184 | 183.4 | 10.15 |
| 35 | 34.89 | 1.93 | 85 | 84.74 | 4.69 | 135 | 134.6 | 7.45 | 185 | 184.4 | 10.20 |
| 36 | 35.89 | 1.99 | 86 | 85.74 | 4.74 | 136 | 135.6 | 7.50 | 186 | 185.4 | 10.26 |
| 37 | 36.89 | 2.04 | 87 | 86.73 | 4.80 | 137 | 136.6 | 7.56 | 187 | 186.4 | 10.31 |
| 38 | 37.88 | 2.10 | 88 | 87.73 | 4.85 | 138 | 137.6 | 7.61 | 188 | 187.4 | 10.37 |
| 39 | 38.88 | 2.15 | 89 | 88.73 | 4.91 | 139 | 138.6 | 7.67 | 189 | 188.4 | 10.42 |
| 40 | 39.88 | 2.21 | 90 | 89.73 | 4.96 | 140 | 139.6 | 7.72 | 190 | 189.4 | 10.48 |
| 41 | 40.87 | 2.26 | 91 | 90.72 | 5.02 | 141 | 140.6 | 7.78 | 191 | 190.4 | 10.53 |
| 42 | 41.87 | 2.32 | 92 | 91.72 | 5.07 | 142 | 141.6 | 7.83 | 192 | 191.4 | 10.59 |
| 43 | 42.87 | 2.37 | 93 | 92.72 | 5.13 | 143 | 142.6 | 7.89 | 193 | 192.4 | 10.65 |
| 44 | 43.87 | 2.43 | 94 | 93.71 | 5.18 | 144 | 143.6 | 7.94 | 194 | 193.4 | 10.70 |
| 45 | 44.86 | 2.48 | 95 | 94.71 | 5.24 | 145 | 144.6 | 8.00 | 195 | 194.4 | 10.76 |
| 46 | 45.86 | 2.54 | 96 | 95.71 | 5.29 | 146 | 145.6 | 8.05 | 196 | 195.4 | 10.81 |
| 47 | 46.86 | 2.59 | 97 | 96.70 | 5.35 | 147 | 146.6 | 8.11 | 197 | 196.4 | 10.87 |
| 48 | 47.85 | 2.65 | 98 | 97.70 | 5.41 | 148 | 147.5 | 8.16 | 198 | 197.4 | 10.92 |
| 49 | 48.85 | 2.70 | 99 | 98.70 | 5.46 | 149 | 148.5 | 8.22 | 199 | 198.4 | 10.98 |
| 50 | 49.85 | 2.76 | 100 | 99.69 | 5.52 | 150 | 149.5 | 8.27 | 200 | 199.4 | 11.03 |
| 51 | 50.84 | 2.81 | 101 | 100.7 | 5.57 | 151 | 150.5 | 8.33 | 201 | 200.4 | 11.09 |
| 52 | 51.84 | 2.87 | 102 | 101.7 | 5.63 | 152 | 151.5 | 8.38 | 202 | 201.4 | 11.14 |
| 53 | 52.84 | 2.92 | 103 | 102.7 | 5.68 | 153 | 152.5 | 8.44 | 203 | 202.4 | 11.20 |
| 54 | 53.84 | 2.98 | 104 | 103.7 | 5.74 | 154 | 153.5 | 8.49 | 204 | 203.4 | 11.25 |
| 55 | 54.83 | 3.03 | 105 | 104.7 | 5.79 | 155 | 154.5 | 8.55 | 205 | 204.4 | 11.31 |
| 56 | 55.83 | 3.09 | 106 | 105.7 | 5.85 | 156 | 155.5 | 8.60 | 206 | 205.4 | 11.36 |
| 57 | 56.83 | 3.14 | 107 | 106.7 | 5.90 | 157 | 156.5 | 8.66 | 207 | 206.4 | 11.42 |
| 58 | 57.82 | 3.20 | 108 | 107.7 | 5.96 | 158 | 157.5 | 8.71 | 208 | 207.4 | 11.47 |
| 59 | 58.82 | 3.25 | 109 | 108.7 | 6.01 | 159 | 158.5 | 8.77 | 209 | 208.4 | 11.53 |
| 60 | 59.82 | 3.31 | 110 | 109.7 | 6.07 | 160 | 159.5 | 8.82 | 210 | 209.4 | 11.58 |

TABLE I

| G | D | H | G | D | H | G | D | H | G | D | H |
|---|---|---|---|---|---|---|---|---|---|---|---|
| 10 | 9·97 | 0·58 | 60 | 59·80 | 3·48 | 110 | 109·6 | 6·39 | 160 | 159·5 | 9·29 |
| 11 | 10·96 | 0·64 | 61 | 60·79 | 3·54 | 111 | 110·6 | 6·44 | 161 | 160·5 | 9·35 |
| 12 | 11·96 | 0·70 | 62 | 61·79 | 3·60 | 112 | 111·6 | 6·50 | 162 | 161·5 | 9·40 |
| 13 | 12·96 | 0·75 | 63 | 62·79 | 3·66 | 113 | 112·6 | 6·56 | 163 | 162·4 | 9·46 |
| 14 | 13·95 | 0·81 | 64 | 63·78 | 3·71 | 114 | 113·6 | 6·62 | 164 | 163·4 | 9·52 |
| 15 | 14·95 | 0·87 | 65 | 64·78 | 3·77 | 115 | 114·6 | 6·68 | 165 | 164·4 | 9·58 |
| 16 | 15·95 | 0·93 | 66 | 65·78 | 3·83 | 116 | 115·6 | 6·73 | 166 | 165·4 | 9·64 |
| 17 | 16·94 | 0·99 | 67 | 66·77 | 3·89 | 117 | 116·6 | 6·79 | 167 | 166·4 | 9·69 |
| 18 | 17·94 | 1·04 | 68 | 67·77 | 3·95 | 118 | 117·6 | 6·85 | 168 | 167·4 | 9·75 |
| 19 | 18·94 | 1·10 | 69 | 68·77 | 4·01 | 119 | 118·6 | 6·91 | 169 | 168·4 | 9·81 |
| 20 | 19·93 | 1·16 | 70 | 69·76 | 4·06 | 120 | 119·6 | 6·97 | 170 | 169·4 | 9·87 |
| 21 | 20·93 | 1·22 | 71 | 70·76 | 4·12 | 121 | 120·6 | 7·02 | 171 | 170·4 | 9·93 |
| 22 | 21·93 | 1·28 | 72 | 71·76 | 4·18 | 122 | 121·6 | 7·08 | 172 | 171·4 | 9·98 |
| 23 | 22·92 | 1·34 | 73 | 72·75 | 4·24 | 123 | 122·6 | 7·14 | 173 | 172·4 | 10·04 |
| 24 | 23·92 | 1·39 | 74 | 73·75 | 4·30 | 124 | 123·6 | 7·20 | 174 | 173·4 | 10·10 |
| 25 | 24·92 | 1·45 | 75 | 74·75 | 4·35 | 125 | 124·6 | 7·26 | 175 | 174·4 | 10·16 |
| 26 | 25·91 | 1·51 | 76 | 75·74 | 4·41 | 126 | 125·6 | 7·31 | 176 | 175·4 | 10·22 |
| 27 | 26·91 | 1·57 | 77 | 76·74 | 4·47 | 127 | 126·6 | 7·37 | 177 | 176·4 | 10·27 |
| 28 | 27·91 | 1·63 | 78 | 77·74 | 4·53 | 128 | 127·6 | 7·43 | 178 | 177·4 | 10·33 |
| 29 | 28·90 | 1·68 | 79 | 78·73 | 4·59 | 129 | 128·6 | 7·49 | 179 | 178·4 | 10·39 |
| 30 | 29·90 | 1·74 | 80 | 79·73 | 4·64 | 130 | 129·6 | 7·55 | 180 | 179·4 | 10·45 |
| 31 | 30·90 | 1·80 | 81 | 80·73 | 4·70 | 131 | 130·6 | 7·60 | 181 | 180·4 | 10·51 |
| 32 | 31·89 | 1·86 | 82 | 81·72 | 4·76 | 132 | 131·6 | 7·66 | 182 | 181·4 | 10·56 |
| 33 | 32·89 | 1·92 | 83 | 82·72 | 4·82 | 133 | 132·6 | 7·72 | 183 | 182·4 | 10·62 |
| 34 | 33·89 | 1·97 | 84 | 83·72 | 4·88 | 134 | 133·5 | 7·78 | 184 | 183·4 | 10·68 |
| 35 | 34·88 | 2·03 | 85 | 84·71 | 4·93 | 135 | 134·5 | 7·84 | 185 | 184·4 | 10·74 |
| 36 | 35·88 | 2·09 | 86 | 85·71 | 4·99 | 136 | 135·5 | 7·89 | 186 | 185·4 | 10·80 |
| 37 | 36·87 | 2·15 | 87 | 86·71 | 5·05 | 137 | 136·5 | 7·95 | 187 | 186·4 | 10·85 |
| 38 | 37·87 | 2·21 | 88 | 87·70 | 5·11 | 138 | 137·5 | 8·01 | 188 | 187·4 | 10·91 |
| 39 | 38·87 | 2·26 | 89 | 88·70 | 5·17 | 139 | 138·5 | 8·07 | 189 | 188·4 | 10·97 |
| 40 | 39·86 | 2·32 | 90 | 89·70 | 5·22 | 140 | 139·5 | 8·13 | 190 | 189·4 | 11·03 |
| 41 | 40·86 | 2·38 | 91 | 90·69 | 5·28 | 141 | 140·5 | 8·18 | 191 | 190·4 | 11·09 |
| 42 | 41·86 | 2·44 | 92 | 91·69 | 5·34 | 142 | 141·5 | 8·24 | 192 | 191·4 | 11·14 |
| 43 | 42·85 | 2·50 | 93 | 92·69 | 5·40 | 143 | 142·5 | 8·30 | 193 | 192·3 | 11·20 |
| 44 | 43·85 | 2·55 | 94 | 93·68 | 5·46 | 144 | 143·5 | 8·36 | 194 | 193·3 | 11·26 |
| 45 | 44·85 | 2·61 | 95 | 94·68 | 5·51 | 145 | 144·5 | 8·42 | 195 | 194·3 | 11·32 |
| 46 | 45·84 | 2·67 | 96 | 95·68 | 5·57 | 146 | 145·5 | 8·47 | 196 | 195·3 | 11·38 |
| 47 | 46·84 | 2·73 | 97 | 96·67 | 5·63 | 147 | 146·5 | 8·53 | 197 | 196·3 | 11·44 |
| 48 | 47·84 | 2·79 | 98 | 97·67 | 5·69 | 148 | 147·5 | 8·59 | 198 | 197·3 | 11·49 |
| 49 | 48·83 | 2·84 | 99 | 98·67 | 5·75 | 149 | 148·5 | 8·65 | 199 | 198·3 | 11·55 |
| 50 | 49·83 | 2·90 | 100 | 99·66 | 5·80 | 150 | 149·5 | 8·71 | 200 | 199·3 | 11·61 |
| 51 | 50·83 | 2·96 | 101 | 100·7 | 5·86 | 151 | 150·5 | 8·76 | 201 | 200·3 | 11·67 |
| 52 | 51·82 | 3·02 | 102 | 101·7 | 5·92 | 152 | 151·5 | 8·82 | 202 | 201·3 | 11·73 |
| 53 | 52·82 | 3·08 | 103 | 102·7 | 5·98 | 153 | 152·5 | 8·88 | 203 | 202·3 | 11·78 |
| 54 | 53·82 | 3·13 | 104 | 103·6 | 6·04 | 154 | 153·5 | 8·94 | 204 | 203·3 | 11·84 |
| 55 | 54·81 | 3·19 | 105 | 104·6 | 6·09 | 155 | 154·5 | 9·00 | 205 | 204·3 | 11·90 |
| 56 | 55·81 | 3·25 | 106 | 105·6 | 6·15 | 156 | 155·5 | 9·06 | 206 | 205·3 | 11·96 |
| 57 | 56·81 | 3·31 | 107 | 106·6 | 6·21 | 157 | 156·5 | 9·11 | 207 | 206·3 | 12·02 |
| 58 | 57·80 | 3·37 | 108 | 107·6 | 6·27 | 158 | 157·5 | 9·17 | 208 | 207·3 | 12·07 |
| 59 | 58·80 | 3·42 | 109 | 108·6 | 6·33 | 159 | 158·5 | 9·23 | 209 | 208·3 | 12·13 |
| 60 | 59·80 | 3·48 | 110 | 109·6 | 6·39 | 160 | 159·5 | 9·29 | 210 | 209·3 | 12·19 |

TABLE I

# 3° 30′

| G | D | H | G | D | H | G | D | H | G | D | H |
|---|---|---|---|---|---|---|---|---|---|---|---|
| 10 | 9·96 | 0·61 | 60 | 59·78 | 3·66 | 110 | 109·6 | 6·70 | 160 | 159·4 | 9·75 |
| 11 | 10·96 | 0·67 | 61 | 60·77 | 3·72 | 111 | 110·6 | 6·76 | 161 | 160·4 | 9·81 |
| 12 | 11·96 | 0·73 | 62 | 61·77 | 3·78 | 112 | 111·6 | 6·82 | 162 | 161·4 | 9·87 |
| 13 | 12·95 | 0·79 | 63 | 62·77 | 3·84 | 113 | 112·6 | 6·89 | 163 | 162·4 | 9·93 |
| 14 | 13·95 | 0·85 | 64 | 63·76 | 3·90 | 114 | 113·6 | 6·95 | 164 | 163·4 | 9·99 |
| 15 | 14·94 | 0·91 | 65 | 64·76 | 3·96 | 115 | 114·6 | 7·01 | 165 | 164·4 | 10·05 |
| 16 | 15·94 | 0·97 | 66 | 65·75 | 4·02 | 116 | 115·6 | 7·07 | 166 | 165·4 | 10·12 |
| 17 | 16·94 | 1·04 | 67 | 66·75 | 4·08 | 117 | 116·6 | 7·13 | 167 | 166·4 | 10·18 |
| 18 | 17·93 | 1·10 | 68 | 67·75 | 4·14 | 118 | 117·6 | 7·19 | 168 | 167·4 | 10·24 |
| 19 | 18·93 | 1·16 | 69 | 68·74 | 4·20 | 119 | 118·6 | 7·25 | 169 | 168·4 | 10·30 |
| 20 | 19·93 | 1·22 | 70 | 69·74 | 4·27 | 120 | 119·6 | 7·31 | 170 | 169·4 | 10·36 |
| 21 | 20·92 | 1·28 | 71 | 70·74 | 4·33 | 121 | 120·5 | 7·37 | 171 | 170·4 | 10·42 |
| 22 | 21·92 | 1·34 | 72 | 71·73 | 4·39 | 122 | 121·5 | 7·43 | 172 | 171·4 | 10·48 |
| 23 | 22·91 | 1·40 | 73 | 72·73 | 4·45 | 123 | 122·5 | 7·49 | 173 | 172·4 | 10·54 |
| 24 | 23·91 | 1·46 | 74 | 73·72 | 4·51 | 124 | 123·5 | 7·56 | 174 | 173·4 | 10·60 |
| 25 | 24·91 | 1·52 | 75 | 74·72 | 4·57 | 125 | 124·5 | 7·62 | 175 | 174·3 | 10·66 |
| 26 | 25·90 | 1·58 | 76 | 75·72 | 4·63 | 126 | 125·5 | 7·68 | 176 | 175·3 | 10·72 |
| 27 | 26·90 | 1·65 | 77 | 76·71 | 4·69 | 127 | 126·5 | 7·74 | 177 | 176·3 | 10·79 |
| 28 | 27·90 | 1·71 | 78 | 77·71 | 4·75 | 128 | 127·5 | 7·80 | 178 | 177·3 | 10·85 |
| 29 | 28·89 | 1·77 | 79 | 78·71 | 4·81 | 129 | 128·5 | 7·86 | 179 | 178·3 | 10·91 |
| 30 | 29·89 | 1·83 | 80 | 79·70 | 4·87 | 130 | 129·5 | 7·92 | 180 | 179·3 | 10·97 |
| 31 | 30·88 | 1·89 | 81 | 80·70 | 4·94 | 131 | 130·5 | 7·98 | 181 | 180·3 | 11·03 |
| 32 | 31·88 | 1·95 | 82 | 81·69 | 5·00 | 132 | 131·5 | 8·04 | 182 | 181·3 | 11·09 |
| 33 | 32·88 | 2·01 | 83 | 82·69 | 5·06 | 133 | 132·5 | 8·10 | 183 | 182·3 | 11·15 |
| 34 | 33·87 | 2·07 | 84 | 83·69 | 5·12 | 134 | 133·5 | 8·17 | 184 | 183·3 | 11·21 |
| 35 | 34·87 | 2·13 | 85 | 84·68 | 5·18 | 135 | 134·5 | 8·23 | 185 | 184·3 | 11·27 |
| 36 | 35·87 | 2·19 | 86 | 85·68 | 5·24 | 136 | 135·5 | 8·29 | 186 | 185·3 | 11·33 |
| 37 | 36·86 | 2·25 | 87 | 86·68 | 5·30 | 137 | 136·5 | 8·35 | 187 | 186·3 | 11·39 |
| 38 | 37·86 | 2·32 | 88 | 87·67 | 5·36 | 138 | 137·5 | 8·41 | 188 | 187·3 | 11·46 |
| 39 | 38·85 | 2·38 | 89 | 88·67 | 5·42 | 139 | 138·5 | 8·47 | 189 | 188·3 | 11·52 |
| 40 | 39·85 | 2·44 | 90 | 89·66 | 5·48 | 140 | 139·5 | 8·53 | 190 | 189·3 | 11·58 |
| 41 | 40·85 | 2·50 | 91 | 90·66 | 5·54 | 141 | 140·5 | 8·59 | 191 | 190·3 | 11·64 |
| 42 | 41·84 | 2·56 | 92 | 91·66 | 5·61 | 142 | 141·5 | 8·65 | 192 | 191·3 | 11·70 |
| 43 | 42·84 | 2·62 | 93 | 92·65 | 5·67 | 143 | 142·5 | 8·71 | 193 | 192·3 | 11·76 |
| 44 | 43·84 | 2·68 | 94 | 93·65 | 5·73 | 144 | 143·5 | 8·77 | 194 | 193·3 | 11·82 |
| 45 | 44·83 | 2·74 | 95 | 94·65 | 5·79 | 145 | 144·5 | 8·84 | 195 | 194·3 | 11·88 |
| 46 | 45·83 | 2·80 | 96 | 95·64 | 5·85 | 146 | 145·5 | 8·90 | 196 | 195·3 | 11·94 |
| 47 | 46·82 | 2·86 | 97 | 96·64 | 5·91 | 147 | 146·5 | 8·96 | 197 | 196·3 | 12·00 |
| 48 | 47·82 | 2·92 | 98 | 97·63 | 5·97 | 148 | 147·4 | 9·02 | 198 | 197·3 | 12·06 |
| 49 | 48·82 | 2·99 | 99 | 98·63 | 6·03 | 149 | 148·4 | 9·08 | 199 | 198·3 | 12·13 |
| 50 | 49·81 | 3·05 | 100 | 99·63 | 6·09 | 150 | 149·4 | 9·14 | 200 | 199·3 | 12·19 |
| 51 | 50·81 | 3·11 | 101 | 100·6 | 6·15 | 151 | 150·4 | 9·20 | 201 | 200·3 | 12·25 |
| 52 | 51·81 | 3·17 | 102 | 101·6 | 6·22 | 152 | 151·4 | 9·26 | 202 | 201·2 | 12·31 |
| 53 | 52·80 | 3·23 | 103 | 102·6 | 6·28 | 153 | 152·4 | 9·32 | 203 | 202·2 | 12·37 |
| 54 | 53·80 | 3·29 | 104 | 103·6 | 6·34 | 154 | 153·4 | 9·38 | 204 | 203·2 | 12·43 |
| 55 | 54·79 | 3·35 | 105 | 104·6 | 6·40 | 155 | 154·4 | 9·44 | 205 | 204·2 | 12·49 |
| 56 | 55·79 | 3·41 | 106 | 105·6 | 6·46 | 156 | 155·4 | 9·51 | 206 | 205·2 | 12·55 |
| 57 | 56·79 | 3·47 | 107 | 106·6 | 6·52 | 157 | 156·4 | 9·57 | 207 | 206·2 | 12·61 |
| 58 | 57·78 | 3·53 | 108 | 107·6 | 6·58 | 158 | 157·4 | 9·63 | 208 | 207·2 | 12·67 |
| 59 | 58·78 | 3·60 | 109 | 108·6 | 6·64 | 159 | 158·4 | 9·69 | 209 | 208·2 | 12·74 |
| 60 | 59·78 | 3·66 | 110 | 109·6 | 6·70 | 160 | 159·4 | 9·75 | 210 | 209·2 | 12·80 |

| G | D | H | G | D | H | G | D | H | G | D | H |
|---|---|---|---|---|---|---|---|---|---|---|---|
| 10 | 9.96 | 0.64 | 60 | 59.75 | 3.83 | 110 | 109.5 | 7.02 | 160 | 159.3 | 10.21 |
| 11 | 10.95 | 0.70 | 61 | 60.75 | 3.89 | 111 | 110.5 | 7.08 | 161 | 160.3 | 10.28 |
| 12 | 11.95 | 0.77 | 62 | 61.75 | 3.96 | 112 | 111.5 | 7.15 | 162 | 161.3 | 10.34 |
| 13 | 12.95 | 0.83 | 63 | 62.74 | 4.02 | 113 | 112.5 | 7.21 | 163 | 162.3 | 10.40 |
| 14 | 13.94 | 0.89 | 64 | 63.74 | 4.08 | 114 | 113.5 | 7.28 | 164 | 163.3 | 10.47 |
| 15 | 14.94 | 0.96 | 65 | 64.73 | 4.15 | 115 | 114.5 | 7.34 | 165 | 164.3 | 10.53 |
| 16 | 15.93 | 1.02 | 66 | 65.73 | 4.21 | 116 | 115.5 | 7.40 | 166 | 165.3 | 10.59 |
| 17 | 16.93 | 1.08 | 67 | 66.73 | 4.28 | 117 | 116.5 | 7.47 | 167 | 166.3 | 10.66 |
| 18 | 17.93 | 1.15 | 68 | 67.72 | 4.34 | 118 | 117.5 | 7.53 | 168 | 167.3 | 10.72 |
| 19 | 18.92 | 1.21 | 69 | 68.72 | 4.40 | 119 | 118.5 | 7.59 | 169 | 168.3 | 10.79 |
| 20 | 19.92 | 1.28 | 70 | 69.71 | 4.47 | 120 | 119.5 | 7.66 | 170 | 169.3 | 10.85 |
| 21 | 20.91 | 1.34 | 71 | 70.71 | 4.53 | 121 | 120.5 | 7.72 | 171 | 170.3 | 10.91 |
| 22 | 21.91 | 1.40 | 72 | 71.71 | 4.60 | 122 | 121.5 | 7.79 | 172 | 171.3 | 10.98 |
| 23 | 22.91 | 1.47 | 73 | 72.70 | 4.66 | 123 | 122.5 | 7.85 | 173 | 172.3 | 11.04 |
| 24 | 23.90 | 1.53 | 74 | 73.70 | 4.72 | 124 | 123.5 | 7.91 | 174 | 173.3 | 11.10 |
| 25 | 24.90 | 1.60 | 75 | 74.69 | 4.79 | 125 | 124.5 | 7.98 | 175 | 174.3 | 11.17 |
| 26 | 25.89 | 1.66 | 76 | 75.69 | 4.85 | 126 | 125.5 | 8.04 | 176 | 175.3 | 11.23 |
| 27 | 26.89 | 1.72 | 77 | 76.68 | 4.91 | 127 | 126.5 | 8.11 | 177 | 176.3 | 11.30 |
| 28 | 27.89 | 1.79 | 78 | 77.68 | 4.98 | 128 | 127.5 | 8.17 | 178 | 177.3 | 11.36 |
| 29 | 28.88 | 1.85 | 79 | 78.68 | 5.04 | 129 | 128.5 | 8.23 | 179 | 178.3 | 11.42 |
| 30 | 29.88 | 1.91 | 80 | 79.67 | 5.11 | 130 | 129.5 | 8.30 | 180 | 179.3 | 11.49 |
| 31 | 30.87 | 1.98 | 81 | 80.67 | 5.17 | 131 | 130.5 | 8.36 | 181 | 180.3 | 11.55 |
| 32 | 31.87 | 2.04 | 82 | 81.66 | 5.23 | 132 | 131.5 | 8.42 | 182 | 181.3 | 11.62 |
| 33 | 32.86 | 2.11 | 83 | 82.66 | 5.30 | 133 | 132.5 | 8.49 | 183 | 182.3 | 11.68 |
| 34 | 33.86 | 2.17 | 84 | 83.66 | 5.36 | 134 | 133.5 | 8.55 | 184 | 183.2 | 11.74 |
| 35 | 34.86 | 2.23 | 85 | 84.65 | 5.42 | 135 | 134.4 | 8.62 | 185 | 184.2 | 11.81 |
| 36 | 35.85 | 2.30 | 86 | 85.65 | 5.49 | 136 | 135.4 | 8.68 | 186 | 185.2 | 11.87 |
| 37 | 36.85 | 2.36 | 87 | 86.64 | 5.55 | 137 | 136.4 | 8.74 | 187 | 186.2 | 11.93 |
| 38 | 37.84 | 2.43 | 88 | 87.64 | 5.62 | 138 | 137.4 | 8.81 | 188 | 187.2 | 12.00 |
| 39 | 38.84 | 2.49 | 89 | 88.64 | 5.68 | 139 | 138.4 | 8.87 | 189 | 188.2 | 12.06 |
| 40 | 39.84 | 2.55 | 90 | 89.63 | 5.74 | 140 | 139.4 | 8.93 | 190 | 189.2 | 12.13 |
| 41 | 40.83 | 2.62 | 91 | 90.63 | 5.81 | 141 | 140.4 | 9.00 | 191 | 190.2 | 12.19 |
| 42 | 41.83 | 2.68 | 92 | 91.62 | 5.87 | 142 | 141.4 | 9.06 | 192 | 191.2 | 12.25 |
| 43 | 42.82 | 2.74 | 93 | 92.62 | 5.94 | 143 | 142.4 | 9.13 | 193 | 192.2 | 12.32 |
| 44 | 43.82 | 2.81 | 94 | 93.62 | 6.00 | 144 | 143.4 | 9.19 | 194 | 193.2 | 12.38 |
| 45 | 44.82 | 2.87 | 95 | 94.61 | 6.06 | 145 | 144.4 | 9.25 | 195 | 194.2 | 12.44 |
| 46 | 45.81 | 2.94 | 96 | 95.61 | 6.13 | 146 | 145.4 | 9.32 | 196 | 195.2 | 12.51 |
| 47 | 46.81 | 3.00 | 97 | 96.60 | 6.19 | 147 | 146.4 | 9.38 | 197 | 196.2 | 12.57 |
| 48 | 47.80 | 3.06 | 98 | 97.60 | 6.25 | 148 | 147.4 | 9.45 | 198 | 197.2 | 12.64 |
| 49 | 48.80 | 3.13 | 99 | 98.59 | 6.32 | 149 | 148.4 | 9.51 | 199 | 198.2 | 12.70 |
| 50 | 49.80 | 3.19 | 100 | 99.59 | 6.38 | 150 | 149.4 | 9.57 | 200 | 199.2 | 12.76 |
| 51 | 50.79 | 3.25 | 101 | 100.6 | 6.45 | 151 | 150.4 | 9.64 | 201 | 200.2 | 12.83 |
| 52 | 51.79 | 3.32 | 102 | 101.6 | 6.51 | 152 | 151.4 | 9.70 | 202 | 201.2 | 12.89 |
| 53 | 52.78 | 3.38 | 103 | 102.6 | 6.57 | 153 | 152.4 | 9.76 | 203 | 202.2 | 12.96 |
| 54 | 53.78 | 3.45 | 104 | 103.6 | 6.64 | 154 | 153.4 | 9.83 | 204 | 203.2 | 13.02 |
| 55 | 54.77 | 3.51 | 105 | 104.6 | 6.70 | 155 | 154.4 | 9.89 | 205 | 204.2 | 13.08 |
| 56 | 55.77 | 3.57 | 106 | 105.6 | 6.76 | 156 | 155.4 | 9.96 | 206 | 205.2 | 13.15 |
| 57 | 56.77 | 3.64 | 107 | 106.6 | 6.83 | 157 | 156.4 | 10.02 | 207 | 206.2 | 13.21 |
| 58 | 57.76 | 3.70 | 108 | 107.6 | 6.89 | 158 | 157.4 | 10.08 | 208 | 207.1 | 13.27 |
| 59 | 58.76 | 3.77 | 109 | 108.6 | 6.96 | 159 | 158.3 | 10.15 | 209 | 208.1 | 13.34 |
| 60 | 59.75 | 3.83 | 110 | 109.5 | 7.02 | 160 | 159.3 | 10.21 | 210 | 209.1 | 13.40 |

TABLE I  3° 50′

| G | D | H | G | D | H | G | D | H | G | D | H |
|---|---|---|---|---|---|---|---|---|---|---|---|
| 10 | 9.96 | 0.67 | 60 | 59.73 | 4.00 | 110 | 109.5 | 7.34 | 160 | 159.3 | 10.67 |
| 11 | 10.95 | 0.73 | 61 | 60.73 | 4.07 | 111 | 110.5 | 7.40 | 161 | 160.3 | 10.74 |
| 12 | 11.95 | 0.80 | 62 | 61.72 | 4.14 | 112 | 111.5 | 7.47 | 162 | 161.3 | 10.81 |
| 13 | 12.94 | 0.87 | 63 | 62.72 | 4.20 | 113 | 112.5 | 7.54 | 163 | 162.3 | 10.87 |
| 14 | 13.94 | 0.93 | 64 | 63.71 | 4.27 | 114 | 113.5 | 7.60 | 164 | 163.3 | 10.94 |
| 15 | 14.93 | 1.00 | 65 | 64.71 | 4.34 | 115 | 114.5 | 7.67 | 165 | 164.3 | 11.01 |
| 16 | 15.93 | 1.07 | 66 | 65.70 | 4.40 | 116 | 115.5 | 7.74 | 166 | 165.3 | 11.07 |
| 17 | 16.92 | 1.13 | 67 | 66.70 | 4.47 | 117 | 116.5 | 7.80 | 167 | 166.3 | 11.14 |
| 18 | 17.92 | 1.20 | 68 | 67.70 | 4.54 | 118 | 117.5 | 7.87 | 168 | 167.2 | 11.21 |
| 19 | 18.92 | 1.27 | 69 | 68.69 | 4.60 | 119 | 118.5 | 7.94 | 169 | 168.2 | 11.27 |
| 20 | 19.91 | 1.33 | 70 | 69.69 | 4.67 | 120 | 119.5 | 8.00 | 170 | 169.2 | 11.34 |
| 21 | 20.91 | 1.40 | 71 | 70.68 | 4.74 | 121 | 120.5 | 8.07 | 171 | 170.2 | 11.41 |
| 22 | 21.90 | 1.47 | 72 | 71.68 | 4.80 | 122 | 121.5 | 8.14 | 172 | 171.2 | 11.47 |
| 23 | 22.90 | 1.53 | 73 | 72.67 | 4.87 | 123 | 122.5 | 8.20 | 173 | 172.2 | 11.54 |
| 24 | 23.89 | 1.60 | 74 | 73.67 | 4.94 | 124 | 123.4 | 8.27 | 174 | 173.2 | 11.61 |
| 25 | 24.89 | 1.67 | 75 | 74.66 | 5.00 | 125 | 124.4 | 8.34 | 175 | 174.2 | 11.67 |
| 26 | 25.88 | 1.73 | 76 | 75.66 | 5.07 | 126 | 125.4 | 8.40 | 176 | 175.2 | 11.74 |
| 27 | 26.88 | 1.80 | 77 | 76.66 | 5.14 | 127 | 126.4 | 8.47 | 177 | 176.2 | 11.81 |
| 28 | 27.87 | 1.87 | 78 | 77.65 | 5.20 | 128 | 127.4 | 8.54 | 178 | 177.2 | 11.87 |
| 29 | 28.87 | 1.93 | 79 | 78.65 | 5.27 | 129 | 128.4 | 8.60 | 179 | 178.2 | 11.94 |
| 30 | 29.87 | 2.00 | 80 | 79.64 | 5.34 | 130 | 129.4 | 8.67 | 180 | 179.2 | 12.01 |
| 31 | 30.86 | 2.07 | 81 | 80.64 | 5.40 | 131 | 130.4 | 8.74 | 181 | 180.2 | 12.07 |
| 32 | 31.86 | 2.13 | 82 | 81.63 | 5.47 | 132 | 131.4 | 8.80 | 182 | 181.2 | 12.14 |
| 33 | 32.85 | 2.20 | 83 | 82.63 | 5.54 | 133 | 132.4 | 8.87 | 183 | 182.2 | 12.21 |
| 34 | 33.85 | 2.27 | 84 | 83.62 | 5.60 | 134 | 133.4 | 8.94 | 184 | 183.2 | 12.27 |
| 35 | 34.84 | 2.33 | 85 | 84.62 | 5.67 | 135 | 134.4 | 9.01 | 185 | 184.2 | 12.34 |
| 36 | 35.84 | 2.40 | 86 | 85.62 | 5.74 | 136 | 135.4 | 9.07 | 186 | 185.2 | 12.41 |
| 37 | 36.83 | 2.47 | 87 | 86.61 | 5.80 | 137 | 136.4 | 9.14 | 187 | 186.2 | 12.47 |
| 38 | 37.83 | 2.53 | 88 | 87.61 | 5.87 | 138 | 137.4 | 9.21 | 188 | 187.2 | 12.54 |
| 39 | 38.83 | 2.60 | 89 | 88.60 | 5.94 | 139 | 138.4 | 9.27 | 189 | 188.2 | 12.61 |
| 40 | 39.82 | 2.67 | 90 | 89.60 | 6.00 | 140 | 139.4 | 9.34 | 190 | 189.2 | 12.67 |
| 41 | 40.82 | 2.73 | 91 | 90.59 | 6.07 | 141 | 140.4 | 9.41 | 191 | 190.1 | 12.74 |
| 42 | 41.81 | 2.80 | 92 | 91.59 | 6.14 | 142 | 141.4 | 9.47 | 192 | 191.1 | 12.81 |
| 43 | 42.81 | 2.87 | 93 | 92.58 | 6.20 | 143 | 142.4 | 9.54 | 193 | 192.1 | 12.87 |
| 44 | 43.80 | 2.93 | 94 | 93.58 | 6.27 | 144 | 143.4 | 9.61 | 194 | 193.1 | 12.94 |
| 45 | 44.80 | 3.00 | 95 | 94.58 | 6.34 | 145 | 144.4 | 9.67 | 195 | 194.1 | 13.01 |
| 46 | 45.79 | 3.07 | 96 | 95.57 | 6.40 | 146 | 145.3 | 9.74 | 196 | 195.1 | 13.07 |
| 47 | 46.79 | 3.14 | 97 | 96.57 | 6.47 | 147 | 146.3 | 9.81 | 197 | 196.1 | 13.14 |
| 48 | 47.79 | 3.20 | 98 | 97.56 | 6.54 | 148 | 147.3 | 9.87 | 198 | 197.1 | 13.21 |
| 49 | 48.78 | 3.27 | 99 | 98.56 | 6.60 | 149 | 148.3 | 9.94 | 199 | 198.1 | 13.27 |
| 50 | 49.78 | 3.34 | 100 | 99.55 | 6.67 | 150 | 149.3 | 10.01 | 200 | 199.1 | 13.34 |
| 51 | 50.77 | 3.40 | 101 | 100.5 | 6.74 | 151 | 150.3 | 10.07 | 201 | 200.1 | 13.41 |
| 52 | 51.77 | 3.47 | 102 | 101.5 | 6.80 | 152 | 151.3 | 10.14 | 202 | 201.1 | 13.47 |
| 53 | 52.76 | 3.54 | 103 | 102.5 | 6.87 | 153 | 152.3 | 10.21 | 203 | 202.1 | 13.54 |
| 54 | 53.76 | 3.60 | 104 | 103.5 | 6.94 | 154 | 153.3 | 10.27 | 204 | 203.1 | 13.61 |
| 55 | 54.75 | 3.67 | 105 | 104.5 | 7.00 | 155 | 154.3 | 10.34 | 205 | 204.1 | 13.67 |
| 56 | 55.75 | 3.74 | 106 | 105.5 | 7.07 | 156 | 155.3 | 10.41 | 206 | 205.1 | 13.74 |
| 57 | 56.75 | 3.80 | 107 | 106.5 | 7.14 | 157 | 156.3 | 10.47 | 207 | 206.1 | 13.81 |
| 58 | 57.74 | 3.87 | 108 | 107.5 | 7.20 | 158 | 157.3 | 10.54 | 208 | 207.1 | 13.87 |
| 59 | 58.74 | 3.94 | 109 | 108.5 | 7.27 | 159 | 158.3 | 10.61 | 209 | 208.1 | 13.94 |
| 60 | 59.73 | 4.00 | 110 | 109.5 | 7.34 | 160 | 159.3 | 10.67 | 210 | 209.1 | 14.01 |

| G | D | H | G | D | H | G | D | H | G | D | H |
|---|---|---|---|---|---|---|---|---|---|---|---|
| 10 | 9.95 | 0.70 | 60 | 59.71 | 4.18 | 110 | 109.5 | 7.65 | 160 | 159.2 | 11.13 |
| 11 | 10.95 | 0.77 | 61 | 60.70 | 4.24 | 111 | 110.5 | 7.72 | 161 | 160.2 | 11.20 |
| 12 | 11.94 | 0.84 | 62 | 61.70 | 4.31 | 112 | 111.5 | 7.79 | 162 | 161.2 | 11.27 |
| 13 | 12.94 | 0.90 | 63 | 62.69 | 4.38 | 113 | 112.5 | 7.86 | 163 | 162.2 | 11.34 |
| 14 | 13.93 | 0.97 | 64 | 63.69 | 4.45 | 114 | 113.4 | 7.93 | 164 | 163.2 | 11.41 |
| 15 | 14.93 | 1.04 | 65 | 64.68 | 4.52 | 115 | 114.4 | 8.00 | 165 | 164.2 | 11.48 |
| 16 | 15.92 | 1.11 | 66 | 65.68 | 4.59 | 116 | 115.4 | 8.07 | 166 | 165.2 | 11.55 |
| 17 | 16.92 | 1.18 | 67 | 66.67 | 4.66 | 117 | 116.4 | 8.14 | 167 | 166.2 | 11.62 |
| 18 | 17.91 | 1.25 | 68 | 67.67 | 4.73 | 118 | 117.4 | 8.21 | 168 | 167.2 | 11.69 |
| 19 | 18.91 | 1.32 | 69 | 68.66 | 4.80 | 119 | 118.4 | 8.28 | 169 | 168.2 | 11.76 |
| 20 | 19.90 | 1.39 | 70 | 69.66 | 4.87 | 120 | 119.4 | 8.35 | 170 | 169.2 | 11.83 |
| 21 | 20.90 | 1.46 | 71 | 70.65 | 4.94 | 121 | 120.4 | 8.42 | 171 | 170.2 | 11.90 |
| 22 | 21.89 | 1.53 | 72 | 71.65 | 5.01 | 122 | 121.4 | 8.49 | 172 | 171.2 | 11.97 |
| 23 | 22.89 | 1.60 | 73 | 72.64 | 5.08 | 123 | 122.4 | 8.56 | 173 | 172.2 | 12.04 |
| 24 | 23.88 | 1.67 | 74 | 73.64 | 5.15 | 124 | 123.4 | 8.63 | 174 | 173.2 | 12.11 |
| 25 | 24.88 | 1.74 | 75 | 74.63 | 5.22 | 125 | 124.4 | 8.70 | 175 | 174.1 | 12.18 |
| 26 | 25.87 | 1.81 | 76 | 75.63 | 5.29 | 126 | 125.4 | 8.77 | 176 | 175.1 | 12.25 |
| 27 | 26.87 | 1.88 | 77 | 76.63 | 5.36 | 127 | 126.4 | 8.84 | 177 | 176.1 | 12.32 |
| 28 | 27.86 | 1.95 | 78 | 77.62 | 5.43 | 128 | 127.4 | 8.91 | 178 | 177.1 | 12.39 |
| 29 | 28.86 | 2.02 | 79 | 78.62 | 5.50 | 129 | 128.4 | 8.98 | 179 | 178.1 | 12.46 |
| 30 | 29.85 | 2.09 | 80 | 79.61 | 5.57 | 130 | 129.4 | 9.05 | 180 | 179.1 | 12.53 |
| 31 | 30.85 | 2.16 | 81 | 80.61 | 5.64 | 131 | 130.4 | 9.12 | 181 | 180.1 | 12.60 |
| 32 | 31.84 | 2.23 | 82 | 81.60 | 5.71 | 132 | 131.4 | 9.19 | 182 | 181.1 | 12.66 |
| 33 | 32.84 | 2.30 | 83 | 82.60 | 5.78 | 133 | 132.4 | 9.25 | 183 | 182.1 | 12.73 |
| 34 | 33.83 | 2.37 | 84 | 83.59 | 5.85 | 134 | 133.3 | 9.32 | 184 | 183.1 | 12.80 |
| 35 | 34.83 | 2.44 | 85 | 84.59 | 5.91 | 135 | 134.3 | 9.39 | 185 | 184.1 | 12.87 |
| 36 | 35.82 | 2.51 | 86 | 85.58 | 5.98 | 136 | 135.3 | 9.46 | 186 | 185.1 | 12.94 |
| 37 | 36.82 | 2.57 | 87 | 86.58 | 6.05 | 137 | 136.3 | 9.53 | 187 | 186.1 | 13.01 |
| 38 | 37.82 | 2.64 | 88 | 87.57 | 6.12 | 138 | 137.3 | 9.60 | 188 | 187.1 | 13.08 |
| 39 | 38.81 | 2.71 | 89 | 88.57 | 6.19 | 139 | 138.3 | 9.67 | 189 | 188.1 | 13.15 |
| 40 | 39.81 | 2.78 | 90 | 89.56 | 6.26 | 140 | 139.3 | 9.74 | 190 | 189.1 | 13.22 |
| 41 | 40.80 | 2.85 | 91 | 90.56 | 6.33 | 141 | 140.3 | 9.81 | 191 | 190.1 | 13.29 |
| 42 | 41.80 | 2.92 | 92 | 91.55 | 6.40 | 142 | 141.3 | 9.88 | 192 | 191.1 | 13.36 |
| 43 | 42.79 | 2.99 | 93 | 92.55 | 6.47 | 143 | 142.3 | 9.95 | 193 | 192.1 | 13.43 |
| 44 | 43.79 | 3.06 | 94 | 93.54 | 6.54 | 144 | 143.3 | 10.02 | 194 | 193.1 | 13.50 |
| 45 | 44.78 | 3.13 | 95 | 94.54 | 6.61 | 145 | 144.3 | 10.09 | 195 | 194.1 | 13.57 |
| 46 | 45.78 | 3.20 | 96 | 95.53 | 6.68 | 146 | 145.3 | 10.16 | 196 | 195.0 | 13.64 |
| 47 | 46.77 | 3.27 | 97 | 96.53 | 6.75 | 147 | 146.3 | 10.23 | 197 | 196.0 | 13.71 |
| 48 | 47.77 | 3.34 | 98 | 97.52 | 6.82 | 148 | 147.3 | 10.30 | 198 | 197.0 | 13.78 |
| 49 | 48.76 | 3.41 | 99 | 98.52 | 6.89 | 149 | 148.3 | 10.37 | 199 | 198.0 | 13.85 |
| 50 | 49.76 | 3.48 | 100 | 99.51 | 6.96 | 150 | 149.3 | 10.44 | 200 | 199.0 | 13.92 |
| 51 | 50.75 | 3.55 | 101 | 100.5 | 7.03 | 151 | 150.3 | 10.51 | 201 | 200.0 | 13.99 |
| 52 | 51.75 | 3.62 | 102 | 101.5 | 7.10 | 152 | 151.3 | 10.58 | 202 | 201.0 | 14.06 |
| 53 | 52.74 | 3.69 | 103 | 102.5 | 7.17 | 153 | 152.3 | 10.65 | 203 | 202.0 | 14.13 |
| 54 | 53.74 | 3.76 | 104 | 103.5 | 7.24 | 154 | 153.3 | 10.72 | 204 | 203.0 | 14.20 |
| 55 | 54.73 | 3.83 | 105 | 104.5 | 7.31 | 155 | 154.2 | 10.79 | 205 | 204.0 | 14.27 |
| 56 | 55.73 | 3.90 | 106 | 105.5 | 7.38 | 156 | 155.2 | 10.86 | 206 | 205.0 | 14.33 |
| 57 | 56.72 | 3.97 | 107 | 106.5 | 7.45 | 157 | 156.2 | 10.93 | 207 | 206.0 | 14.40 |
| 58 | 57.72 | 4.04 | 108 | 107.5 | 7.52 | 158 | 157.2 | 10.99 | 208 | 207.0 | 14.47 |
| 59 | 58.71 | 4.11 | 109 | 108.5 | 7.58 | 159 | 158.2 | 11.06 | 209 | 208.0 | 14.54 |
| 60 | 59.71 | 4.18 | 110 | 109.5 | 7.65 | 160 | 159.2 | 11.13 | 210 | 209.0 | 14.61 |

TABLE I     **4° 10′**

| G | D | H | G | D | H | G | D | H | G | D | H |
|---|---|---|---|---|---|---|---|---|---|---|---|
| 10 | 9·95 | 0·72 | 60 | 59·68 | 4·35 | 110 | 109·4 | 7·97 | 160 | 159·2 | 11·59 |
| 11 | 10·94 | 0·80 | 61 | 60·68 | 4·42 | 111 | 110·4 | 8·04 | 161 | 160·1 | 11·67 |
| 12 | 11·94 | 0·87 | 62 | 61·67 | 4·49 | 112 | 111·4 | 8·12 | 162 | 161·1 | 11·74 |
| 13 | 12·93 | 0·94 | 63 | 62·67 | 4·57 | 113 | 112·4 | 8·19 | 163 | 162·1 | 11·81 |
| 14 | 13·93 | 1·01 | 64 | 63·66 | 4·64 | 114 | 113·4 | 8·26 | 164 | 163·1 | 11·88 |
| 15 | 14·92 | 1·09 | 65 | 64·66 | 4·71 | 115 | 114·4 | 8·33 | 165 | 164·1 | 11·96 |
| 16 | 15·92 | 1·16 | 66 | 65·65 | 4·78 | 116 | 115·4 | 8·41 | 166 | 165·1 | 12·03 |
| 17 | 16·91 | 1·23 | 67 | 66·65 | 4·86 | 117 | 116·4 | 8·48 | 167 | 166·1 | 12·10 |
| 18 | 17·90 | 1·30 | 68 | 67·64 | 4·93 | 118 | 117·4 | 8·55 | 168 | 167·1 | 12·17 |
| 19 | 18·90 | 1·38 | 69 | 68·64 | 5·00 | 119 | 118·4 | 8·62 | 169 | 168·1 | 12·25 |
| 20 | 19·89 | 1·45 | 70 | 69·63 | 5·07 | 120 | 119·4 | 8·70 | 170 | 169·1 | 12·32 |
| 21 | 20·89 | 1·52 | 71 | 70·62 | 5·15 | 121 | 120·4 | 8·77 | 171 | 170·1 | 12·39 |
| 22 | 21·88 | 1·59 | 72 | 71·62 | 5·22 | 122 | 121·4 | 8·84 | 172 | 171·1 | 12·46 |
| 23 | 22·88 | 1·67 | 73 | 72·61 | 5·29 | 123 | 122·4 | 8·91 | 173 | 172·1 | 12·54 |
| 24 | 23·87 | 1·74 | 74 | 73·61 | 5·36 | 124 | 123·3 | 8·99 | 174 | 173·1 | 12·61 |
| 25 | 24·87 | 1·81 | 75 | 74·60 | 5·43 | 125 | 124·3 | 9·06 | 175 | 174·1 | 12·68 |
| 26 | 25·86 | 1·88 | 76 | 75·60 | 5·51 | 126 | 125·3 | 9·13 | 176 | 175·1 | 12·75 |
| 27 | 26·86 | 1·96 | 77 | 76·59 | 5·58 | 127 | 126·3 | 9·20 | 177 | 176·1 | 12·83 |
| 28 | 27·85 | 2·03 | 78 | 77·59 | 5·65 | 128 | 127·3 | 9·28 | 178 | 177·1 | 12·90 |
| 29 | 28·85 | 2·10 | 79 | 78·58 | 5·72 | 129 | 128·3 | 9·35 | 179 | 178·1 | 12·97 |
| 30 | 29·84 | 2·17 | 80 | 79·58 | 5·80 | 130 | 129·3 | 9·42 | 180 | 179·0 | 13·04 |
| 31 | 30·84 | 2·25 | 81 | 80·57 | 5·87 | 131 | 130·3 | 9·49 | 181 | 180·0 | 13·12 |
| 32 | 31·83 | 2·32 | 82 | 81·57 | 5·94 | 132 | 131·3 | 9·57 | 182 | 181·0 | 13·19 |
| 33 | 32·83 | 2·39 | 83 | 82·56 | 6·01 | 133 | 132·3 | 9·64 | 183 | 182·0 | 13·26 |
| 34 | 33·82 | 2·46 | 84 | 83·56 | 6·09 | 134 | 133·3 | 9·71 | 184 | 183·0 | 13·33 |
| 35 | 34·82 | 2·54 | 85 | 84·55 | 6·16 | 135 | 134·3 | 9·78 | 185 | 184·0 | 13·41 |
| 36 | 35·81 | 2·61 | 86 | 85·55 | 6·23 | 136 | 135·3 | 9·86 | 186 | 185·0 | 13·48 |
| 37 | 36·80 | 2·68 | 87 | 86·54 | 6·30 | 137 | 136·3 | 9·93 | 187 | 186·0 | 13·55 |
| 38 | 37·80 | 2·75 | 88 | 87·54 | 6·38 | 138 | 137·3 | 10·00 | 188 | 187·0 | 13·62 |
| 39 | 38·79 | 2·83 | 89 | 88·53 | 6·45 | 139 | 138·3 | 10·07 | 189 | 188·0 | 13·70 |
| 40 | 39·79 | 2·90 | 90 | 89·52 | 6·52 | 140 | 139·3 | 10·15 | 190 | 189·0 | 13·77 |
| 41 | 40·78 | 2·97 | 91 | 90·52 | 6·59 | 141 | 140·3 | 10·22 | 191 | 190·0 | 13·84 |
| 42 | 41·78 | 3·04 | 92 | 91·51 | 6·67 | 142 | 141·2 | 10·29 | 192 | 191·0 | 13·91 |
| 43 | 42·77 | 3·12 | 93 | 92·51 | 6·74 | 143 | 142·2 | 10·36 | 193 | 192·0 | 13·99 |
| 44 | 43·77 | 3·19 | 94 | 93·50 | 6·81 | 144 | 143·2 | 10·43 | 194 | 193·0 | 14·06 |
| 45 | 44·76 | 3·26 | 95 | 94·50 | 6·88 | 145 | 144·2 | 10·51 | 195 | 194·0 | 14·13 |
| 46 | 45·76 | 3·33 | 96 | 95·49 | 6·96 | 146 | 145·2 | 10·58 | 196 | 195·0 | 14·20 |
| 47 | 46·75 | 3·41 | 97 | 96·49 | 7·03 | 147 | 146·2 | 10·65 | 197 | 196·0 | 14·28 |
| 48 | 47·75 | 3·48 | 98 | 97·48 | 7·10 | 148 | 147·2 | 10·72 | 198 | 197·0 | 14·35 |
| 49 | 48·74 | 3·55 | 99 | 98·48 | 7·17 | 149 | 148·2 | 10·80 | 199 | 197·9 | 14·42 |
| 50 | 49·74 | 3·62 | 100 | 99·47 | 7·25 | 150 | 149·2 | 10·87 | 200 | 198·9 | 14·49 |
| 51 | 50·73 | 3·70 | 101 | 100·5 | 7·32 | 151 | 150·2 | 10·94 | 201 | 199·9 | 14·57 |
| 52 | 51·73 | 3·77 | 102 | 101·5 | 7·39 | 152 | 151·2 | 11·01 | 202 | 200·9 | 14·64 |
| 53 | 52·72 | 3·84 | 103 | 102·5 | 7·46 | 153 | 152·2 | 11·09 | 203 | 201·9 | 14·71 |
| 54 | 53·71 | 3·91 | 104 | 103·5 | 7·54 | 154 | 153·2 | 11·16 | 204 | 202·9 | 14·78 |
| 55 | 54·71 | 3·99 | 105 | 104·4 | 7·61 | 155 | 154·2 | 11·23 | 205 | 203·9 | 14·86 |
| 56 | 55·70 | 4·06 | 106 | 105·4 | 7·68 | 156 | 155·2 | 11·30 | 206 | 204·9 | 14·93 |
| 57 | 56·70 | 4·13 | 107 | 106·4 | 7·75 | 157 | 156·2 | 11·38 | 207 | 205·9 | 15·00 |
| 58 | 57·69 | 4·20 | 108 | 107·4 | 7·83 | 158 | 157·2 | 11·45 | 208 | 206·9 | 15·07 |
| 59 | 58·69 | 4·28 | 109 | 108·4 | 7·90 | 159 | 158·2 | 11·52 | 209 | 207·9 | 15·15 |
| 60 | 59·68 | 4·35 | 110 | 109·4 | 7·97 | 160 | 159·2 | 11·59 | 210 | 208·9 | 15·22 |

| G | D | H | G | D | H | G | D | H | G | D | H |
|---|---|---|---|---|---|---|---|---|---|---|---|
| 10 | 9.94 | 0.75 | 60 | 59.66 | 4.52 | 110 | 109.4 | 8.29 | 160 | 159.1 | 12.05 |
| 11 | 10.94 | 0.83 | 61 | 60.65 | 4.60 | 111 | 110.4 | 8.36 | 161 | 160.1 | 12.13 |
| 12 | 11.93 | 0.90 | 62 | 61.65 | 4.67 | 112 | 111.4 | 8.44 | 162 | 161.1 | 12.21 |
| 13 | 12.93 | 0.98 | 63 | 62.64 | 4.75 | 113 | 112.4 | 8.51 | 163 | 162.1 | 12.28 |
| 14 | 13.92 | 1.05 | 64 | 63.63 | 4.82 | 114 | 113.3 | 8.59 | 164 | 163.1 | 12.36 |
| 15 | 14.91 | 1.13 | 65 | 64.63 | 4.90 | 115 | 114.3 | 8.66 | 165 | 164.1 | 12.43 |
| 16 | 15.91 | 1.21 | 66 | 65.62 | 4.97 | 116 | 115.3 | 8.74 | 166 | 165.1 | 12.51 |
| 17 | 16.90 | 1.28 | 67 | 66.62 | 5.05 | 117 | 116.3 | 8.82 | 167 | 166.0 | 12.58 |
| 18 | 17.90 | 1.36 | 68 | 67.61 | 5.12 | 118 | 117.3 | 8.89 | 168 | 167.0 | 12.66 |
| 19 | 18.89 | 1.43 | 69 | 68.61 | 5.20 | 119 | 118.3 | 8.97 | 169 | 168.0 | 12.73 |
| 20 | 19.89 | 1.51 | 70 | 69.60 | 5.27 | 120 | 119.3 | 9.04 | 170 | 169.0 | 12.81 |
| 21 | 20.88 | 1.58 | 71 | 70.59 | 5.35 | 121 | 120.3 | 9.12 | 171 | 170.0 | 12.88 |
| 22 | 21.87 | 1.66 | 72 | 71.59 | 5.42 | 122 | 121.3 | 9.19 | 172 | 171.0 | 12.96 |
| 23 | 22.87 | 1.73 | 73 | 72.58 | 5.50 | 123 | 122.3 | 9.27 | 173 | 172.0 | 13.03 |
| 24 | 23.86 | 1.81 | 74 | 73.58 | 5.58 | 124 | 123.3 | 9.34 | 174 | 173.0 | 13.11 |
| 25 | 24.86 | 1.88 | 75 | 74.57 | 5.65 | 125 | 124.3 | 9.42 | 175 | 174.0 | 13.18 |
| 26 | 25.85 | 1.96 | 76 | 75.57 | 5.73 | 126 | 125.3 | 9.49 | 176 | 175.0 | 13.26 |
| 27 | 26.85 | 2.03 | 77 | 76.56 | 5.80 | 127 | 126.3 | 9.57 | 177 | 176.0 | 13.34 |
| 28 | 27.84 | 2.11 | 78 | 77.55 | 5.88 | 128 | 127.3 | 9.64 | 178 | 177.0 | 13.41 |
| 29 | 28.83 | 2.18 | 79 | 78.55 | 5.95 | 129 | 128.3 | 9.72 | 179 | 178.0 | 13.49 |
| 30 | 29.83 | 2.26 | 80 | 79.54 | 6.03 | 130 | 129.3 | 9.79 | 180 | 179.0 | 13.56 |
| 31 | 30.82 | 2.34 | 81 | 80.54 | 6.10 | 131 | 130.3 | 9.87 | 181 | 180.0 | 13.64 |
| 32 | 31.82 | 2.41 | 82 | 81.53 | 6.18 | 132 | 131.2 | 9.95 | 182 | 181.0 | 13.71 |
| 33 | 32.81 | 2.49 | 83 | 82.53 | 6.25 | 133 | 132.2 | 10.02 | 183 | 182.0 | 13.79 |
| 34 | 33.81 | 2.56 | 84 | 83.52 | 6.33 | 134 | 133.2 | 10.10 | 184 | 182.9 | 13.86 |
| 35 | 34.80 | 2.64 | 85 | 84.51 | 6.40 | 135 | 134.2 | 10.17 | 185 | 183.9 | 13.94 |
| 36 | 35.79 | 2.71 | 86 | 85.51 | 6.48 | 136 | 135.2 | 10.25 | 186 | 184.9 | 14.01 |
| 37 | 36.79 | 2.79 | 87 | 86.50 | 6.55 | 137 | 136.2 | 10.32 | 187 | 185.9 | 14.09 |
| 38 | 37.78 | 2.86 | 88 | 87.50 | 6.63 | 138 | 137.2 | 10.40 | 188 | 186.9 | 14.16 |
| 39 | 38.78 | 2.94 | 89 | 88.49 | 6.71 | 139 | 138.2 | 10.47 | 189 | 187.9 | 14.24 |
| 40 | 39.77 | 3.01 | 90 | 89.49 | 6.78 | 140 | 139.2 | 10.55 | 190 | 188.9 | 14.31 |
| 41 | 40.77 | 3.09 | 91 | 90.48 | 6.86 | 141 | 140.2 | 10.62 | 191 | 189.9 | 14.39 |
| 42 | 41.76 | 3.16 | 92 | 91.47 | 6.93 | 142 | 141.2 | 10.70 | 192 | 190.9 | 14.47 |
| 43 | 42.75 | 3.24 | 93 | 92.47 | 7.01 | 143 | 142.2 | 10.77 | 193 | 191.9 | 14.54 |
| 44 | 43.75 | 3.32 | 94 | 93.46 | 7.08 | 144 | 143.2 | 10.85 | 194 | 192.9 | 14.62 |
| 45 | 44.74 | 3.39 | 95 | 94.46 | 7.16 | 145 | 144.2 | 10.92 | 195 | 193.9 | 14.69 |
| 46 | 45.74 | 3.47 | 96 | 95.45 | 7.23 | 146 | 145.2 | 11.00 | 196 | 194.9 | 14.77 |
| 47 | 46.73 | 3.54 | 97 | 96.45 | 7.31 | 147 | 146.2 | 11.08 | 197 | 195.9 | 14.84 |
| 48 | 47.73 | 3.62 | 98 | 97.44 | 7.38 | 148 | 147.2 | 11.15 | 198 | 196.9 | 14.92 |
| 49 | 48.72 | 3.69 | 99 | 98.43 | 7.46 | 149 | 148.1 | 11.23 | 199 | 197.9 | 14.99 |
| 50 | 49.71 | 3.77 | 100 | 99.43 | 7.53 | 150 | 149.1 | 11.30 | 200 | 198.9 | 15.07 |
| 51 | 50.71 | 3.84 | 101 | 100.4 | 7.61 | 151 | 150.1 | 11.38 | 201 | 199.9 | 15.14 |
| 52 | 51.70 | 3.92 | 102 | 101.4 | 7.68 | 152 | 151.1 | 11.45 | 202 | 200.8 | 15.22 |
| 53 | 52.70 | 3.99 | 103 | 102.4 | 7.76 | 153 | 152.1 | 11.53 | 203 | 201.8 | 15.29 |
| 54 | 53.69 | 4.07 | 104 | 103.4 | 7.84 | 154 | 153.1 | 11.60 | 204 | 202.8 | 15.37 |
| 55 | 54.69 | 4.14 | 105 | 104.4 | 7.91 | 155 | 154.1 | 11.68 | 205 | 203.8 | 15.45 |
| 56 | 55.68 | 4.22 | 106 | 105.4 | 7.99 | 156 | 155.1 | 11.75 | 206 | 204.8 | 15.52 |
| 57 | 56.67 | 4.29 | 107 | 106.4 | 8.06 | 157 | 156.1 | 11.83 | 207 | 205.8 | 15.60 |
| 58 | 57.67 | 4.37 | 108 | 107.4 | 8.14 | 158 | 157.1 | 11.90 | 208 | 206.8 | 15.67 |
| 59 | 58.66 | 4.45 | 109 | 108.4 | 8.21 | 159 | 158.1 | 11.98 | 209 | 207.8 | 15.75 |
| 60 | 59.66 | 4.52 | 110 | 109.4 | 8.29 | 160 | 159.1 | 12.05 | 210 | 208.8 | 15.82 |

TABLE I

# 4° 30'

| G | D | H | G | D | H | G | D | H | G | D | H |
|---|---|---|---|---|---|---|---|---|---|---|---|
| 10 | 9.94 | 0.78 | 60 | 59.63 | 4.69 | 110 | 109.3 | 8.60 | 160 | 159.0 | 12.51 |
| 11 | 10.93 | 0.86 | 61 | 60.62 | 4.77 | 111 | 110.3 | 8.68 | 161 | 160.0 | 12.59 |
| 12 | 11.93 | 0.94 | 62 | 61.62 | 4.85 | 112 | 111.3 | 8.76 | 162 | 161.0 | 12.67 |
| 13 | 12.92 | 1.02 | 63 | 62.61 | 4.93 | 113 | 112.3 | 8.84 | 163 | 162.0 | 12.75 |
| 14 | 13.91 | 1.10 | 64 | 63.61 | 5.01 | 114 | 113.3 | 8.92 | 164 | 163.0 | 12.83 |
| 15 | 14.91 | 1.17 | 65 | 64.60 | 5.08 | 115 | 114.3 | 8.99 | 165 | 164.0 | 12.91 |
| 16 | 15.90 | 1.25 | 66 | 65.59 | 5.16 | 116 | 115.3 | 9.07 | 166 | 165.0 | 12.98 |
| 17 | 16.90 | 1.33 | 67 | 66.59 | 5.24 | 117 | 116.3 | 9.15 | 167 | 166.0 | 13.06 |
| 18 | 17.89 | 1.41 | 68 | 67.58 | 5.32 | 118 | 117.3 | 9.23 | 168 | 167.0 | 13.14 |
| 19 | 18.88 | 1.49 | 69 | 68.58 | 5.40 | 119 | 118.3 | 9.31 | 169 | 168.0 | 13.22 |
| 20 | 19.88 | 1.56 | 70 | 69.57 | 5.48 | 120 | 119.3 | 9.39 | 170 | 169.0 | 13.30 |
| 21 | 20.87 | 1.64 | 71 | 70.56 | 5.55 | 121 | 120.3 | 9.46 | 171 | 169.9 | 13.38 |
| 22 | 21.86 | 1.72 | 72 | 71.56 | 5.63 | 122 | 121.2 | 9.54 | 172 | 170.9 | 13.45 |
| 23 | 22.86 | 1.80 | 73 | 72.55 | 5.71 | 123 | 122.2 | 9.62 | 173 | 171.9 | 13.53 |
| 24 | 23.85 | 1.88 | 74 | 73.54 | 5.79 | 124 | 123.2 | 9.70 | 174 | 172.9 | 13.61 |
| 25 | 24.85 | 1.96 | 75 | 74.54 | 5.87 | 125 | 124.2 | 9.78 | 175 | 173.9 | 13.69 |
| 26 | 25.84 | 2.03 | 76 | 75.53 | 5.94 | 126 | 125.2 | 9.86 | 176 | 174.9 | 13.77 |
| 27 | 26.83 | 2.11 | 77 | 76.53 | 6.02 | 127 | 126.2 | 9.93 | 177 | 175.9 | 13.84 |
| 28 | 27.83 | 2.19 | 78 | 77.52 | 6.10 | 128 | 127.2 | 10.01 | 178 | 176.9 | 13.92 |
| 29 | 28.82 | 2.27 | 79 | 78.51 | 6.18 | 129 | 128.2 | 10.09 | 179 | 177.9 | 14.00 |
| 30 | 29.82 | 2.35 | 80 | 79.51 | 6.26 | 130 | 129.2 | 10.17 | 180 | 178.9 | 14.08 |
| 31 | 30.81 | 2.42 | 81 | 80.50 | 6.34 | 131 | 130.2 | 10.25 | 181 | 179.9 | 14.16 |
| 32 | 31.80 | 2.50 | 82 | 81.50 | 6.41 | 132 | 131.2 | 10.32 | 182 | 180.9 | 14.24 |
| 33 | 32.80 | 2.58 | 83 | 82.49 | 6.49 | 133 | 132.2 | 10.40 | 183 | 181.9 | 14.31 |
| 34 | 33.79 | 2.66 | 84 | 83.48 | 6.57 | 134 | 133.2 | 10.48 | 184 | 182.9 | 14.39 |
| 35 | 34.78 | 2.74 | 85 | 84.48 | 6.65 | 135 | 134.2 | 10.56 | 185 | 183.9 | 14.47 |
| 36 | 35.78 | 2.82 | 86 | 85.47 | 6.73 | 136 | 135.2 | 10.64 | 186 | 184.9 | 14.55 |
| 37 | 36.77 | 2.89 | 87 | 86.46 | 6.80 | 137 | 136.2 | 10.72 | 187 | 185.8 | 14.63 |
| 38 | 37.77 | 2.97 | 88 | 87.46 | 6.88 | 138 | 137.2 | 10.79 | 188 | 186.8 | 14.70 |
| 39 | 38.76 | 3.05 | 89 | 88.45 | 6.96 | 139 | 138.1 | 10.87 | 189 | 187.8 | 14.78 |
| 40 | 39.75 | 3.13 | 90 | 89.45 | 7.04 | 140 | 139.1 | 10.95 | 190 | 188.8 | 14.86 |
| 41 | 40.75 | 3.21 | 91 | 90.44 | 7.12 | 141 | 140.1 | 11.03 | 191 | 189.8 | 14.94 |
| 42 | 41.74 | 3.29 | 92 | 91.43 | 7.20 | 142 | 141.1 | 11.11 | 192 | 190.8 | 15.02 |
| 43 | 42.74 | 3.36 | 93 | 92.43 | 7.27 | 143 | 142.1 | 11.19 | 193 | 191.8 | 15.10 |
| 44 | 43.73 | 3.44 | 94 | 93.42 | 7.35 | 144 | 143.1 | 11.26 | 194 | 192.8 | 15.17 |
| 45 | 44.72 | 3.52 | 95 | 94.42 | 7.43 | 145 | 144.1 | 11.34 | 195 | 193.8 | 15.25 |
| 46 | 45.72 | 3.60 | 96 | 95.41 | 7.51 | 146 | 145.1 | 11.42 | 196 | 194.8 | 15.33 |
| 47 | 46.71 | 3.68 | 97 | 96.40 | 7.59 | 147 | 146.1 | 11.50 | 197 | 195.8 | 15.41 |
| 48 | 47.70 | 3.75 | 98 | 97.40 | 7.67 | 148 | 147.1 | 11.58 | 198 | 196.8 | 15.49 |
| 49 | 48.70 | 3.83 | 99 | 98.39 | 7.74 | 149 | 148.1 | 11.65 | 199 | 197.8 | 15.57 |
| 50 | 49.69 | 3.91 | 100 | 99.38 | 7.82 | 150 | 149.1 | 11.73 | 200 | 198.8 | 15.64 |
| 51 | 50.69 | 3.99 | 101 | 100.4 | 7.90 | 151 | 150.1 | 11.81 | 201 | 199.8 | 15.72 |
| 52 | 51.68 | 4.07 | 102 | 101.4 | 7.98 | 152 | 151.1 | 11.89 | 202 | 200.8 | 15.80 |
| 53 | 52.67 | 4.15 | 103 | 102.4 | 8.06 | 153 | 152.1 | 11.97 | 203 | 201.8 | 15.88 |
| 54 | 53.67 | 4.22 | 104 | 103.4 | 8.13 | 154 | 153.1 | 12.05 | 204 | 202.7 | 15.96 |
| 55 | 54.66 | 4.30 | 105 | 104.4 | 8.21 | 155 | 154.0 | 12.12 | 205 | 203.7 | 16.03 |
| 56 | 55.66 | 4.38 | 106 | 105.3 | 8.29 | 156 | 155.0 | 12.20 | 206 | 204.7 | 16.11 |
| 57 | 56.65 | 4.46 | 107 | 106.3 | 8.37 | 157 | 156.0 | 12.28 | 207 | 205.7 | 16.19 |
| 58 | 57.64 | 4.54 | 108 | 107.3 | 8.45 | 158 | 157.0 | 12.36 | 208 | 206.7 | 16.27 |
| 59 | 58.64 | 4.61 | 109 | 108.3 | 8.53 | 159 | 158.0 | 12.44 | 209 | 207.7 | 16.35 |
| 60 | 59.63 | 4.69 | 110 | 109.3 | 8.60 | 160 | 159.0 | 12.51 | 210 | 208.7 | 16.43 |

TABLE I

| G | D | H | G | D | H | G | D | H | G | D | H |
|---|---|---|---|---|---|---|---|---|---|---|---|
| 10 | 9·93 | 0·81 | 60 | 59·60 | 4·87 | 110 | 109·3 | 8·92 | 160 | 158·9 | 12·97 |
| 11 | 10·93 | 0·89 | 61 | 60·60 | 4·95 | 111 | 110·3 | 9·00 | 161 | 159·9 | 13·06 |
| 12 | 11·92 | 0·97 | 62 | 61·59 | 5·03 | 112 | 111·3 | 9·08 | 162 | 160·9 | 13·14 |
| 13 | 12·91 | 1·05 | 63 | 62·58 | 5·11 | 113 | 112·3 | 9·16 | 163 | 161·9 | 13·22 |
| 14 | 13·91 | 1·14 | 64 | 63·58 | 5·19 | 114 | 113·2 | 9·24 | 164 | 162·9 | 13·30 |
| 15 | 14·90 | 1·22 | 65 | 64·57 | 5·27 | 115 | 114·2 | 9·33 | 165 | 163·9 | 13·38 |
| 16 | 15·89 | 1·30 | 66 | 65·56 | 5·35 | 116 | 115·2 | 9·41 | 166 | 164·9 | 13·46 |
| 17 | 16·89 | 1·38 | 67 | 66·56 | 5·43 | 117 | 116·2 | 9·49 | 167 | 165·9 | 13·54 |
| 18 | 17·88 | 1·46 | 68 | 67·55 | 5·51 | 118 | 117·2 | 9·57 | 168 | 166·9 | 13·62 |
| 19 | 18·87 | 1·54 | 69 | 68·54 | 5·60 | 119 | 118·2 | 9·65 | 169 | 167·9 | 13·70 |
| 20 | 19·87 | 1·62 | 70 | 69·54 | 5·68 | 120 | 119·2 | 9·73 | 170 | 168·9 | 13·78 |
| 21 | 20·86 | 1·70 | 71 | 70·53 | 5·76 | 121 | 120·2 | 9·81 | 171 | 169·9 | 13·87 |
| 22 | 21·85 | 1·78 | 72 | 71·52 | 5·84 | 122 | 121·2 | 9·89 | 172 | 170·9 | 13·95 |
| 23 | 22·85 | 1·87 | 73 | 72·52 | 5·92 | 123 | 122·2 | 9·97 | 173 | 171·9 | 14·03 |
| 24 | 23·84 | 1·95 | 74 | 73·51 | 6·00 | 124 | 123·2 | 10·05 | 174 | 172·8 | 14·11 |
| 25 | 24·83 | 2·03 | 75 | 74·50 | 6·08 | 125 | 124·2 | 10·14 | 175 | 173·8 | 14·19 |
| 26 | 25·83 | 2·11 | 76 | 75·50 | 6·16 | 126 | 125·2 | 10·22 | 176 | 174·8 | 14·27 |
| 27 | 26·82 | 2·19 | 77 | 76·49 | 6·24 | 127 | 126·2 | 10·30 | 177 | 175·8 | 14·35 |
| 28 | 27·81 | 2·27 | 78 | 77·48 | 6·32 | 128 | 127·2 | 10·38 | 178 | 176·8 | 14·43 |
| 29 | 28·81 | 2·35 | 79 | 78·48 | 6·41 | 129 | 128·1 | 10·46 | 179 | 177·8 | 14·51 |
| 30 | 29·80 | 2·43 | 80 | 79·47 | 6·49 | 130 | 129·1 | 10·54 | 180 | 178·8 | 14·60 |
| 31 | 30·79 | 2·51 | 81 | 80·46 | 6·57 | 131 | 130·1 | 10·62 | 181 | 179·8 | 14·68 |
| 32 | 31·79 | 2·59 | 82 | 81·46 | 6·65 | 132 | 131·1 | 10·70 | 182 | 180·8 | 14·76 |
| 33 | 32·78 | 2·68 | 83 | 82·45 | 6·73 | 133 | 132·1 | 10·78 | 183 | 181·8 | 14·84 |
| 34 | 33·77 | 2·76 | 84 | 83·44 | 6·81 | 134 | 133·1 | 10·87 | 184 | 182·8 | 14·92 |
| 35 | 34·77 | 2·84 | 85 | 84·44 | 6·89 | 135 | 134·1 | 10·95 | 185 | 183·8 | 15·00 |
| 36 | 35·76 | 2·92 | 86 | 85·43 | 6·97 | 136 | 135·1 | 11·03 | 186 | 184·8 | 15·08 |
| 37 | 36·75 | 3·00 | 87 | 86·42 | 7·05 | 137 | 136·1 | 11·11 | 187 | 185·8 | 15·16 |
| 38 | 37·75 | 3·08 | 88 | 87·42 | 7·14 | 138 | 137·1 | 11·19 | 188 | 186·8 | 15·24 |
| 39 | 38·74 | 3·16 | 89 | 88·41 | 7·22 | 139 | 138·1 | 11·27 | 189 | 187·7 | 15·33 |
| 40 | 39·74 | 3·24 | 90 | 89·40 | 7·30 | 140 | 139·1 | 11·35 | 190 | 188·7 | 15·41 |
| 41 | 40·73 | 3·32 | 91 | 90·40 | 7·38 | 141 | 140·1 | 11·43 | 191 | 189·7 | 15·49 |
| 42 | 41·72 | 3·41 | 92 | 91·39 | 7·46 | 142 | 141·1 | 11·51 | 192 | 190·7 | 15·57 |
| 43 | 42·72 | 3·49 | 93 | 92·38 | 7·54 | 143 | 142·1 | 11·60 | 193 | 191·7 | 15·65 |
| 44 | 43·71 | 3·57 | 94 | 93·38 | 7·62 | 144 | 143·0 | 11·68 | 194 | 192·7 | 15·73 |
| 45 | 44·70 | 3·65 | 95 | 94·37 | 7·70 | 145 | 144·0 | 11·76 | 195 | 193·7 | 15·81 |
| 46 | 45·70 | 3·73 | 96 | 95·36 | 7·78 | 146 | 145·0 | 11·84 | 196 | 194·7 | 15·89 |
| 47 | 46·69 | 3·81 | 97 | 96·36 | 7·87 | 147 | 146·0 | 11·92 | 197 | 195·7 | 15·97 |
| 48 | 47·68 | 3·89 | 98 | 97·35 | 7·95 | 148 | 147·0 | 12·00 | 198 | 196·7 | 16·06 |
| 49 | 48·68 | 3·97 | 99 | 98·34 | 8·03 | 149 | 148·0 | 12·08 | 199 | 197·7 | 16·14 |
| 50 | 49·67 | 4·05 | 100 | 99·34 | 8·11 | 150 | 149·0 | 12·16 | 200 | 198·7 | 16·22 |
| 51 | 50·66 | 4·14 | 101 | 100·3 | 8·19 | 151 | 150·0 | 12·24 | 201 | 199·7 | 16·30 |
| 52 | 51·66 | 4·22 | 102 | 101·3 | 8·27 | 152 | 151·0 | 12·33 | 202 | 200·7 | 16·38 |
| 53 | 52·65 | 4·30 | 103 | 102·3 | 8·35 | 153 | 152·0 | 12·41 | 203 | 201·7 | 16·46 |
| 54 | 53·64 | 4·38 | 104 | 103·3 | 8·43 | 154 | 153·0 | 12·49 | 204 | 202·6 | 16·54 |
| 55 | 54·64 | 4·46 | 105 | 104·3 | 8·51 | 155 | 154·0 | 12·57 | 205 | 203·6 | 16·62 |
| 56 | 55·63 | 4·54 | 106 | 105·3 | 8·60 | 156 | 155·0 | 12·65 | 206 | 204·6 | 16·70 |
| 57 | 56·62 | 4·62 | 107 | 106·3 | 8·68 | 157 | 156·0 | 12·73 | 207 | 205·6 | 16·79 |
| 58 | 57·62 | 4·70 | 108 | 107·3 | 8·76 | 158 | 157·0 | 12·81 | 208 | 206·6 | 16·87 |
| 59 | 58·61 | 4·78 | 109 | 108·3 | 8·84 | 159 | 157·9 | 12·89 | 209 | 207·6 | 16·95 |
| 60 | 59·60 | 4·87 | 110 | 109·3 | 8·92 | 160 | 158·9 | 12·97 | 210 | 208·6 | 17·03 |

TABLE I

# 4° 50′

| G | D | H | G | D | H | G | D | H | G | D | H |
|---|---|---|---|---|---|---|---|---|---|---|---|
| 10 | 9·93 | 0·84 | 60 | 59·57 | 5·04 | 110 | 109·2 | 9·24 | 160 | 158·9 | 13·43 |
| 11 | 10·92 | 0·92 | 61 | 60·57 | 5·12 | 111 | 110·2 | 9·32 | 161 | 159·9 | 13·52 |
| 12 | 11·91 | 1·01 | 62 | 61·56 | 5·21 | 112 | 111·2 | 9·40 | 162 | 160·8 | 13·60 |
| 13 | 12·91 | 1·09 | 63 | 62·55 | 5·29 | 113 | 112·2 | 9·49 | 163 | 161·8 | 13·68 |
| 14 | 13·90 | 1·18 | 64 | 63·55 | 5·37 | 114 | 113·2 | 9·57 | 164 | 162·8 | 13·77 |
| 15 | 14·89 | 1·26 | 65 | 64·54 | 5·46 | 115 | 114·2 | 9·66 | 165 | 163·8 | 13·85 |
| 16 | 15·89 | 1·34 | 66 | 65·53 | 5·54 | 116 | 115·2 | 9·74 | 166 | 164·8 | 13·94 |
| 17 | 16·88 | 1·43 | 67 | 66·52 | 5·63 | 117 | 116·2 | 9·82 | 167 | 165·8 | 14·02 |
| 18 | 17·87 | 1·51 | 68 | 67·52 | 5·71 | 118 | 117·2 | 9·91 | 168 | 166·8 | 14·10 |
| 19 | 18·87 | 1·60 | 69 | 68·51 | 5·79 | 119 | 118·2 | 9·99 | 169 | 167·8 | 14·19 |
| 20 | 19·86 | 1·68 | 70 | 69·50 | 5·88 | 120 | 119·1 | 10·07 | 170 | 168·8 | 14·27 |
| 21 | 20·85 | 1·76 | 71 | 70·50 | 5·96 | 121 | 120·1 | 10·16 | 171 | 169·8 | 14·36 |
| 22 | 21·84 | 1·85 | 72 | 71·49 | 6·04 | 122 | 121·1 | 10·24 | 172 | 170·8 | 14·44 |
| 23 | 22·84 | 1·93 | 73 | 72·48 | 6·13 | 123 | 122·1 | 10·33 | 173 | 171·8 | 14·52 |
| 24 | 23·83 | 2·01 | 74 | 73·47 | 6·21 | 124 | 123·1 | 10·41 | 174 | 172·8 | 14·61 |
| 25 | 24·82 | 2·10 | 75 | 74·47 | 6·30 | 125 | 124·1 | 10·49 | 175 | 173·8 | 14·69 |
| 26 | 25·82 | 2·18 | 76 | 75·46 | 6·38 | 126 | 125·1 | 10·58 | 176 | 174·8 | 14·78 |
| 27 | 26·81 | 2·27 | 77 | 76·45 | 6·46 | 127 | 126·1 | 10·66 | 177 | 175·7 | 14·86 |
| 28 | 27·80 | 2·35 | 78 | 77·45 | 6·55 | 128 | 127·1 | 10·75 | 178 | 176·7 | 14·94 |
| 29 | 28·79 | 2·43 | 79 | 78·44 | 6·63 | 129 | 128·1 | 10·83 | 179 | 177·7 | 15·03 |
| 30 | 29·79 | 2·52 | 80 | 79·43 | 6·72 | 130 | 129·1 | 10·91 | 180 | 178·7 | 15·11 |
| 31 | 30·78 | 2·60 | 81 | 80·42 | 6·80 | 131 | 130·1 | 11·00 | 181 | 179·7 | 15·20 |
| 32 | 31·77 | 2·69 | 82 | 81·42 | 6·88 | 132 | 131·1 | 11·08 | 182 | 180·7 | 15·28 |
| 33 | 32·77 | 2·77 | 83 | 82·41 | 6·97 | 133 | 132·1 | 11·17 | 183 | 181·7 | 15·36 |
| 34 | 33·76 | 2·85 | 84 | 83·40 | 7·05 | 134 | 133·0 | 11·25 | 184 | 182·7 | 15·45 |
| 35 | 34·75 | 2·94 | 85 | 84·40 | 7·14 | 135 | 134·0 | 11·33 | 185 | 183·7 | 15·53 |
| 36 | 35·74 | 3·02 | 86 | 85·39 | 7·22 | 136 | 135·0 | 11·42 | 186 | 184·7 | 15·62 |
| 37 | 36·74 | 3·11 | 87 | 86·38 | 7·30 | 137 | 136·0 | 11·50 | 187 | 185·7 | 15·70 |
| 38 | 37·73 | 3·19 | 88 | 87·38 | 7·39 | 138 | 137·0 | 11·59 | 188 | 186·7 | 15·78 |
| 39 | 38·72 | 3·27 | 89 | 88·37 | 7·47 | 139 | 138·0 | 11·67 | 189 | 187·7 | 15·87 |
| 40 | 39·72 | 3·36 | 90 | 89·36 | 7·56 | 140 | 139·0 | 11·75 | 190 | 188·7 | 15·95 |
| 41 | 40·71 | 3·44 | 91 | 90·35 | 7·64 | 141 | 140·0 | 11·84 | 191 | 189·6 | 16·04 |
| 42 | 41·70 | 3·53 | 92 | 91·35 | 7·72 | 142 | 141·0 | 11·92 | 192 | 190·6 | 16·12 |
| 43 | 42·69 | 3·61 | 93 | 92·34 | 7·81 | 143 | 142·0 | 12·01 | 193 | 191·6 | 16·20 |
| 44 | 43·69 | 3·69 | 94 | 93·33 | 7·89 | 144 | 143·0 | 12·09 | 194 | 192·6 | 16·29 |
| 45 | 44·68 | 3·78 | 95 | 94·33 | 7·98 | 145 | 144·0 | 12·17 | 195 | 193·6 | 16·37 |
| 46 | 45·67 | 3·86 | 96 | 95·32 | 8·06 | 146 | 145·0 | 12·26 | 196 | 194·6 | 16·46 |
| 47 | 46·67 | 3·95 | 97 | 96·31 | 8·14 | 147 | 146·0 | 12·34 | 197 | 195·6 | 16·54 |
| 48 | 47·66 | 4·03 | 98 | 97·30 | 8·23 | 148 | 146·9 | 12·43 | 198 | 196·6 | 16·62 |
| 49 | 48·65 | 4·11 | 99 | 98·30 | 8·31 | 149 | 147·9 | 12·51 | 199 | 197·6 | 16·71 |
| 50 | 49·65 | 4·20 | 100 | 99·29 | 8·40 | 150 | 148·9 | 12·59 | 200 | 198·6 | 16·79 |
| 51 | 50·64 | 4·28 | 101 | 100·3 | 8·48 | 151 | 149·9 | 12·68 | 201 | 199·6 | 16·88 |
| 52 | 51·63 | 4·37 | 102 | 101·3 | 8·56 | 152 | 150·9 | 12·76 | 202 | 200·6 | 16·96 |
| 53 | 52·62 | 4·45 | 103 | 102·3 | 8·65 | 153 | 151·9 | 12·85 | 203 | 201·6 | 17·04 |
| 54 | 53·62 | 4·53 | 104 | 103·3 | 8·73 | 154 | 152·9 | 12·93 | 204 | 202·6 | 17·13 |
| 55 | 54·61 | 4·62 | 105 | 104·3 | 8·82 | 155 | 153·9 | 13·01 | 205 | 203·5 | 17·21 |
| 56 | 55·60 | 4·70 | 106 | 105·2 | 8·90 | 156 | 154·9 | 13·10 | 206 | 204·5 | 17·30 |
| 57 | 56·60 | 4·79 | 107 | 106·2 | 8·98 | 157 | 155·9 | 13·18 | 207 | 205·5 | 17·38 |
| 58 | 57·59 | 4·87 | 108 | 107·2 | 9·07 | 158 | 156·9 | 13·27 | 208 | 206·5 | 17·46 |
| 59 | 58·58 | 4·95 | 109 | 108·2 | 9·15 | 159 | 157·9 | 13·35 | 209 | 207·5 | 17·55 |
| 60 | 59·57 | 5·04 | 110 | 109·2 | 9·24 | 160 | 158·9 | 13·43 | 210 | 208·5 | 17·63 |

| G | D | H | G | D | H | G | D | H | G | D | H |
|---|---|---|---|---|---|---|---|---|---|---|---|
| 10 | 9·92 | 0·87 | 60 | 59·54 | 5·21 | 110 | 109·2 | 9·55 | 160 | 158·8 | 13·89 |
| 11 | 10·92 | 0·96 | 61 | 60·54 | 5·30 | 111 | 110·2 | 9·64 | 161 | 159·8 | 13·98 |
| 12 | 11·91 | 1·04 | 62 | 61·53 | 5·38 | 112 | 111·1 | 9·72 | 162 | 160·8 | 14·07 |
| 13 | 12·90 | 1·13 | 63 | 62·52 | 5·47 | 113 | 112·1 | 9·81 | 163 | 161·8 | 14·15 |
| 14 | 13·89 | 1·22 | 64 | 63·51 | 5·56 | 114 | 113·1 | 9·90 | 164 | 162·8 | 14·24 |
| 15 | 14·89 | 1·30 | 65 | 64·51 | 5·64 | 115 | 114·1 | 9·98 | 165 | 163·7 | 14·33 |
| 16 | 15·88 | 1·39 | 66 | 65·50 | 5·73 | 116 | 115·1 | 10·07 | 166 | 164·7 | 14·41 |
| 17 | 16·87 | 1·48 | 67 | 66·49 | 5·82 | 117 | 116·1 | 10·16 | 167 | 165·7 | 14·50 |
| 18 | 17·86 | 1·56 | 68 | 67·48 | 5·90 | 118 | 117·1 | 10·25 | 168 | 166·7 | 14·59 |
| 19 | 18·86 | 1·65 | 69 | 68·48 | 5·99 | 119 | 118·1 | 10·33 | 169 | 167·7 | 14·67 |
| 20 | 19·85 | 1·74 | 70 | 69·47 | 6·08 | 120 | 119·1 | 10·42 | 170 | 168·7 | 14·76 |
| 21 | 20·84 | 1·82 | 71 | 70·46 | 6·16 | 121 | 120·1 | 10·51 | 171 | 169·7 | 14·85 |
| 22 | 21·83 | 1·91 | 72 | 71·45 | 6·25 | 122 | 121·1 | 10·59 | 172 | 170·7 | 14·93 |
| 23 | 22·83 | 2·00 | 73 | 72·45 | 6·34 | 123 | 122·1 | 10·68 | 173 | 171·7 | 15·02 |
| 24 | 23·82 | 2·08 | 74 | 73·44 | 6·42 | 124 | 123·1 | 10·77 | 174 | 172·7 | 15·11 |
| 25 | 24·81 | 2·17 | 75 | 74·43 | 6·51 | 125 | 124·1 | 10·85 | 175 | 173·7 | 15·19 |
| 26 | 25·80 | 2·26 | 76 | 75·42 | 6·60 | 126 | 125·0 | 10·94 | 176 | 174·7 | 15·28 |
| 27 | 26·79 | 2·34 | 77 | 76·41 | 6·69 | 127 | 126·0 | 11·03 | 177 | 175·7 | 15·37 |
| 28 | 27·79 | 2·43 | 78 | 77·41 | 6·77 | 128 | 127·0 | 11·11 | 178 | 176·6 | 15·45 |
| 29 | 28·78 | 2·52 | 79 | 78·40 | 6·86 | 129 | 128·0 | 11·20 | 179 | 177·6 | 15·54 |
| 30 | 29·77 | 2·60 | 80 | 79·39 | 6·95 | 130 | 129·0 | 11·29 | 180 | 178·6 | 15·63 |
| 31 | 30·76 | 2·69 | 81 | 80·38 | 7·03 | 131 | 130·0 | 11·37 | 181 | 179·6 | 15·72 |
| 32 | 31·76 | 2·78 | 82 | 81·38 | 7·12 | 132 | 131·0 | 11·46 | 182 | 180·6 | 15·80 |
| 33 | 32·75 | 2·87 | 83 | 82·37 | 7·21 | 133 | 132·0 | 11·55 | 183 | 181·6 | 15·89 |
| 34 | 33·74 | 2·95 | 84 | 83·36 | 7·29 | 134 | 133·0 | 11·63 | 184 | 182·6 | 15·98 |
| 35 | 34·73 | 3·04 | 85 | 84·35 | 7·38 | 135 | 134·0 | 11·72 | 185 | 183·6 | 16·06 |
| 36 | 35·73 | 3·13 | 86 | 85·35 | 7·47 | 136 | 135·0 | 11·81 | 186 | 184·6 | 16·15 |
| 37 | 36·72 | 3·21 | 87 | 86·34 | 7·55 | 137 | 136·0 | 11·89 | 187 | 185·6 | 16·24 |
| 38 | 37·71 | 3·30 | 88 | 87·33 | 7·64 | 138 | 137·0 | 11·98 | 188 | 186·6 | 16·32 |
| 39 | 38·70 | 3·39 | 89 | 88·32 | 7·73 | 139 | 137·9 | 12·07 | 189 | 187·6 | 16·41 |
| 40 | 39·70 | 3·47 | 90 | 89·32 | 7·81 | 140 | 138·9 | 12·16 | 190 | 188·6 | 16·50 |
| 41 | 40·69 | 3·56 | 91 | 90·31 | 7·90 | 141 | 139·9 | 12·24 | 191 | 189·5 | 16·58 |
| 42 | 41·68 | 3·65 | 92 | 91·30 | 7·99 | 142 | 140·9 | 12·33 | 192 | 190·5 | 16·67 |
| 43 | 42·67 | 3·73 | 93 | 92·29 | 8·07 | 143 | 141·9 | 12·42 | 193 | 191·5 | 16·76 |
| 44 | 43·67 | 3·82 | 94 | 93·29 | 8·16 | 144 | 142·9 | 12·50 | 194 | 192·5 | 16·84 |
| 45 | 44·66 | 3·91 | 95 | 94·28 | 8·25 | 145 | 143·9 | 12·59 | 195 | 193·5 | 16·93 |
| 46 | 45·65 | 3·99 | 96 | 95·27 | 8·34 | 146 | 144·9 | 12·68 | 196 | 194·5 | 17·02 |
| 47 | 46·64 | 4·08 | 97 | 96·26 | 8·42 | 147 | 145·9 | 12·76 | 197 | 195·5 | 17·10 |
| 48 | 47·64 | 4·17 | 98 | 97·26 | 8·51 | 148 | 146·9 | 12·85 | 198 | 196·5 | 17·19 |
| 49 | 48·63 | 4·25 | 99 | 98·25 | 8·60 | 149 | 147·9 | 12·94 | 199 | 197·5 | 17·28 |
| 50 | 49·62 | 4·34 | 100 | 99·24 | 8·68 | 150 | 148·9 | 13·02 | 200 | 198·5 | 17·36 |
| 51 | 50·61 | 4·43 | 101 | 100·2 | 8·77 | 151 | 149·9 | 13·11 | 201 | 199·5 | 17·45 |
| 52 | 51·60 | 4·51 | 102 | 101·2 | 8·86 | 152 | 150·8 | 13·20 | 202 | 200·5 | 17·54 |
| 53 | 52·60 | 4·60 | 103 | 102·2 | 8·94 | 153 | 151·8 | 13·28 | 203 | 201·5 | 17·63 |
| 54 | 53·59 | 4·69 | 104 | 103·2 | 9·03 | 154 | 152·8 | 13·37 | 204 | 202·5 | 17·71 |
| 55 | 54·58 | 4·78 | 105 | 104·2 | 9·12 | 155 | 153·8 | 13·46 | 205 | 203·4 | 17·80 |
| 56 | 55·57 | 4·86 | 106 | 105·2 | 9·20 | 156 | 154·8 | 13·54 | 206 | 204·4 | 17·89 |
| 57 | 56·57 | 4·95 | 107 | 106·2 | 9·29 | 157 | 155·8 | 13·63 | 207 | 205·4 | 17·97 |
| 58 | 57·56 | 5·04 | 108 | 107·2 | 9·38 | 158 | 156·8 | 13·72 | 208 | 206·4 | 18·06 |
| 59 | 58·55 | 5·12 | 109 | 108·2 | 9·46 | 159 | 157·8 | 13·81 | 209 | 207·4 | 18·15 |
| 60 | 59·54 | 5·21 | 110 | 109·2 | 9·55 | 160 | 158·8 | 13·89 | 210 | 208·4 | 18·23 |

TABLE I       **5° 10′**

| G | D | H | G | D | H | G | D | H | G | D | H |
|---|---|---|---|---|---|---|---|---|---|---|---|
| 10 | 9·92 | 0·90 | 60 | 59·51 | 5·38 | 110 | 109·1 | 9·87 | 160 | 158·7 | 14·35 |
| 11 | 10·91 | 0·99 | 61 | 60·51 | 5·47 | 111 | 110·1 | 9·96 | 161 | 159·7 | 14·44 |
| 12 | 11·90 | 1·08 | 62 | 61·50 | 5·56 | 112 | 111·1 | 10·04 | 162 | 160·7 | 14·53 |
| 13 | 12·89 | 1·17 | 63 | 62·49 | 5·65 | 113 | 112·1 | 10·13 | 163 | 161·7 | 14·62 |
| 14 | 13·89 | 1·26 | 64 | 63·48 | 5·74 | 114 | 113·1 | 10·22 | 164 | 162·7 | 14·71 |
| 15 | 14·88 | 1·35 | 65 | 64·47 | 5·83 | 115 | 114·1 | 10·31 | 165 | 163·7 | 14·80 |
| 16 | 15·87 | 1·43 | 66 | 65·46 | 5·92 | 116 | 115·1 | 10·40 | 166 | 164·7 | 14·89 |
| 17 | 16·86 | 1·52 | 67 | 66·46 | 6·01 | 117 | 116·1 | 10·49 | 167 | 165·6 | 14·98 |
| 18 | 17·85 | 1·61 | 68 | 67·45 | 6·10 | 118 | 117·0 | 10·58 | 168 | 166·6 | 15·07 |
| 19 | 18·85 | 1·70 | 69 | 68·44 | 6·19 | 119 | 118·0 | 10·67 | 169 | 167·6 | 15·16 |
| 20 | 19·84 | 1·79 | 70 | 69·43 | 6·28 | 120 | 119·0 | 10·76 | 170 | 168·6 | 15·25 |
| 21 | 20·83 | 1·88 | 71 | 70·42 | 6·37 | 121 | 120·0 | 10·85 | 171 | 169·6 | 15·34 |
| 22 | 21·82 | 1·97 | 72 | 71·42 | 6·46 | 122 | 121·0 | 10·94 | 172 | 170·6 | 15·43 |
| 23 | 22·81 | 2·06 | 73 | 72·41 | 6·55 | 123 | 122·0 | 11·03 | 173 | 171·6 | 15·52 |
| 24 | 23·81 | 2·15 | 74 | 73·40 | 6·64 | 124 | 123·0 | 11·12 | 174 | 172·6 | 15·61 |
| 25 | 24·80 | 2·24 | 75 | 74·39 | 6·73 | 125 | 124·0 | 11·21 | 175 | 173·6 | 15·70 |
| 26 | 25·79 | 2·33 | 76 | 75·38 | 6·82 | 126 | 125·0 | 11·30 | 176 | 174·6 | 15·78 |
| 27 | 26·78 | 2·42 | 77 | 76·38 | 6·91 | 127 | 126·0 | 11·39 | 177 | 175·6 | 15·87 |
| 28 | 27·77 | 2·51 | 78 | 77·37 | 7·00 | 128 | 127·0 | 11·48 | 178 | 176·6 | 15·96 |
| 29 | 28·76 | 2·60 | 79 | 78·36 | 7·09 | 129 | 128·0 | 11·57 | 179 | 177·5 | 16·05 |
| 30 | 29·76 | 2·69 | 80 | 79·35 | 7·17 | 130 | 128·9 | 11·66 | 180 | 178·5 | 16·14 |
| 31 | 30·75 | 2·78 | 81 | 80·34 | 7·26 | 131 | 129·9 | 11·75 | 181 | 179·5 | 16·23 |
| 32 | 31·74 | 2·87 | 82 | 81·33 | 7·35 | 132 | 130·9 | 11·84 | 182 | 180·5 | 16·32 |
| 33 | 32·73 | 2·96 | 83 | 82·33 | 7·44 | 133 | 131·9 | 11·93 | 183 | 181·5 | 16·41 |
| 34 | 33·72 | 3·05 | 84 | 83·32 | 7·53 | 134 | 132·9 | 12·02 | 184 | 182·5 | 16·50 |
| 35 | 34·72 | 3·14 | 85 | 84·31 | 7·62 | 135 | 133·9 | 12·11 | 185 | 183·5 | 16·59 |
| 36 | 35·71 | 3·23 | 86 | 85·30 | 7·71 | 136 | 134·9 | 12·20 | 186 | 184·5 | 16·68 |
| 37 | 36·70 | 3·32 | 87 | 86·29 | 7·80 | 137 | 135·9 | 12·29 | 187 | 185·5 | 16·77 |
| 38 | 37·69 | 3·41 | 88 | 87·29 | 7·89 | 138 | 136·9 | 12·38 | 188 | 186·5 | 16·86 |
| 39 | 38·68 | 3·50 | 89 | 88·28 | 7·98 | 139 | 137·9 | 12·47 | 189 | 187·5 | 16·95 |
| 40 | 39·68 | 3·59 | 90 | 89·27 | 8·07 | 140 | 138·9 | 12·56 | 190 | 188·5 | 17·04 |
| 41 | 40·67 | 3·68 | 91 | 90·26 | 8·16 | 141 | 139·9 | 12·65 | 191 | 189·5 | 17·13 |
| 42 | 41·66 | 3·77 | 92 | 91·25 | 8·25 | 142 | 140·8 | 12·74 | 192 | 190·4 | 17·22 |
| 43 | 42·65 | 3·86 | 93 | 92·25 | 8·34 | 143 | 141·8 | 12·83 | 193 | 191·4 | 17·31 |
| 44 | 43·64 | 3·95 | 94 | 93·24 | 8·43 | 144 | 142·8 | 12·91 | 194 | 192·4 | 17·40 |
| 45 | 44·63 | 4·04 | 95 | 94·23 | 8·52 | 145 | 143·8 | 13·00 | 195 | 193·4 | 17·49 |
| 46 | 45·63 | 4·13 | 96 | 95·22 | 8·61 | 146 | 144·8 | 13·09 | 196 | 194·4 | 17·58 |
| 47 | 46·62 | 4·22 | 97 | 96·21 | 8·70 | 147 | 145·8 | 13·18 | 197 | 195·4 | 17·67 |
| 48 | 47·61 | 4·30 | 98 | 97·21 | 8·79 | 148 | 146·8 | 13·27 | 198 | 196·4 | 17·76 |
| 49 | 48·60 | 4·39 | 99 | 98·20 | 8·88 | 149 | 147·8 | 13·36 | 199 | 197·4 | 17·85 |
| 50 | 49·59 | 4·48 | 100 | 99·19 | 8·97 | 150 | 148·8 | 13·45 | 200 | 198·4 | 17·94 |
| 51 | 50·59 | 4·57 | 101 | 100·2 | 9·06 | 151 | 149·8 | 13·54 | 201 | 199·4 | 18·03 |
| 52 | 51·58 | 4·66 | 102 | 101·2 | 9·15 | 152 | 150·8 | 13·63 | 202 | 200·4 | 18·12 |
| 53 | 52·57 | 4·75 | 103 | 102·2 | 9·24 | 153 | 151·8 | 13·72 | 203 | 201·4 | 18·21 |
| 54 | 53·56 | 4·84 | 104 | 103·2 | 9·33 | 154 | 152·8 | 13·81 | 204 | 202·3 | 18·30 |
| 55 | 54·55 | 4·93 | 105 | 104·1 | 9·42 | 155 | 153·7 | 13·90 | 205 | 203·3 | 18·39 |
| 56 | 55·55 | 5·02 | 106 | 105·1 | 9·51 | 156 | 154·7 | 13·99 | 206 | 204·3 | 18·48 |
| 57 | 56·54 | 5·11 | 107 | 106·1 | 9·60 | 157 | 155·7 | 14·08 | 207 | 205·3 | 18·57 |
| 58 | 57·53 | 5·20 | 108 | 107·1 | 9·69 | 158 | 156·7 | 14·17 | 208 | 206·3 | 18·65 |
| 59 | 58·52 | 5·29 | 109 | 108·1 | 9·78 | 159 | 157·7 | 14·26 | 209 | 207·3 | 18·74 |
| 60 | 59·51 | 5·38 | 110 | 109·1 | 9·87 | 160 | 158·7 | 14·35 | 210 | 208·3 | 18·83 |

| G | D | H | G | D | H | G | D | H | G | D | H |
|---|---|---|---|---|---|---|---|---|---|---|---|
| 10 | 9·91 | 0·93 | 60 | 59·48 | 5·55 | 110 | 109·0 | 10·18 | 160 | 158·6 | 14·81 |
| 11 | 10·90 | 1·02 | 61 | 60·47 | 5·65 | 111 | 110·0 | 10·27 | 161 | 159·6 | 14·90 |
| 12 | 11·90 | 1·11 | 62 | 61·46 | 5·74 | 112 | 111·0 | 10·37 | 162 | 160·6 | 14·99 |
| 13 | 12·89 | 1·20 | 63 | 62·46 | 5·83 | 113 | 112·0 | 10·46 | 163 | 161·6 | 15·09 |
| 14 | 13·88 | 1·30 | 64 | 63·45 | 5·92 | 114 | 113·0 | 10·55 | 164 | 162·6 | 15·18 |
| 15 | 14·87 | 1·39 | 65 | 64·44 | 6·02 | 115 | 114·0 | 10·64 | 165 | 163·6 | 15·27 |
| 16 | 15·86 | 1·48 | 66 | 65·43 | 6·11 | 116 | 115·0 | 10·74 | 166 | 164·6 | 15·36 |
| 17 | 16·85 | 1·57 | 67 | 66·42 | 6·20 | 117 | 116·0 | 10·83 | 167 | 165·6 | 15·46 |
| 18 | 17·84 | 1·67 | 68 | 67·41 | 6·29 | 118 | 117·0 | 10·92 | 168 | 166·5 | 15·55 |
| 19 | 18·84 | 1·76 | 69 | 68·40 | 6·39 | 119 | 118·0 | 11·01 | 169 | 167·5 | 15·64 |
| 20 | 19·83 | 1·85 | 70 | 69·40 | 6·48 | 120 | 119·0 | 11·11 | 170 | 168·5 | 15·73 |
| 21 | 20·82 | 1·94 | 71 | 70·39 | 6·57 | 121 | 120·0 | 11·20 | 171 | 169·5 | 15·83 |
| 22 | 21·81 | 2·04 | 72 | 71·38 | 6·66 | 122 | 120·9 | 11·29 | 172 | 170·5 | 15·92 |
| 23 | 22·80 | 2·13 | 73 | 72·37 | 6·76 | 123 | 121·9 | 11·38 | 173 | 171·5 | 16·01 |
| 24 | 23·79 | 2·22 | 74 | 73·36 | 6·85 | 124 | 122·9 | 11·48 | 174 | 172·5 | 16·10 |
| 25 | 24·78 | 2·31 | 75 | 74·35 | 6·94 | 125 | 123·9 | 11·57 | 175 | 173·5 | 16·20 |
| 26 | 25·78 | 2·41 | 76 | 75·34 | 7·03 | 126 | 124·9 | 11·66 | 176 | 174·5 | 16·29 |
| 27 | 26·77 | 2·50 | 77 | 76·33 | 7·13 | 127 | 125·9 | 11·75 | 177 | 175·5 | 16·38 |
| 28 | 27·76 | 2·59 | 78 | 77·33 | 7·22 | 128 | 126·9 | 11·85 | 178 | 176·5 | 16·47 |
| 29 | 28·75 | 2·68 | 79 | 78·32 | 7·31 | 129 | 127·9 | 11·94 | 179 | 177·5 | 16·57 |
| 30 | 29·74 | 2·78 | 80 | 79·31 | 7·40 | 130 | 128·9 | 12·03 | 180 | 178·4 | 16·66 |
| 31 | 30·73 | 2·87 | 81 | 80·30 | 7·50 | 131 | 129·9 | 12·12 | 181 | 179·4 | 16·75 |
| 32 | 31·72 | 2·96 | 82 | 81·29 | 7·59 | 132 | 130·9 | 12·22 | 182 | 180·4 | 16·84 |
| 33 | 32·71 | 3·05 | 83 | 82·28 | 7·68 | 133 | 131·9 | 12·31 | 183 | 181·4 | 16·94 |
| 34 | 33·71 | 3·15 | 84 | 83·27 | 7·77 | 134 | 132·8 | 12·40 | 184 | 182·4 | 17·03 |
| 35 | 34·70 | 3·24 | 85 | 84·27 | 7·87 | 135 | 133·8 | 12·49 | 185 | 183·4 | 17·12 |
| 36 | 35·69 | 3·33 | 86 | 85·26 | 7·96 | 136 | 134·8 | 12·59 | 186 | 184·4 | 17·21 |
| 37 | 36·68 | 3·42 | 87 | 86·25 | 8·05 | 137 | 135·8 | 12·68 | 187 | 185·4 | 17·31 |
| 38 | 37·67 | 3·52 | 88 | 87·24 | 8·14 | 138 | 136·8 | 12·77 | 188 | 186·4 | 17·40 |
| 39 | 38·66 | 3·61 | 89 | 88·23 | 8·24 | 139 | 137·8 | 12·86 | 189 | 187·4 | 17·49 |
| 40 | 39·65 | 3·70 | 90 | 89·22 | 8·33 | 140 | 138·8 | 12·96 | 190 | 188·4 | 17·58 |
| 41 | 40·65 | 3·79 | 91 | 90·21 | 8·42 | 141 | 139·8 | 13·05 | 191 | 189·3 | 17·68 |
| 42 | 41·64 | 3·89 | 92 | 91·20 | 8·51 | 142 | 140·8 | 13·14 | 192 | 190·3 | 17·77 |
| 43 | 42·63 | 3·98 | 93 | 92·20 | 8·61 | 143 | 141·8 | 13·23 | 193 | 191·3 | 17·86 |
| 44 | 43·62 | 4·07 | 94 | 93·19 | 8·70 | 144 | 142·8 | 13·33 | 194 | 192·3 | 17·95 |
| 45 | 44·61 | 4·16 | 95 | 94·18 | 8·79 | 145 | 143·7 | 13·42 | 195 | 193·3 | 18·05 |
| 46 | 45·60 | 4·26 | 96 | 95·17 | 8·88 | 146 | 144·7 | 13·51 | 196 | 194·3 | 18·14 |
| 47 | 46·59 | 4·35 | 97 | 96·16 | 8·98 | 147 | 145·7 | 13·60 | 197 | 195·3 | 18·23 |
| 48 | 47·59 | 4·44 | 98 | 97·15 | 9·07 | 148 | 146·7 | 13·70 | 198 | 196·3 | 18·32 |
| 49 | 48·58 | 4·53 | 99 | 98·14 | 9·16 | 149 | 147·7 | 13·79 | 199 | 197·3 | 18·42 |
| 50 | 49·57 | 4·63 | 100 | 99·14 | 9·25 | 150 | 148·7 | 13·88 | 200 | 198·3 | 18·51 |
| 51 | 50·56 | 4·72 | 101 | 100·1 | 9·35 | 151 | 149·7 | 13·97 | 201 | 199·3 | 18·60 |
| 52 | 51·55 | 4·81 | 102 | 101·1 | 9·44 | 152 | 150·7 | 14·07 | 202 | 200·3 | 18·69 |
| 53 | 52·54 | 4·90 | 103 | 102·1 | 9·53 | 153 | 151·7 | 14·16 | 203 | 201·2 | 18·79 |
| 54 | 53·53 | 5·00 | 104 | 103·1 | 9·62 | 154 | 152·7 | 14·25 | 204 | 202·2 | 18·88 |
| 55 | 54·52 | 5·09 | 105 | 104·1 | 9·72 | 155 | 153·7 | 14·34 | 205 | 203·2 | 18·97 |
| 56 | 55·52 | 5·18 | 106 | 105·1 | 9·81 | 156 | 154·7 | 14·44 | 206 | 204·2 | 19·06 |
| 57 | 56·51 | 5·28 | 107 | 106·1 | 9·90 | 157 | 155·6 | 14·53 | 207 | 205·2 | 19·16 |
| 58 | 57·50 | 5·37 | 108 | 107·1 | 10·00 | 158 | 156·6 | 14·62 | 208 | 206·2 | 19·25 |
| 59 | 58·49 | 5·46 | 109 | 108·1 | 10·09 | 159 | 157·6 | 14·71 | 209 | 207·2 | 19·34 |
| 60 | 59·48 | 5·55 | 110 | 109·0 | 10·18 | 160 | 158·6 | 14·81 | 210 | 208·2 | 19·43 |

TABLE I

| G | D | H | G | D | H | G | D | H | G | D | H |
|---|---|---|---|---|---|---|---|---|---|---|---|
| 10 | 9·91 | 0·95 | 60 | 59·45 | 5·72 | 110 | 109·0 | 10·49 | 160 | 158·5 | 15·26 |
| 11 | 10·90 | 1·05 | 61 | 60·44 | 5·82 | 111 | 110·0 | 10·59 | 161 | 159·5 | 15·36 |
| 12 | 11·89 | 1·14 | 62 | 61·43 | 5·92 | 112 | 111·0 | 10·69 | 162 | 160·5 | 15·46 |
| 13 | 12·88 | 1·24 | 63 | 62·42 | 6·01 | 113 | 112·0 | 10·78 | 163 | 161·5 | 15·55 |
| 14 | 13·87 | 1·34 | 64 | 63·41 | 6·11 | 114 | 113·0 | 10·88 | 164 | 162·5 | 15·65 |
| 15 | 14·86 | 1·43 | 65 | 64·40 | 6·20 | 115 | 113·9 | 10·97 | 165 | 163·5 | 15·74 |
| 16 | 15·85 | 1·53 | 66 | 65·39 | 6·30 | 116 | 114·9 | 11·07 | 166 | 164·5 | 15·84 |
| 17 | 16·84 | 1·62 | 67 | 66·38 | 6·39 | 117 | 115·9 | 11·16 | 167 | 165·5 | 15·93 |
| 18 | 17·83 | 1·72 | 68 | 67·38 | 6·49 | 118 | 116·9 | 11·26 | 168 | 166·5 | 16·03 |
| 19 | 18·83 | 1·81 | 69 | 68·37 | 6·58 | 119 | 117·9 | 11·35 | 169 | 167·4 | 16·12 |
| 20 | 19·82 | 1·91 | 70 | 69·36 | 6·68 | 120 | 118·9 | 11·45 | 170 | 168·4 | 16·22 |
| 21 | 20·81 | 2·00 | 71 | 70·35 | 6·77 | 121 | 119·9 | 11·54 | 171 | 169·4 | 16·31 |
| 22 | 21·80 | 2·10 | 72 | 71·34 | 6·87 | 122 | 120·9 | 11·64 | 172 | 170·4 | 16·41 |
| 23 | 22·79 | 2·19 | 73 | 72·33 | 6·96 | 123 | 121·9 | 11·73 | 173 | 171·4 | 16·50 |
| 24 | 23·78 | 2·29 | 74 | 73·32 | 7·06 | 124 | 122·9 | 11·83 | 174 | 172·4 | 16·60 |
| 25 | 24·77 | 2·39 | 75 | 74·31 | 7·16 | 125 | 123·9 | 11·93 | 175 | 173·4 | 16·70 |
| 26 | 25·76 | 2·48 | 76 | 75·30 | 7·25 | 126 | 124·8 | 12·02 | 176 | 174·4 | 16·79 |
| 27 | 26·75 | 2·58 | 77 | 76·29 | 7·35 | 127 | 125·8 | 12·12 | 177 | 175·4 | 16·89 |
| 28 | 27·74 | 2·67 | 78 | 77·28 | 7·44 | 128 | 126·8 | 12·21 | 178 | 176·4 | 16·98 |
| 29 | 28·73 | 2·77 | 79 | 78·27 | 7·54 | 129 | 127·8 | 12·31 | 179 | 177·4 | 17·08 |
| 30 | 29·72 | 2·86 | 80 | 79·27 | 7·63 | 130 | 128·8 | 12·40 | 180 | 178·3 | 17·17 |
| 31 | 30·72 | 2·96 | 81 | 80·26 | 7·73 | 131 | 129·8 | 12·50 | 181 | 179·3 | 17·27 |
| 32 | 31·71 | 3·05 | 82 | 81·25 | 7·82 | 132 | 130·8 | 12·59 | 182 | 180·3 | 17·36 |
| 33 | 32·70 | 3·15 | 83 | 82·24 | 7·92 | 133 | 131·8 | 12·69 | 183 | 181·3 | 17·46 |
| 34 | 33·69 | 3·24 | 84 | 83·23 | 8·01 | 134 | 132·8 | 12·78 | 184 | 182·3 | 17·55 |
| 35 | 34·68 | 3·34 | 85 | 84·22 | 8·11 | 135 | 133·8 | 12·88 | 185 | 183·3 | 17·65 |
| 36 | 35·67 | 3·43 | 86 | 85·21 | 8·20 | 136 | 134·8 | 12·97 | 186 | 184·3 | 17·75 |
| 37 | 36·66 | 3·53 | 87 | 86·20 | 8·30 | 137 | 135·7 | 13·07 | 187 | 185·3 | 17·84 |
| 38 | 37·65 | 3·63 | 88 | 87·19 | 8·40 | 138 | 136·7 | 13·17 | 188 | 186·3 | 17·94 |
| 39 | 38·64 | 3·72 | 89 | 88·18 | 8·49 | 139 | 137·7 | 13·26 | 189 | 187·3 | 18·03 |
| 40 | 39·63 | 3·82 | 90 | 89·17 | 8·59 | 140 | 138·7 | 13·36 | 190 | 188·3 | 18·13 |
| 41 | 40·62 | 3·91 | 91 | 90·16 | 8·68 | 141 | 139·7 | 13·45 | 191 | 189·2 | 18·22 |
| 42 | 41·61 | 4·01 | 92 | 91·15 | 8·78 | 142 | 140·7 | 13·55 | 192 | 190·2 | 18·32 |
| 43 | 42·60 | 4·10 | 93 | 92·15 | 8·87 | 143 | 141·7 | 13·64 | 193 | 191·2 | 18·41 |
| 44 | 43·60 | 4·20 | 94 | 93·14 | 8·97 | 144 | 142·7 | 13·74 | 194 | 192·2 | 18·51 |
| 45 | 44·59 | 4·29 | 95 | 94·13 | 9·06 | 145 | 143·7 | 13·83 | 195 | 193·2 | 18·60 |
| 46 | 45·58 | 4·39 | 96 | 95·12 | 9·16 | 146 | 144·7 | 13·93 | 196 | 194·2 | 18·70 |
| 47 | 46·57 | 4·48 | 97 | 96·11 | 9·25 | 147 | 145·6 | 14·02 | 197 | 195·2 | 18·79 |
| 48 | 47·56 | 4·58 | 98 | 97·10 | 9·35 | 148 | 146·6 | 14·12 | 198 | 196·2 | 18·89 |
| 49 | 48·55 | 4·67 | 99 | 98·09 | 9·44 | 149 | 147·6 | 14·22 | 199 | 197·2 | 18·99 |
| 50 | 49·54 | 4·77 | 100 | 99·08 | 9·54 | 150 | 148·6 | 14·31 | 200 | 198·2 | 19·08 |
| 51 | 50·53 | 4·87 | 101 | 100·1 | 9·64 | 151 | 149·6 | 14·41 | 201 | 199·2 | 19·18 |
| 52 | 51·52 | 4·96 | 102 | 101·1 | 9·73 | 152 | 150·6 | 14·50 | 202 | 200·1 | 19·27 |
| 53 | 52·51 | 5·06 | 103 | 102·1 | 9·83 | 153 | 151·6 | 14·60 | 203 | 201·1 | 19·37 |
| 54 | 53·50 | 5·15 | 104 | 103·0 | 9·92 | 154 | 152·6 | 14·69 | 204 | 202·1 | 19·46 |
| 55 | 54·49 | 5·25 | 105 | 104·0 | 10·02 | 155 | 153·6 | 14·79 | 205 | 203·1 | 19·56 |
| 56 | 55·49 | 5·34 | 106 | 105·0 | 10·11 | 156 | 154·6 | 14·88 | 206 | 204·1 | 19·65 |
| 57 | 56·48 | 5·44 | 107 | 106·0 | 10·21 | 157 | 155·6 | 14·98 | 207 | 205·1 | 19·75 |
| 58 | 57·47 | 5·53 | 108 | 107·0 | 10·30 | 158 | 156·5 | 15·07 | 208 | 206·1 | 19·84 |
| 59 | 58·46 | 5·63 | 109 | 108·0 | 10·40 | 159 | 157·5 | 15·17 | 209 | 207·1 | 19·94 |
| 60 | 59·45 | 5·72 | 110 | 109·0 | 10·49 | 160 | 158·5 | 15·26 | 210 | 208·1 | 20·03 |

TABLE I

| G | D | H | G | D | H | G | D | H | G | D | H |
|---|---|---|---|---|---|---|---|---|---|---|---|
| 10 | 9·90 | 0·98 | 60 | 59·41 | 5·90 | 110 | 108·9 | 10·81 | 160 | 158·4 | 15·72 |
| 11 | 10·89 | 1·08 | 61 | 60·41 | 5·99 | 111 | 109·9 | 10·91 | 161 | 159·4 | 15·82 |
| 12 | 11·88 | 1·18 | 62 | 61·40 | 6·09 | 112 | 110·9 | 11·00 | 162 | 160·4 | 15·92 |
| 13 | 12·87 | 1·28 | 63 | 62·39 | 6·19 | 113 | 111·9 | 11·10 | 163 | 161·4 | 16·02 |
| 14 | 13·86 | 1·38 | 64 | 63·38 | 6·29 | 114 | 112·9 | 11·20 | 164 | 162·4 | 16·11 |
| 15 | 14·85 | 1·47 | 65 | 64·37 | 6·39 | 115 | 113·9 | 11·30 | 165 | 163·4 | 16·21 |
| 16 | 15·84 | 1·57 | 66 | 65·36 | 6·49 | 116 | 114·9 | 11·40 | 166 | 164·4 | 16·31 |
| 17 | 16·83 | 1·67 | 67 | 66·35 | 6·58 | 117 | 115·9 | 11·50 | 167 | 165·4 | 16·41 |
| 18 | 17·82 | 1·77 | 68 | 67·34 | 6·68 | 118 | 116·8 | 11·59 | 168 | 166·4 | 16·51 |
| 19 | 18·81 | 1·87 | 69 | 68·33 | 6·78 | 119 | 117·8 | 11·69 | 169 | 167·4 | 16·61 |
| 20 | 19·80 | 1·97 | 70 | 69·32 | 6·88 | 120 | 118·8 | 11·79 | 170 | 168·3 | 16·70 |
| 21 | 20·80 | 2·06 | 71 | 70·31 | 6·98 | 121 | 119·8 | 11·89 | 171 | 169·3 | 16·80 |
| 22 | 21·79 | 2·16 | 72 | 71·30 | 7·07 | 122 | 120·8 | 11·99 | 172 | 170·3 | 16·90 |
| 23 | 22·78 | 2·26 | 73 | 72·29 | 7·17 | 123 | 121·8 | 12·09 | 173 | 171·3 | 17·00 |
| 24 | 23·77 | 2·36 | 74 | 73·28 | 7·27 | 124 | 122·8 | 12·18 | 174 | 172·3 | 17·10 |
| 25 | 24·76 | 2·46 | 75 | 74·27 | 7·37 | 125 | 123·8 | 12·28 | 175 | 173·3 | 17·20 |
| 26 | 25·75 | 2·55 | 76 | 75·26 | 7·47 | 126 | 124·8 | 12·38 | 176 | 174·3 | 17·29 |
| 27 | 26·74 | 2·65 | 77 | 76·25 | 7·57 | 127 | 125·8 | 12·48 | 177 | 175·3 | 17·39 |
| 28 | 27·73 | 2·75 | 78 | 77·24 | 7·66 | 128 | 126·8 | 12·58 | 178 | 176·3 | 17·49 |
| 29 | 28·72 | 2·85 | 79 | 78·23 | 7·76 | 129 | 127·7 | 12·68 | 179 | 177·3 | 17·59 |
| 30 | 29·71 | 2·95 | 80 | 79·22 | 7·86 | 130 | 128·7 | 12·77 | 180 | 178·2 | 17·69 |
| 31 | 30·70 | 3·05 | 81 | 80·21 | 7·96 | 131 | 129·7 | 12·87 | 181 | 179·2 | 17·78 |
| 32 | 31·69 | 3·14 | 82 | 81·20 | 8·06 | 132 | 130·7 | 12·97 | 182 | 180·2 | 17·88 |
| 33 | 32·68 | 3·24 | 83 | 82·19 | 8·16 | 133 | 131·7 | 13·07 | 183 | 181·2 | 17·98 |
| 34 | 33·67 | 3·34 | 84 | 83·18 | 8·25 | 134 | 132·7 | 13·17 | 184 | 182·2 | 18·08 |
| 35 | 34·66 | 3·44 | 85 | 84·17 | 8·35 | 135 | 133·7 | 13·26 | 185 | 183·2 | 18·18 |
| 36 | 35·65 | 3·54 | 86 | 85·16 | 8·45 | 136 | 134·7 | 13·36 | 186 | 184·2 | 18·28 |
| 37 | 36·64 | 3·64 | 87 | 86·15 | 8·55 | 137 | 135·7 | 13·46 | 187 | 185·2 | 18·37 |
| 38 | 37·63 | 3·73 | 88 | 87·14 | 8·65 | 138 | 136·7 | 13·56 | 188 | 186·2 | 18·47 |
| 39 | 38·62 | 3·83 | 89 | 88·13 | 8·74 | 139 | 137·6 | 13·66 | 189 | 187·2 | 18·57 |
| 40 | 39·61 | 3·93 | 90 | 89·12 | 8·84 | 140 | 138·6 | 13·76 | 190 | 188·1 | 18·67 |
| 41 | 40·60 | 4·03 | 91 | 90·11 | 8·94 | 141 | 139·6 | 13·85 | 191 | 189·1 | 18·77 |
| 42 | 41·59 | 4·13 | 92 | 91·10 | 9·04 | 142 | 140·6 | 13·95 | 192 | 190·1 | 18·87 |
| 43 | 42·58 | 4·23 | 93 | 92·09 | 9·14 | 143 | 141·6 | 14·05 | 193 | 191·1 | 18·96 |
| 44 | 43·57 | 4·32 | 94 | 93·08 | 9·24 | 144 | 142·6 | 14·15 | 194 | 192·1 | 19·06 |
| 45 | 44·56 | 4·42 | 95 | 94·07 | 9·33 | 145 | 143·6 | 14·25 | 195 | 193·1 | 19·16 |
| 46 | 45·55 | 4·52 | 96 | 95·06 | 9·43 | 146 | 144·6 | 14·35 | 196 | 194·1 | 19·26 |
| 47 | 46·54 | 4·62 | 97 | 96·05 | 9·53 | 147 | 145·6 | 14·44 | 197 | 195·1 | 19·36 |
| 48 | 47·53 | 4·72 | 98 | 97·04 | 9·63 | 148 | 146·6 | 14·54 | 198 | 196·1 | 19·46 |
| 49 | 48·52 | 4·81 | 99 | 98·03 | 9·73 | 149 | 147·5 | 14·64 | 199 | 197·1 | 19·55 |
| 50 | 49·51 | 4·91 | 100 | 99·02 | 9·83 | 150 | 148·5 | 14·74 | 200 | 198·0 | 19·65 |
| 51 | 50·50 | 5·01 | 101 | 100·0 | 9·92 | 151 | 149·5 | 14·84 | 201 | 199·0 | 19·75 |
| 52 | 51·49 | 5·11 | 102 | 101·0 | 10·02 | 152 | 150·5 | 14·94 | 202 | 200·0 | 19·85 |
| 53 | 52·48 | 5·21 | 103 | 102·0 | 10·12 | 153 | 151·5 | 15·03 | 203 | 201·0 | 19·95 |
| 54 | 53·47 | 5·31 | 104 | 103·0 | 10·22 | 154 | 152·5 | 15·13 | 204 | 202·0 | 20·04 |
| 55 | 54·46 | 5·40 | 105 | 104·0 | 10·32 | 155 | 153·5 | 15·23 | 205 | 203·0 | 20·14 |
| 56 | 55·45 | 5·50 | 106 | 105·0 | 10·42 | 156 | 154·5 | 15·33 | 206 | 204·0 | 20·24 |
| 57 | 56·44 | 5·60 | 107 | 106·0 | 10·51 | 157 | 155·5 | 15·43 | 207 | 205·0 | 20·34 |
| 58 | 57·43 | 5·70 | 108 | 106·9 | 10·61 | 158 | 156·5 | 15·52 | 208 | 206·0 | 20·44 |
| 59 | 58·42 | 5·80 | 109 | 107·9 | 10·71 | 159 | 157·4 | 15·62 | 209 | 207·0 | 20·54 |
| 60 | 59·41 | 5·90 | 110 | 108·9 | 10·81 | 160 | 158·4 | 15·72 | 210 | 208·0 | 20·63 |

TABLE I       **5° 50′**

| G | D | H | G | D | H | G | D | H | G | D | H |
|---|---|---|---|---|---|---|---|---|---|---|---|
| 10 | 9·90 | 1·01 | 60 | 59·38 | 6·07 | 110 | 108·9 | 11·12 | 160 | 158·3 | 16·18 |
| 11 | 10·89 | 1·11 | 61 | 60·37 | 6·17 | 111 | 109·9 | 11·22 | 161 | 159·3 | 16·28 |
| 12 | 11·88 | 1·21 | 62 | 61·36 | 6·27 | 112 | 110·8 | 11·32 | 162 | 160·3 | 16·38 |
| 13 | 12·87 | 1·31 | 63 | 62·35 | 6·37 | 113 | 111·8 | 11·43 | 163 | 161·3 | 16·48 |
| 14 | 13·86 | 1·42 | 64 | 63·34 | 6·47 | 114 | 112·8 | 11·53 | 164 | 162·3 | 16·58 |
| 15 | 14·85 | 1·52 | 65 | 64·33 | 6·57 | 115 | 113·8 | 11·63 | 165 | 163·3 | 16·68 |
| 16 | 15·83 | 1·62 | 66 | 65·32 | 6·67 | 116 | 114·8 | 11·73 | 166 | 164·3 | 16·78 |
| 17 | 16·82 | 1·72 | 67 | 66·31 | 6·77 | 117 | 115·8 | 11·83 | 167 | 165·3 | 16·89 |
| 18 | 17·81 | 1·82 | 68 | 67·30 | 6·88 | 118 | 116·8 | 11·93 | 168 | 166·3 | 16·99 |
| 19 | 18·80 | 1·92 | 69 | 68·29 | 6·98 | 119 | 117·8 | 12·03 | 169 | 167·3 | 17·09 |
| 20 | 19·79 | 2·02 | 70 | 69·28 | 7·08 | 120 | 118·8 | 12·13 | 170 | 168·2 | 17·19 |
| 21 | 20·78 | 2·12 | 71 | 70·27 | 7·18 | 121 | 119·7 | 12·23 | 171 | 169·2 | 17·29 |
| 22 | 21·77 | 2·22 | 72 | 71·26 | 7·28 | 122 | 120·7 | 12·34 | 172 | 170·2 | 17·39 |
| 23 | 22·76 | 2·33 | 73 | 72·25 | 7·38 | 123 | 121·7 | 12·44 | 173 | 171·2 | 17·49 |
| 24 | 23·75 | 2·43 | 74 | 73·24 | 7·48 | 124 | 122·7 | 12·54 | 174 | 172·2 | 17·59 |
| 25 | 24·74 | 2·53 | 75 | 74·23 | 7·58 | 125 | 123·7 | 12·64 | 175 | 173·2 | 17·69 |
| 26 | 25·73 | 2·63 | 76 | 75·21 | 7·68 | 126 | 124·7 | 12·74 | 176 | 174·2 | 17·80 |
| 27 | 26·72 | 2·73 | 77 | 76·20 | 7·79 | 127 | 125·7 | 12·84 | 177 | 175·2 | 17·90 |
| 28 | 27·71 | 2·83 | 78 | 77·19 | 7·89 | 128 | 126·7 | 12·94 | 178 | 176·2 | 18·00 |
| 29 | 28·70 | 2·93 | 79 | 78·18 | 7·99 | 129 | 127·7 | 13·04 | 179 | 177·2 | 18·10 |
| 30 | 29·69 | 3·03 | 80 | 79·17 | 8·09 | 130 | 128·7 | 13·14 | 180 | 178·1 | 18·20 |
| 31 | 30·68 | 3·13 | 81 | 80·16 | 8·19 | 131 | 129·6 | 13·25 | 181 | 179·1 | 18·30 |
| 32 | 31·67 | 3·24 | 82 | 81·15 | 8·29 | 132 | 130·6 | 13·35 | 182 | 180·1 | 18·40 |
| 33 | 32·66 | 3·34 | 83 | 82·14 | 8·39 | 133 | 131·6 | 13·45 | 183 | 181·1 | 18·50 |
| 34 | 33·65 | 3·44 | 84 | 83·13 | 8·49 | 134 | 132·6 | 13·55 | 184 | 182·1 | 18·60 |
| 35 | 34·64 | 3·54 | 85 | 84·12 | 8·59 | 135 | 133·6 | 13·65 | 185 | 183·1 | 18·70 |
| 36 | 35·63 | 3·64 | 86 | 85·11 | 8·70 | 136 | 134·6 | 13·75 | 186 | 184·1 | 18·81 |
| 37 | 36·62 | 3·74 | 87 | 86·10 | 8·80 | 137 | 135·6 | 13·85 | 187 | 185·1 | 18·91 |
| 38 | 37·61 | 3·84 | 88 | 87·09 | 8·90 | 138 | 136·6 | 13·95 | 188 | 186·1 | 19·01 |
| 39 | 38·60 | 3·94 | 89 | 88·08 | 9·00 | 139 | 137·6 | 14·05 | 189 | 187·0 | 19·11 |
| 40 | 39·59 | 4·04 | 90 | 89·07 | 9·10 | 140 | 138·6 | 14·16 | 190 | 188·0 | 19·21 |
| 41 | 40·58 | 4·15 | 91 | 90·06 | 9·20 | 141 | 139·5 | 14·26 | 191 | 189·0 | 19·31 |
| 42 | 41·57 | 4·25 | 92 | 91·05 | 9·30 | 142 | 140·5 | 14·36 | 192 | 190·0 | 19·41 |
| 43 | 42·56 | 4·35 | 93 | 92·04 | 9·40 | 143 | 141·5 | 14·46 | 193 | 191·0 | 19·51 |
| 44 | 43·55 | 4·45 | 94 | 93·03 | 9·50 | 144 | 142·5 | 14·56 | 194 | 192·0 | 19·61 |
| 45 | 44·54 | 4·55 | 95 | 94·02 | 9·61 | 145 | 143·5 | 14·66 | 195 | 193·0 | 19·72 |
| 46 | 45·52 | 4·65 | 96 | 95·01 | 9·71 | 146 | 144·5 | 14·76 | 196 | 194·0 | 19·82 |
| 47 | 46·51 | 4·75 | 97 | 96·00 | 9·81 | 147 | 145·5 | 14·86 | 197 | 195·0 | 19·92 |
| 48 | 47·50 | 4·85 | 98 | 96·99 | 9·91 | 148 | 146·5 | 14·96 | 198 | 196·0 | 20·02 |
| 49 | 48·49 | 4·95 | 99 | 97·98 | 10·01 | 149 | 147·5 | 15·07 | 199 | 196·9 | 20·12 |
| 50 | 49·48 | 5·06 | 100 | 98·97 | 10·11 | 150 | 148·5 | 15·17 | 200 | 197·9 | 20·22 |
| 51 | 50·47 | 5·16 | 101 | 99·96 | 10·21 | 151 | 149·4 | 15·27 | 201 | 198·9 | 20·32 |
| 52 | 51·46 | 5·26 | 102 | 100·9 | 10·31 | 152 | 150·4 | 15·37 | 202 | 199·9 | 20·42 |
| 53 | 52·45 | 5·36 | 103 | 101·9 | 10·41 | 153 | 151·4 | 15·47 | 203 | 200·9 | 20·52 |
| 54 | 53·44 | 5·46 | 104 | 102·9 | 10·52 | 154 | 152·4 | 15·57 | 204 | 201·9 | 20·63 |
| 55 | 54·43 | 5·56 | 105 | 103·9 | 10·62 | 155 | 153·4 | 15·67 | 205 | 202·9 | 20·73 |
| 56 | 55·42 | 5·66 | 106 | 104·9 | 10·72 | 156 | 154·4 | 15·77 | 206 | 203·9 | 20·83 |
| 57 | 56·41 | 5·76 | 107 | 105·9 | 10·82 | 157 | 155·4 | 15·87 | 207 | 204·9 | 20·93 |
| 58 | 57·40 | 5·86 | 108 | 106·9 | 10·92 | 158 | 156·4 | 15·98 | 208 | 205·9 | 21·03 |
| 59 | 58·39 | 5·97 | 109 | 107·9 | 11·02 | 159 | 157·4 | 16·08 | 209 | 206·8 | 21·13 |
| 60 | 59·38 | 6·07 | 110 | 108·9 | 11·12 | 160 | 158·3 | 16·18 | 210 | 207·8 | 21·23 |

| G | D | H | G | D | H | G | D | H | G | D | H |
|---|---|---|---|---|---|---|---|---|---|---|---|
| 10 | 9·89 | 1·04 | 60 | 59·34 | 6·24 | 110 | 108·8 | 11·44 | 160 | 158·3 | 16·63 |
| 11 | 10·88 | 1·14 | 61 | 60·33 | 6·34 | 111 | 109·8 | 11·54 | 161 | 159·2 | 16·74 |
| 12 | 11·87 | 1·25 | 62 | 61·32 | 6·45 | 112 | 110·8 | 11·64 | 162 | 160·2 | 16·84 |
| 13 | 12·86 | 1·35 | 63 | 62·31 | 6·55 | 113 | 111·8 | 11·75 | 163 | 161·2 | 16·94 |
| 14 | 13·85 | 1·46 | 64 | 63·30 | 6·65 | 114 | 112·8 | 11·85 | 164 | 162·2 | 17·05 |
| 15 | 14·84 | 1·56 | 65 | 64·29 | 6·76 | 115 | 113·7 | 11·95 | 165 | 163·2 | 17·15 |
| 16 | 15·83 | 1·66 | 66 | 65·28 | 6·86 | 116 | 114·7 | 12·06 | 166 | 164·2 | 17·26 |
| 17 | 16·81 | 1·77 | 67 | 66·27 | 6·96 | 117 | 115·7 | 12·16 | 167 | 165·2 | 17·36 |
| 18 | 17·80 | 1·87 | 68 | 67·26 | 7·07 | 118 | 116·7 | 12·27 | 168 | 166·2 | 17·46 |
| 19 | 18·79 | 1·98 | 69 | 68·25 | 7·17 | 119 | 117·7 | 12·37 | 169 | 167·2 | 17·57 |
| 20 | 19·78 | 2·08 | 70 | 69·24 | 7·28 | 120 | 118·7 | 12·47 | 170 | 168·1 | 17·67 |
| 21 | 20·77 | 2·18 | 71 | 70·22 | 7·38 | 121 | 119·7 | 12·58 | 171 | 169·1 | 17·78 |
| 22 | 21·76 | 2·29 | 72 | 71·21 | 7·48 | 122 | 120·7 | 12·68 | 172 | 170·1 | 17·88 |
| 23 | 22·75 | 2·39 | 73 | 72·20 | 7·59 | 123 | 121·7 | 12·79 | 173 | 171·1 | 17·98 |
| 24 | 23·74 | 2·49 | 74 | 73·19 | 7·69 | 124 | 122·6 | 12·89 | 174 | 172·1 | 18·09 |
| 25 | 24·73 | 2·60 | 75 | 74·18 | 7·80 | 125 | 123·6 | 12·99 | 175 | 173·1 | 18·19 |
| 26 | 25·72 | 2·70 | 76 | 75·17 | 7·90 | 126 | 124·6 | 13·10 | 176 | 174·1 | 18·30 |
| 27 | 26·70 | 2·81 | 77 | 76·16 | 8·00 | 127 | 125·6 | 13·20 | 177 | 175·1 | 18·40 |
| 28 | 27·69 | 2·91 | 78 | 77·15 | 8·11 | 128 | 126·6 | 13·31 | 178 | 176·1 | 18·50 |
| 29 | 28·68 | 3·01 | 79 | 78·14 | 8·21 | 129 | 127·6 | 13·41 | 179 | 177·0 | 18·61 |
| 30 | 29·67 | 3·12 | 80 | 79·13 | 8·32 | 130 | 128·6 | 13·51 | 180 | 178·0 | 18·71 |
| 31 | 30·66 | 3·22 | 81 | 80·11 | 8·42 | 131 | 129·6 | 13·62 | 181 | 179·0 | 18·82 |
| 32 | 31·65 | 3·33 | 82 | 81·10 | 8·52 | 132 | 130·6 | 13·72 | 182 | 180·0 | 18·92 |
| 33 | 32·64 | 3·43 | 83 | 82·09 | 8·63 | 133 | 131·5 | 13·83 | 183 | 181·0 | 19·02 |
| 34 | 33·63 | 3·53 | 84 | 83·08 | 8·73 | 134 | 132·5 | 13·93 | 184 | 182·0 | 19·13 |
| 35 | 34·62 | 3·64 | 85 | 84·07 | 8·84 | 135 | 133·5 | 14·03 | 185 | 183·0 | 19·23 |
| 36 | 35·61 | 3·74 | 86 | 85·06 | 8·94 | 136 | 134·5 | 14·14 | 186 | 184·0 | 19·34 |
| 37 | 36·60 | 3·85 | 87 | 86·05 | 9·04 | 137 | 135·5 | 14·24 | 187 | 185·0 | 19·44 |
| 38 | 37·58 | 3·95 | 88 | 87·04 | 9·15 | 138 | 136·5 | 14·35 | 188 | 185·9 | 19·54 |
| 39 | 38·57 | 4·05 | 89 | 88·03 | 9·25 | 139 | 137·5 | 14·45 | 189 | 186·9 | 19·65 |
| 40 | 39·56 | 4·16 | 90 | 89·02 | 9·36 | 140 | 138·5 | 14·55 | 190 | 187·9 | 19·75 |
| 41 | 40·55 | 4·26 | 91 | 90·01 | 9·46 | 141 | 139·5 | 14·66 | 191 | 188·9 | 19·86 |
| 42 | 41·54 | 4·37 | 92 | 90·99 | 9·56 | 142 | 140·4 | 14·76 | 192 | 189·9 | 19·96 |
| 43 | 42·53 | 4·47 | 93 | 91·98 | 9·67 | 143 | 141·4 | 14·87 | 193 | 190·9 | 20·06 |
| 44 | 43·52 | 4·57 | 94 | 92·97 | 9·77 | 144 | 142·4 | 14·97 | 194 | 191·9 | 20·17 |
| 45 | 44·51 | 4·68 | 95 | 93·96 | 9·88 | 145 | 143·4 | 15·07 | 195 | 192·9 | 20·27 |
| 46 | 45·50 | 4·78 | 96 | 94·95 | 9·98 | 146 | 144·4 | 15·18 | 196 | 193·9 | 20·38 |
| 47 | 46·49 | 4·89 | 97 | 95·94 | 10·08 | 147 | 145·4 | 15·28 | 197 | 194·8 | 20·48 |
| 48 | 47·48 | 4·99 | 98 | 96·93 | 10·19 | 148 | 146·4 | 15·39 | 198 | 195·8 | 20·58 |
| 49 | 48·46 | 5·09 | 99 | 97·92 | 10·29 | 149 | 147·4 | 15·49 | 199 | 196·8 | 20·69 |
| 50 | 49·45 | 5·20 | 100 | 98·91 | 10·40 | 150 | 148·4 | 15·59 | 200 | 197·8 | 20·79 |
| 51 | 50·44 | 5·30 | 101 | 99·90 | 10·50 | 151 | 149·3 | 15·70 | 201 | 198·8 | 20·89 |
| 52 | 51·43 | 5·41 | 102 | 100·9 | 10·60 | 152 | 150·3 | 15·80 | 202 | 199·8 | 21·00 |
| 53 | 52·42 | 5·51 | 103 | 101·9 | 10·71 | 153 | 151·3 | 15·91 | 203 | 200·8 | 21·10 |
| 54 | 53·41 | 5·61 | 104 | 102·9 | 10·81 | 154 | 152·3 | 16·01 | 204 | 201·8 | 21·21 |
| 55 | 54·40 | 5·72 | 105 | 103·9 | 10·92 | 155 | 153·3 | 16·11 | 205 | 202·8 | 21·31 |
| 56 | 55·39 | 5·82 | 106 | 104·8 | 11·02 | 156 | 154·3 | 16·22 | 206 | 203·7 | 21·41 |
| 57 | 56·38 | 5·93 | 107 | 105·8 | 11·12 | 157 | 155·3 | 16·32 | 207 | 204·7 | 21·52 |
| 58 | 57·37 | 6·03 | 108 | 106·8 | 11·23 | 158 | 156·3 | 16·42 | 208 | 205·7 | 21·62 |
| 59 | 58·36 | 6·13 | 109 | 107·8 | 11·33 | 159 | 157·3 | 16·53 | 209 | 206·7 | 21·73 |
| 60 | 59·34 | 6·24 | 110 | 108·8 | 11·44 | 160 | 158·3 | 16·63 | 210 | 207·7 | 21·83 |

TABLE I 　　　　　　　　　　　　　　　　　　　　　　　　 **6° 10′**

| G | D | H | G | D | H | G | D | H | G | D | H |
|---|---|---|---|---|---|---|---|---|---|---|---|
| 10 | 9·88 | 1·07 | 60 | 59·31 | 6·41 | 110 | 108·7 | 11·75 | 160 | 158·2 | 17·09 |
| 11 | 10·87 | 1·17 | 61 | 60·30 | 6·51 | 111 | 109·7 | 11·85 | 161 | 159·1 | 17·19 |
| 12 | 11·86 | 1·28 | 62 | 61·28 | 6·62 | 112 | 110·7 | 11·96 | 162 | 160·1 | 17·30 |
| 13 | 12·85 | 1·39 | 63 | 62·27 | 6·73 | 113 | 111·7 | 12·07 | 163 | 161·1 | 17·41 |
| 14 | 13·84 | 1·50 | 64 | 63·26 | 6·84 | 114 | 112·7 | 12·18 | 164 | 162·1 | 17·52 |
| 15 | 14·83 | 1·60 | 65 | 64·25 | 6·94 | 115 | 113·7 | 12·28 | 165 | 163·1 | 17·62 |
| 16 | 15·82 | 1·71 | 66 | 65·24 | 7·05 | 116 | 114·7 | 12·39 | 166 | 164·1 | 17·73 |
| 17 | 16·80 | 1·82 | 67 | 66·23 | 7·16 | 117 | 115·6 | 12·50 | 167 | 165·1 | 17·84 |
| 18 | 17·79 | 1·92 | 68 | 67·22 | 7·26 | 118 | 116·6 | 12·60 | 168 | 166·1 | 17·94 |
| 19 | 18·78 | 2·03 | 69 | 68·20 | 7·37 | 119 | 117·6 | 12·71 | 169 | 167·0 | 18·05 |
| 20 | 19·77 | 2·14 | 70 | 69·19 | 7·48 | 120 | 118·6 | 12·82 | 170 | 168·0 | 18·16 |
| 21 | 20·76 | 2·24 | 71 | 70·18 | 7·58 | 121 | 119·6 | 12·92 | 171 | 169·0 | 18·26 |
| 22 | 21·75 | 2·35 | 72 | 71·17 | 7·69 | 122 | 120·6 | 13·03 | 172 | 170·0 | 18·37 |
| 23 | 22·73 | 2·46 | 73 | 72·16 | 7·80 | 123 | 121·6 | 13·14 | 173 | 171·0 | 18·48 |
| 24 | 23·72 | 2·56 | 74 | 73·15 | 7·90 | 124 | 122·6 | 13·24 | 174 | 172·0 | 18·58 |
| 25 | 24·71 | 2·67 | 75 | 74·13 | 8·01 | 125 | 123·6 | 13·35 | 175 | 173·0 | 18·69 |
| 26 | 25·70 | 2·78 | 76 | 75·12 | 8·12 | 126 | 124·5 | 13·46 | 176 | 174·0 | 18·80 |
| 27 | 26·69 | 2·88 | 77 | 76·11 | 8·22 | 127 | 125·5 | 13·56 | 177 | 175·0 | 18·90 |
| 28 | 27·68 | 2·99 | 78 | 77·10 | 8·33 | 128 | 126·5 | 13·67 | 178 | 175·9 | 19·01 |
| 29 | 28·67 | 3·10 | 79 | 78·09 | 8·44 | 129 | 127·5 | 13·78 | 179 | 176·9 | 19·12 |
| 30 | 29·65 | 3·20 | 80 | 79·08 | 8·54 | 130 | 128·5 | 13·88 | 180 | 177·9 | 19·22 |
| 31 | 30·64 | 3·31 | 81 | 80·07 | 8·65 | 131 | 129·5 | 13·99 | 181 | 178·9 | 19·33 |
| 32 | 31·63 | 3·42 | 82 | 81·05 | 8·76 | 132 | 130·5 | 14·10 | 182 | 179·9 | 19·44 |
| 33 | 32·62 | 3·52 | 83 | 82·04 | 8·86 | 133 | 131·5 | 14·20 | 183 | 180·9 | 19·54 |
| 34 | 33·61 | 3·63 | 84 | 83·03 | 8·97 | 134 | 132·5 | 14·31 | 184 | 181·9 | 19·65 |
| 35 | 34·60 | 3·74 | 85 | 84·02 | 9·08 | 135 | 133·4 | 14·42 | 185 | 182·9 | 19·76 |
| 36 | 35·58 | 3·84 | 86 | 85·01 | 9·18 | 136 | 134·4 | 14·52 | 186 | 183·9 | 19·86 |
| 37 | 36·57 | 3·95 | 87 | 86·00 | 9·29 | 137 | 135·4 | 14·63 | 187 | 184·8 | 19·97 |
| 38 | 37·56 | 4·06 | 88 | 86·98 | 9·40 | 138 | 136·4 | 14·74 | 188 | 185·8 | 20·08 |
| 39 | 38·55 | 4·17 | 89 | 87·97 | 9·51 | 139 | 137·4 | 14·85 | 189 | 186·8 | 20·19 |
| 40 | 39·54 | 4·27 | 90 | 88·96 | 9·61 | 140 | 138·4 | 14·95 | 190 | 187·8 | 20·29 |
| 41 | 40·53 | 4·38 | 91 | 89·95 | 9·72 | 141 | 139·4 | 15·06 | 191 | 188·8 | 20·40 |
| 42 | 41·52 | 4·49 | 92 | 90·94 | 9·83 | 142 | 140·4 | 15·17 | 192 | 189·8 | 20·51 |
| 43 | 42·50 | 4·59 | 93 | 91·93 | 9·93 | 143 | 141·3 | 15·27 | 193 | 190·8 | 20·61 |
| 44 | 43·49 | 4·70 | 94 | 92·92 | 10·04 | 144 | 142·3 | 15·38 | 194 | 191·8 | 20·72 |
| 45 | 44·48 | 4·81 | 95 | 93·90 | 10·15 | 145 | 143·3 | 15·49 | 195 | 192·7 | 20·83 |
| 46 | 45·47 | 4·91 | 96 | 94·89 | 10·25 | 146 | 144·3 | 15·59 | 196 | 193·7 | 20·93 |
| 47 | 46·46 | 5·02 | 97 | 95·88 | 10·36 | 147 | 145·3 | 15·70 | 197 | 194·7 | 21·04 |
| 48 | 47·45 | 5·13 | 98 | 96·87 | 10·47 | 148 | 146·3 | 15·81 | 198 | 195·7 | 21·15 |
| 49 | 48·43 | 5·23 | 99 | 97·86 | 10·57 | 149 | 147·3 | 15·91 | 199 | 196·7 | 21·25 |
| 50 | 49·42 | 5·34 | 100 | 98·85 | 10·68 | 150 | 148·3 | 16·02 | 200 | 197·7 | 21·36 |
| 51 | 50·41 | 5·45 | 101 | 99·83 | 10·79 | 151 | 149·3 | 16·13 | 201 | 198·7 | 21·47 |
| 52 | 51·40 | 5·55 | 102 | 100·8 | 10·89 | 152 | 150·2 | 16·23 | 202 | 199·7 | 21·57 |
| 53 | 52·39 | 5·66 | 103 | 101·8 | 11·00 | 153 | 151·2 | 16·34 | 203 | 200·7 | 21·68 |
| 54 | 53·38 | 5·77 | 104 | 102·8 | 11·11 | 154 | 152·2 | 16·45 | 204 | 201·6 | 21·79 |
| 55 | 54·37 | 5·87 | 105 | 103·8 | 11·21 | 155 | 153·2 | 16·55 | 205 | 202·6 | 21·89 |
| 56 | 55·35 | 5·98 | 106 | 104·8 | 11·32 | 156 | 154·2 | 16·66 | 206 | 203·6 | 22·00 |
| 57 | 56·34 | 6·09 | 107 | 105·8 | 11·43 | 157 | 155·2 | 16·77 | 207 | 204·6 | 22·11 |
| 58 | 57·33 | 6·19 | 108 | 106·8 | 11·53 | 158 | 156·2 | 16·87 | 208 | 205·6 | 22·21 |
| 59 | 58·32 | 6·30 | 109 | 107·7 | 11·64 | 159 | 157·2 | 16·98 | 209 | 206·6 | 22·32 |
| 60 | 59·31 | 6·41 | 110 | 108·7 | 11·75 | 160 | 158·2 | 17·09 | 210 | 207·6 | 22·43 |

| G | D | H | G | D | H | G | D | H | G | D | H |
|---|---|---|---|---|---|---|---|---|---|---|---|
| 10 | 9·88 | 1·10 | 60 | 59·27 | 6·58 | 110 | 108·7 | 12·06 | 160 | 158·1 | 17·54 |
| 11 | 10·87 | 1·21 | 61 | 60·26 | 6·69 | 111 | 109·6 | 12·17 | 161 | 159·0 | 17·65 |
| 12 | 11·85 | 1·32 | 62 | 61·25 | 6·80 | 112 | 110·6 | 12·28 | 162 | 160·0 | 17·76 |
| 13 | 12·84 | 1·43 | 63 | 62·23 | 6·91 | 113 | 111·6 | 12·39 | 163 | 161·0 | 17·87 |
| 14 | 13·83 | 1·53 | 64 | 63·22 | 7·02 | 114 | 112·6 | 12·50 | 164 | 162·0 | 17·98 |
| 15 | 14·82 | 1·64 | 65 | 64·21 | 7·13 | 115 | 113·6 | 12·61 | 165 | 163·0 | 18·09 |
| 16 | 15·81 | 1·75 | 66 | 65·20 | 7·24 | 116 | 114·6 | 12·72 | 166 | 164·0 | 18·20 |
| 17 | 16·79 | 1·86 | 67 | 66·18 | 7·35 | 117 | 115·6 | 12·83 | 167 | 165·0 | 18·31 |
| 18 | 17·78 | 1·97 | 68 | 67·17 | 7·46 | 118 | 116·6 | 12·94 | 168 | 166·0 | 18·42 |
| 19 | 18·77 | 2·08 | 69 | 68·16 | 7·57 | 119 | 117·6 | 13·05 | 169 | 166·9 | 18·53 |
| 20 | 19·76 | 2·19 | 70 | 69·15 | 7·67 | 120 | 118·5 | 13·16 | 170 | 167·9 | 18·64 |
| 21 | 20·74 | 2·30 | 71 | 70·14 | 7·78 | 121 | 119·5 | 13·27 | 171 | 168·9 | 18·75 |
| 22 | 21·73 | 2·41 | 72 | 71·12 | 7·89 | 122 | 120·5 | 13·38 | 172 | 169·9 | 18·86 |
| 23 | 22·72 | 2·52 | 73 | 72·11 | 8·00 | 123 | 121·5 | 13·49 | 173 | 170·9 | 18·97 |
| 24 | 23·71 | 2·63 | 74 | 73·10 | 8·11 | 124 | 122·5 | 13·60 | 174 | 171·9 | 19·08 |
| 25 | 24·70 | 2·74 | 75 | 74·09 | 8·22 | 125 | 123·5 | 13·70 | 175 | 172·9 | 19·19 |
| 26 | 25·68 | 2·85 | 76 | 75·08 | 8·33 | 126 | 124·5 | 13·81 | 176 | 173·9 | 19·30 |
| 27 | 26·67 | 2·96 | 77 | 76·06 | 8·44 | 127 | 125·5 | 13·92 | 177 | 174·8 | 19·41 |
| 28 | 27·66 | 3·07 | 78 | 77·05 | 8·55 | 128 | 126·4 | 14·03 | 178 | 175·8 | 19·52 |
| 29 | 28·65 | 3·18 | 79 | 78·04 | 8·66 | 129 | 127·4 | 14·14 | 179 | 176·8 | 19·63 |
| 30 | 29·63 | 3·29 | 80 | 79·03 | 8·77 | 130 | 128·4 | 14·25 | 180 | 177·8 | 19·74 |
| 31 | 30·62 | 3·40 | 81 | 80·01 | 8·88 | 131 | 129·4 | 14·36 | 181 | 178·8 | 19·84 |
| 32 | 31·61 | 3·51 | 82 | 81·00 | 8·99 | 132 | 130·4 | 14·47 | 182 | 179·8 | 19·95 |
| 33 | 32·60 | 3·62 | 83 | 81·99 | 9·10 | 133 | 131·4 | 14·58 | 183 | 180·8 | 20·06 |
| 34 | 33·59 | 3·73 | 84 | 82·98 | 9·21 | 134 | 132·4 | 14·69 | 184 | 181·8 | 20·17 |
| 35 | 34·57 | 3·84 | 85 | 83·97 | 9·32 | 135 | 133·4 | 14·80 | 185 | 182·7 | 20·28 |
| 36 | 35·56 | 3·95 | 86 | 84·95 | 9·43 | 136 | 134·3 | 14·91 | 186 | 183·7 | 20·39 |
| 37 | 36·55 | 4·06 | 87 | 85·94 | 9·54 | 137 | 135·3 | 15·02 | 187 | 184·7 | 20·50 |
| 38 | 37·54 | 4·17 | 88 | 86·93 | 9·65 | 138 | 136·3 | 15·13 | 188 | 185·7 | 20·61 |
| 39 | 38·53 | 4·28 | 89 | 87·92 | 9·76 | 139 | 137·3 | 15·24 | 189 | 186·7 | 20·72 |
| 40 | 39·51 | 4·39 | 90 | 88·90 | 9·87 | 140 | 138·3 | 15·35 | 190 | 187·7 | 20·83 |
| 41 | 40·50 | 4·50 | 91 | 89·89 | 9·98 | 141 | 139·3 | 15·46 | 191 | 188·7 | 20·94 |
| 42 | 41·49 | 4·60 | 92 | 90·88 | 10·09 | 142 | 140·3 | 15·57 | 192 | 189·7 | 21·05 |
| 43 | 42·48 | 4·71 | 93 | 91·87 | 10·20 | 143 | 141·3 | 15·68 | 193 | 190·7 | 21·16 |
| 44 | 43·46 | 4·82 | 94 | 92·86 | 10·31 | 144 | 142·2 | 15·79 | 194 | 191·6 | 21·27 |
| 45 | 44·45 | 4·93 | 95 | 93·84 | 10·42 | 145 | 143·2 | 15·90 | 195 | 192·6 | 21·38 |
| 46 | 45·44 | 5·04 | 96 | 94·83 | 10·53 | 146 | 144·2 | 16·01 | 196 | 193·6 | 21·49 |
| 47 | 46·43 | 5·15 | 97 | 95·82 | 10·63 | 147 | 145·2 | 16·12 | 197 | 194·6 | 21·60 |
| 48 | 47·42 | 5·26 | 98 | 96·81 | 10·74 | 148 | 146·2 | 16·23 | 198 | 195·6 | 21·71 |
| 49 | 48·40 | 5·37 | 99 | 97·80 | 10·85 | 149 | 147·2 | 16·34 | 199 | 196·6 | 21·82 |
| 50 | 49·39 | 5·48 | 100 | 98·78 | 10·96 | 150 | 148·2 | 16·45 | 200 | 197·6 | 21·93 |
| 51 | 50·38 | 5·59 | 101 | 99·77 | 11·07 | 151 | 149·2 | 16·56 | 201 | 198·6 | 22·04 |
| 52 | 51·37 | 5·70 | 102 | 100·8 | 11·18 | 152 | 150·2 | 16·67 | 202 | 199·5 | 22·15 |
| 53 | 52·35 | 5·81 | 103 | 101·7 | 11·29 | 153 | 151·1 | 16·77 | 203 | 200·5 | 22·26 |
| 54 | 53·34 | 5·92 | 104 | 102·7 | 11·40 | 154 | 152·1 | 16·88 | 204 | 201·5 | 22·37 |
| 55 | 54·33 | 6·03 | 105 | 103·7 | 11·51 | 155 | 153·1 | 16·99 | 205 | 202·5 | 22·48 |
| 56 | 55·32 | 6·14 | 106 | 104·7 | 11·62 | 156 | 154·1 | 17·10 | 206 | 203·5 | 22·59 |
| 57 | 56·31 | 6·25 | 107 | 105·7 | 11·73 | 157 | 155·1 | 17·21 | 207 | 204·5 | 22·70 |
| 58 | 57·29 | 6·36 | 108 | 106·7 | 11·84 | 158 | 156·1 | 17·32 | 208 | 205·5 | 22·80 |
| 59 | 58·28 | 6·47 | 109 | 107·7 | 11·95 | 159 | 157·1 | 17·43 | 209 | 206·5 | 22·91 |
| 60 | 59·27 | 6·58 | 110 | 108·7 | 12·06 | 160 | 158·1 | 17·54 | 210 | 207·4 | 23·02 |

TABLE I

6° 30′

| G | D | H | G | D | H | G | D | H | G | D | H |
|---|---|---|---|---|---|---|---|---|---|---|---|
| 10 | 9.87 | 1.12 | 60 | 59.23 | 6.75 | 110 | 108.6 | 12.37 | 160 | 157.9 | 18.00 |
| 11 | 10.86 | 1.24 | 61 | 60.22 | 6.86 | 111 | 109.6 | 12.48 | 161 | 158.9 | 18.11 |
| 12 | 11.85 | 1.35 | 62 | 61.21 | 6.97 | 112 | 110.6 | 12.60 | 162 | 159.9 | 18.22 |
| 13 | 12.83 | 1.46 | 63 | 62.19 | 7.09 | 113 | 111.6 | 12.71 | 163 | 160.9 | 18.33 |
| 14 | 13.82 | 1.57 | 64 | 63.18 | 7.20 | 114 | 112.5 | 12.82 | 164 | 161.9 | 18.45 |
| 15 | 14.81 | 1.69 | 65 | 64.17 | 7.31 | 115 | 113.5 | 12.93 | 165 | 162.9 | 18.56 |
| 16 | 15.79 | 1.80 | 66 | 65.15 | 7.42 | 116 | 114.5 | 13.05 | 166 | 163.9 | 18.67 |
| 17 | 16.78 | 1.91 | 67 | 66.14 | 7.54 | 117 | 115.5 | 13.16 | 167 | 164.9 | 18.78 |
| 18 | 17.77 | 2.02 | 68 | 67.13 | 7.65 | 118 | 116.5 | 13.27 | 168 | 165.8 | 18.90 |
| 19 | 18.76 | 2.14 | 69 | 68.12 | 7.76 | 119 | 117.5 | 13.38 | 169 | 166.8 | 19.01 |
| 20 | 19.74 | 2.25 | 70 | 69.10 | 7.87 | 120 | 118.5 | 13.50 | 170 | 167.8 | 19.12 |
| 21 | 20.73 | 2.36 | 71 | 70.09 | 7.99 | 121 | 119.4 | 13.61 | 171 | 168.8 | 19.23 |
| 22 | 21.72 | 2.47 | 72 | 71.08 | 8.10 | 122 | 120.4 | 13.72 | 172 | 169.8 | 19.35 |
| 23 | 22.71 | 2.59 | 73 | 72.06 | 8.21 | 123 | 121.4 | 13.83 | 173 | 170.8 | 19.46 |
| 24 | 23.69 | 2.70 | 74 | 73.05 | 8.32 | 124 | 122.4 | 13.95 | 174 | 171.8 | 19.57 |
| 25 | 24.68 | 2.81 | 75 | 74.04 | 8.44 | 125 | 123.4 | 14.06 | 175 | 172.8 | 19.68 |
| 26 | 25.67 | 2.92 | 76 | 75.03 | 8.55 | 126 | 124.4 | 14.17 | 176 | 173.7 | 19.80 |
| 27 | 26.65 | 3.04 | 77 | 76.01 | 8.66 | 127 | 125.4 | 14.28 | 177 | 174.7 | 19.91 |
| 28 | 27.64 | 3.15 | 78 | 77.00 | 8.77 | 128 | 126.4 | 14.40 | 178 | 175.7 | 20.02 |
| 29 | 28.63 | 3.26 | 79 | 77.99 | 8.89 | 129 | 127.3 | 14.51 | 179 | 176.7 | 20.13 |
| 30 | 29.62 | 3.37 | 80 | 78.97 | 9.00 | 130 | 128.3 | 14.62 | 180 | 177.7 | 20.25 |
| 31 | 30.60 | 3.49 | 81 | 79.96 | 9.11 | 131 | 129.3 | 14.73 | 181 | 178.7 | 20.36 |
| 32 | 31.59 | 3.60 | 82 | 80.95 | 9.22 | 132 | 130.3 | 14.85 | 182 | 179.7 | 20.47 |
| 33 | 32.58 | 3.71 | 83 | 81.94 | 9.34 | 133 | 131.3 | 14.96 | 183 | 180.7 | 20.58 |
| 34 | 33.56 | 3.82 | 84 | 82.92 | 9.45 | 134 | 132.3 | 15.07 | 184 | 181.6 | 20.70 |
| 35 | 34.55 | 3.94 | 85 | 83.91 | 9.56 | 135 | 133.3 | 15.18 | 185 | 182.6 | 20.81 |
| 36 | 35.54 | 4.05 | 86 | 84.90 | 9.67 | 136 | 134.3 | 15.30 | 186 | 183.6 | 20.92 |
| 37 | 36.53 | 4.16 | 87 | 85.88 | 9.79 | 137 | 135.2 | 15.41 | 187 | 184.6 | 21.03 |
| 38 | 37.51 | 4.27 | 88 | 86.87 | 9.90 | 138 | 136.2 | 15.52 | 188 | 185.6 | 21.15 |
| 39 | 38.50 | 4.39 | 89 | 87.86 | 10.01 | 139 | 137.2 | 15.63 | 189 | 186.6 | 21.26 |
| 40 | 39.49 | 4.50 | 90 | 88.85 | 10.12 | 140 | 138.2 | 15.75 | 190 | 187.6 | 21.37 |
| 41 | 40.47 | 4.61 | 91 | 89.83 | 10.24 | 141 | 139.2 | 15.86 | 191 | 188.6 | 21.48 |
| 42 | 41.46 | 4.72 | 92 | 90.82 | 10.35 | 142 | 140.2 | 15.97 | 192 | 189.5 | 21.60 |
| 43 | 42.45 | 4.84 | 93 | 91.81 | 10.46 | 143 | 141.2 | 16.08 | 193 | 190.5 | 21.71 |
| 44 | 43.44 | 4.95 | 94 | 92.80 | 10.57 | 144 | 142.2 | 16.20 | 194 | 191.5 | 21.82 |
| 45 | 44.42 | 5.06 | 95 | 93.78 | 10.69 | 145 | 143.1 | 16.31 | 195 | 192.5 | 21.93 |
| 46 | 45.41 | 5.17 | 96 | 94.77 | 10.80 | 146 | 144.1 | 16.42 | 196 | 193.5 | 22.05 |
| 47 | 46.40 | 5.29 | 97 | 95.76 | 10.91 | 147 | 145.1 | 16.53 | 197 | 194.5 | 22.16 |
| 48 | 47.38 | 5.40 | 98 | 96.74 | 11.02 | 148 | 146.1 | 16.65 | 198 | 195.5 | 22.27 |
| 49 | 48.37 | 5.51 | 99 | 97.73 | 11.14 | 149 | 147.1 | 16.76 | 199 | 196.4 | 22.38 |
| 50 | 49.36 | 5.62 | 100 | 98.72 | 11.25 | 150 | 148.1 | 16.87 | 200 | 197.4 | 22.50 |
| 51 | 50.35 | 5.74 | 101 | 99.71 | 11.36 | 151 | 149.1 | 16.98 | 201 | 198.4 | 22.61 |
| 52 | 51.33 | 5.85 | 102 | 100.7 | 11.47 | 152 | 150.1 | 17.10 | 202 | 199.4 | 22.72 |
| 53 | 52.32 | 5.96 | 103 | 101.7 | 11.58 | 153 | 151.0 | 17.21 | 203 | 200.4 | 22.83 |
| 54 | 53.31 | 6.07 | 104 | 102.7 | 11.70 | 154 | 152.0 | 17.32 | 204 | 201.4 | 22.94 |
| 55 | 54.30 | 6.19 | 105 | 103.7 | 11.81 | 155 | 153.0 | 17.43 | 205 | 202.4 | 23.06 |
| 56 | 55.28 | 6.30 | 106 | 104.6 | 11.92 | 156 | 154.0 | 17.55 | 206 | 203.4 | 23.17 |
| 57 | 56.27 | 6.41 | 107 | 105.6 | 12.03 | 157 | 155.0 | 17.66 | 207 | 204.3 | 23.28 |
| 58 | 57.26 | 6.52 | 108 | 106.6 | 12.15 | 158 | 156.0 | 17.77 | 208 | 205.3 | 23.39 |
| 59 | 58.24 | 6.64 | 109 | 107.6 | 12.26 | 159 | 157.0 | 17.88 | 209 | 206.3 | 23.51 |
| 60 | 59.23 | 6.75 | 110 | 108.6 | 12.37 | 160 | 157.9 | 18.00 | 210 | 207.3 | 23.62 |

| G | D | H | G | D | H | G | D | H | G | D | H |
|---|---|---|---|---|---|---|---|---|---|---|---|
| 10 | 9·87 | 1·15 | 60 | 59·19 | 6·92 | 110 | 108·5 | 12·68 | 160 | 157·8 | 18·45 |
| 11 | 10·85 | 1·27 | 61 | 60·18 | 7·03 | 111 | 109·5 | 12·80 | 161 | 158·8 | 18·56 |
| 12 | 11·84 | 1·38 | 62 | 61·16 | 7·15 | 112 | 110·5 | 12·91 | 162 | 159·8 | 18·68 |
| 13 | 12·82 | 1·50 | 63 | 62·15 | 7·26 | 113 | 111·5 | 13·03 | 163 | 160·8 | 18·80 |
| 14 | 13·81 | 1·61 | 64 | 63·14 | 7·38 | 114 | 112·5 | 13·14 | 164 | 161·8 | 18·91 |
| 15 | 14·80 | 1·73 | 65 | 64·12 | 7·49 | 115 | 113·4 | 13·26 | 165 | 162·8 | 19·03 |
| 16 | 15·78 | 1·84 | 66 | 65·11 | 7·61 | 116 | 114·4 | 13·38 | 166 | 163·8 | 19·14 |
| 17 | 16·77 | 1·96 | 67 | 66·10 | 7·73 | 117 | 115·4 | 13·49 | 167 | 164·7 | 19·26 |
| 18 | 17·76 | 2·08 | 68 | 67·08 | 7·84 | 118 | 116·4 | 13·61 | 168 | 165·7 | 19·37 |
| 19 | 18·74 | 2·19 | 69 | 68·07 | 7·96 | 119 | 117·4 | 13·72 | 169 | 166·7 | 19·49 |
| 20 | 19·73 | 2·31 | 70 | 69·06 | 8·07 | 120 | 118·4 | 13·84 | 170 | 167·7 | 19·60 |
| 21 | 20·72 | 2·42 | 71 | 70·04 | 8·19 | 121 | 119·4 | 13·95 | 171 | 168·7 | 19·72 |
| 22 | 21·70 | 2·54 | 72 | 71·03 | 8·30 | 122 | 120·4 | 14·07 | 172 | 169·7 | 19·83 |
| 23 | 22·69 | 2·65 | 73 | 72·02 | 8·42 | 123 | 121·3 | 14·18 | 173 | 170·7 | 19·95 |
| 24 | 23·68 | 2·77 | 74 | 73·00 | 8·53 | 124 | 122·3 | 14·30 | 174 | 171·7 | 20·06 |
| 25 | 24·66 | 2·88 | 75 | 73·99 | 8·65 | 125 | 123·3 | 14·41 | 175 | 172·6 | 20·18 |
| 26 | 25·65 | 3·00 | 76 | 74·98 | 8·76 | 126 | 124·3 | 14·53 | 176 | 173·6 | 20·29 |
| 27 | 26·64 | 3·11 | 77 | 75·96 | 8·88 | 127 | 125·3 | 14·64 | 177 | 174·6 | 20·41 |
| 28 | 27·62 | 3·23 | 78 | 76·95 | 8·99 | 128 | 126·3 | 14·76 | 178 | 175·6 | 20·52 |
| 29 | 28·61 | 3·34 | 79 | 77·94 | 9·11 | 129 | 127·3 | 14·87 | 179 | 176·6 | 20·64 |
| 30 | 29·60 | 3·46 | 80 | 78·92 | 9·22 | 130 | 128·2 | 14·99 | 180 | 177·6 | 20·76 |
| 31 | 30·58 | 3·57 | 81 | 79·91 | 9·34 | 131 | 129·2 | 15·11 | 181 | 178·6 | 20·87 |
| 32 | 31·57 | 3·69 | 82 | 80·89 | 9·46 | 132 | 130·2 | 15·22 | 182 | 179·5 | 20·99 |
| 33 | 32·56 | 3·81 | 83 | 81·88 | 9·57 | 133 | 131·2 | 15·34 | 183 | 180·5 | 21·10 |
| 34 | 33·54 | 3·92 | 84 | 82·87 | 9·69 | 134 | 132·2 | 15·45 | 184 | 181·5 | 21·22 |
| 35 | 34·53 | 4·04 | 85 | 83·85 | 9·80 | 135 | 133·2 | 15·57 | 185 | 182·5 | 21·33 |
| 36 | 35·51 | 4·15 | 86 | 84·84 | 9·92 | 136 | 134·2 | 15·68 | 186 | 183·5 | 21·45 |
| 37 | 36·50 | 4·27 | 87 | 85·83 | 10·03 | 137 | 135·2 | 15·80 | 187 | 184·5 | 21·56 |
| 38 | 37·49 | 4·38 | 88 | 86·81 | 10·15 | 138 | 136·1 | 15·91 | 188 | 185·5 | 21·68 |
| 39 | 38·47 | 4·50 | 89 | 87·80 | 10·26 | 139 | 137·1 | 16·03 | 189 | 186·5 | 21·79 |
| 40 | 39·46 | 4·61 | 90 | 88·79 | 10·38 | 140 | 138·1 | 16·14 | 190 | 187·4 | 21·91 |
| 41 | 40·45 | 4·73 | 91 | 89·77 | 10·49 | 141 | 139·1 | 16·26 | 191 | 188·4 | 22·02 |
| 42 | 41·43 | 4·84 | 92 | 90·76 | 10·61 | 142 | 140·1 | 16·37 | 192 | 189·4 | 22·14 |
| 43 | 42·42 | 4·96 | 93 | 91·75 | 10·72 | 143 | 141·1 | 16·49 | 193 | 190·4 | 22·25 |
| 44 | 43·41 | 5·07 | 94 | 92·73 | 10·84 | 144 | 142·1 | 16·60 | 194 | 191·4 | 22·37 |
| 45 | 44·39 | 5·19 | 95 | 93·72 | 10·95 | 145 | 143·0 | 16·72 | 195 | 192·4 | 22·48 |
| 46 | 45·38 | 5·30 | 96 | 94·71 | 11·07 | 146 | 144·0 | 16·83 | 196 | 193·4 | 22·60 |
| 47 | 46·37 | 5·42 | 97 | 95·69 | 11·18 | 147 | 145·0 | 16·95 | 197 | 194·3 | 22·72 |
| 48 | 47·35 | 5·53 | 98 | 96·68 | 11·30 | 148 | 146·0 | 17·07 | 198 | 195·3 | 22·83 |
| 49 | 48·34 | 5·65 | 99 | 97·67 | 11·42 | 149 | 147·0 | 17·18 | 199 | 196·3 | 22·95 |
| 50 | 49·33 | 5·77 | 100 | 98·65 | 11·53 | 150 | 148·0 | 17·30 | 200 | 197·3 | 23·06 |
| 51 | 50·31 | 5·88 | 101 | 99·64 | 11·65 | 151 | 149·0 | 17·41 | 201 | 198·3 | 23·18 |
| 52 | 51·30 | 6·00 | 102 | 100·6 | 11·76 | 152 | 150·0 | 17·53 | 202 | 199·3 | 23·29 |
| 53 | 52·29 | 6·11 | 103 | 101·6 | 11·88 | 153 | 150·9 | 17·64 | 203 | 200·3 | 23·41 |
| 54 | 53·27 | 6·23 | 104 | 102·6 | 11·99 | 154 | 151·9 | 17·76 | 204 | 201·3 | 23·52 |
| 55 | 54·26 | 6·34 | 105 | 103·6 | 12·11 | 155 | 152·9 | 17·87 | 205 | 202·2 | 23·64 |
| 56 | 55·25 | 6·46 | 106 | 104·6 | 12·22 | 156 | 153·9 | 17·99 | 206 | 203·2 | 23·75 |
| 57 | 56·23 | 6·57 | 107 | 105·6 | 12·34 | 157 | 154·9 | 18·10 | 207 | 204·2 | 23·87 |
| 58 | 57·22 | 6·69 | 108 | 106·5 | 12·45 | 158 | 155·9 | 18·22 | 208 | 205·2 | 23·98 |
| 59 | 58·20 | 6·80 | 109 | 107·5 | 12·57 | 159 | 156·9 | 18·33 | 209 | 206·2 | 24·10 |
| 60 | 59·19 | 6·92 | 110 | 108·5 | 12·68 | 160 | 157·8 | 18·45 | 210 | 207·2 | 24·21 |

TABLE I

# 6° 50′

| G | D | H | G | D | H | G | D | H | G | D | H |
|---|---|---|---|---|---|---|---|---|---|---|---|
| 10 | 9·86 | 1·18 | 60 | 59·15 | 7·09 | 110 | 108·4 | 12·99 | 160 | 157·7 | 18·90 |
| 11 | 10·84 | 1·30 | 61 | 60·14 | 7·21 | 111 | 109·4 | 13·11 | 161 | 158·7 | 19·02 |
| 12 | 11·83 | 1·42 | 62 | 61·12 | 7·32 | 112 | 110·4 | 13·23 | 162 | 159·7 | 19·14 |
| 13 | 12·82 | 1·54 | 63 | 62·11 | 7·44 | 113 | 111·4 | 13·35 | 163 | 160·7 | 19·26 |
| 14 | 13·80 | 1·65 | 64 | 63·09 | 7·56 | 114 | 112·4 | 13·47 | 164 | 161·7 | 19·37 |
| 15 | 14·79 | 1·77 | 65 | 64·08 | 7·68 | 115 | 113·4 | 13·59 | 165 | 162·7 | 19·49 |
| 16 | 15·77 | 1·89 | 66 | 65·07 | 7·80 | 116 | 114·4 | 13·70 | 166 | 163·6 | 19·61 |
| 17 | 16·76 | 2·01 | 67 | 66·05 | 7·92 | 117 | 115·3 | 13·82 | 167 | 164·6 | 19·73 |
| 18 | 17·75 | 2·13 | 68 | 67·04 | 8·03 | 118 | 116·3 | 13·94 | 168 | 165·6 | 19·85 |
| 19 | 18·73 | 2·24 | 69 | 68·02 | 8·15 | 119 | 117·3 | 14·06 | 169 | 166·6 | 19·96 |
| 20 | 19·72 | 2·36 | 70 | 69·01 | 8·27 | 120 | 118·3 | 14·18 | 170 | 167·6 | 20·08 |
| 21 | 20·70 | 2·48 | 71 | 69·99 | 8·39 | 121 | 119·3 | 14·29 | 171 | 168·6 | 20·20 |
| 22 | 21·69 | 2·60 | 72 | 70·98 | 8·51 | 122 | 120·3 | 14·41 | 172 | 169·6 | 20·32 |
| 23 | 22·67 | 2·72 | 73 | 71·97 | 8·62 | 123 | 121·3 | 14·53 | 173 | 170·6 | 20·44 |
| 24 | 23·66 | 2·84 | 74 | 72·95 | 8·74 | 124 | 122·2 | 14·65 | 174 | 171·5 | 20·56 |
| 25 | 24·65 | 2·95 | 75 | 73·94 | 8·86 | 125 | 123·2 | 14·77 | 175 | 172·5 | 20·67 |
| 26 | 25·63 | 3·07 | 76 | 74·92 | 8·98 | 126 | 124·2 | 14·89 | 176 | 173·5 | 20·79 |
| 27 | 26·62 | 3·19 | 77 | 75·91 | 9·10 | 127 | 125·2 | 15·00 | 177 | 174·5 | 20·91 |
| 28 | 27·60 | 3·31 | 78 | 76·90 | 9·21 | 128 | 126·2 | 15·12 | 178 | 175·5 | 21·03 |
| 29 | 28·59 | 3·43 | 79 | 77·88 | 9·33 | 129 | 127·2 | 15·24 | 179 | 176·5 | 21·15 |
| 30 | 29·58 | 3·54 | 80 | 78·87 | 9·45 | 130 | 128·2 | 15·36 | 180 | 177·5 | 21·26 |
| 31 | 30·56 | 3·66 | 81 | 79·85 | 9·57 | 131 | 129·1 | 15·48 | 181 | 178·4 | 21·38 |
| 32 | 31·55 | 3·78 | 82 | 80·84 | 9·69 | 132 | 130·1 | 15·59 | 182 | 179·4 | 21·50 |
| 33 | 32·53 | 3·90 | 83 | 81·82 | 9·81 | 133 | 131·1 | 15·71 | 183 | 180·4 | 21·62 |
| 34 | 33·52 | 4·02 | 84 | 82·81 | 9·92 | 134 | 132·1 | 15·83 | 184 | 181·4 | 21·74 |
| 35 | 34·50 | 4·13 | 85 | 83·80 | 10·04 | 135 | 133·1 | 15·95 | 185 | 182·4 | 21·86 |
| 36 | 35·49 | 4·25 | 86 | 84·78 | 10·16 | 136 | 134·1 | 16·07 | 186 | 183·4 | 21·97 |
| 37 | 36·48 | 4·37 | 87 | 85·77 | 10·28 | 137 | 135·1 | 16·18 | 187 | 184·4 | 22·09 |
| 38 | 37·46 | 4·49 | 88 | 86·75 | 10·40 | 138 | 136·0 | 16·30 | 188 | 185·3 | 22·21 |
| 39 | 38·45 | 4·61 | 89 | 87·74 | 10·51 | 139 | 137·0 | 16·42 | 189 | 186·3 | 22·33 |
| 40 | 39·43 | 4·73 | 90 | 88·73 | 10·63 | 140 | 138·0 | 16·54 | 190 | 187·3 | 22·45 |
| 41 | 40·42 | 4·84 | 91 | 89·71 | 10·75 | 141 | 139·0 | 16·66 | 191 | 188·3 | 22·56 |
| 42 | 41·41 | 4·96 | 92 | 90·70 | 10·87 | 142 | 140·0 | 16·78 | 192 | 189·3 | 22·68 |
| 43 | 42·39 | 5·08 | 93 | 91·68 | 10·99 | 143 | 141·0 | 16·89 | 193 | 190·3 | 22·80 |
| 44 | 43·38 | 5·20 | 94 | 92·67 | 11·10 | 144 | 142·0 | 17·01 | 194 | 191·3 | 22·92 |
| 45 | 44·36 | 5·32 | 95 | 93·65 | 11·22 | 145 | 142·9 | 17·13 | 195 | 192·2 | 23·04 |
| 46 | 45·35 | 5·43 | 96 | 94·64 | 11·34 | 146 | 143·9 | 17·25 | 196 | 193·2 | 23·15 |
| 47 | 46·33 | 5·55 | 97 | 95·63 | 11·46 | 147 | 144·9 | 17·37 | 197 | 194·2 | 23·27 |
| 48 | 47·32 | 5·67 | 98 | 96·61 | 11·58 | 148 | 145·9 | 17·48 | 198 | 195·2 | 23·39 |
| 49 | 48·31 | 5·79 | 99 | 97·60 | 11·70 | 149 | 146·9 | 17·60 | 199 | 196·2 | 23·51 |
| 50 | 49·29 | 5·91 | 100 | 98·58 | 11·81 | 150 | 147·9 | 17·72 | 200 | 197·2 | 23·63 |
| 51 | 50·28 | 6·02 | 101 | 99·57 | 11·93 | 151 | 148·9 | 17·84 | 201 | 198·2 | 23·75 |
| 52 | 51·26 | 6·14 | 102 | 100·6 | 12·05 | 152 | 149·8 | 17·96 | 202 | 199·1 | 23·86 |
| 53 | 52·25 | 6·26 | 103 | 101·5 | 12·17 | 153 | 150·8 | 18·07 | 203 | 200·1 | 23·98 |
| 54 | 53·24 | 6·38 | 104 | 102·5 | 12·29 | 154 | 151·8 | 18·19 | 204 | 201·1 | 24·10 |
| 55 | 54·22 | 6·50 | 105 | 103·5 | 12·40 | 155 | 152·8 | 18·31 | 205 | 202·1 | 24·22 |
| 56 | 55·21 | 6·62 | 106 | 104·5 | 12·52 | 156 | 153·8 | 18·43 | 206 | 203·1 | 24·34 |
| 57 | 56·19 | 6·73 | 107 | 105·5 | 12·64 | 157 | 154·8 | 18·55 | 207 | 204·1 | 24·45 |
| 58 | 57·18 | 6·85 | 108 | 106·5 | 12·76 | 158 | 155·8 | 18·67 | 208 | 205·1 | 24·57 |
| 59 | 58·16 | 6·97 | 109 | 107·5 | 12·88 | 159 | 156·7 | 18·78 | 209 | 206·0 | 24·69 |
| 60 | 59·15 | 7·09 | 110 | 108·4 | 12·99 | 160 | 157·7 | 18·90 | 210 | 207·0 | 24·81 |

TABLE I

| G | D | H | G | D | H | G | D | H | G | D | H |
|---|---|---|---|---|---|---|---|---|---|---|---|
| 10 | 9·85 | 1·21 | 60 | 59·11 | 7·26 | 110 | 108·4 | 13·31 | 160 | 157·6 | 19·35 |
| 11 | 10·84 | 1·33 | 61 | 60·09 | 7·38 | 111 | 109·4 | 13·43 | 161 | 158·6 | 19·47 |
| 12 | 11·82 | 1·45 | 62 | 61·08 | 7·50 | 112 | 110·3 | 13·55 | 162 | 159·6 | 19·60 |
| 13 | 12·81 | 1·57 | 63 | 62·06 | 7·62 | 113 | 111·3 | 13·67 | 163 | 160·6 | 19·72 |
| 14 | 13·79 | 1·69 | 64 | 63·05 | 7·74 | 114 | 112·3 | 13·79 | 164 | 161·6 | 19·84 |
| 15 | 14·78 | 1·81 | 65 | 64·03 | 7·86 | 115 | 113·3 | 13·91 | 165 | 162·5 | 19·96 |
| 16 | 15·76 | 1·94 | 66 | 65·02 | 7·98 | 116 | 114·3 | 14·03 | 166 | 163·5 | 20·08 |
| 17 | 16·75 | 2·06 | 67 | 66·00 | 8·10 | 117 | 115·3 | 14·15 | 167 | 164·5 | 20·20 |
| 18 | 17·73 | 2·18 | 68 | 66·99 | 8·23 | 118 | 116·2 | 14·27 | 168 | 165·5 | 20·32 |
| 19 | 18·72 | 2·30 | 69 | 67·98 | 8·35 | 119 | 117·2 | 14·39 | 169 | 166·5 | 20·44 |
| 20 | 19·70 | 2·42 | 70 | 68·96 | 8·47 | 120 | 118·2 | 14·52 | 170 | 167·5 | 20·56 |
| 21 | 20·69 | 2·54 | 71 | 69·95 | 8·59 | 121 | 119·2 | 14·64 | 171 | 168·5 | 20·68 |
| 22 | 21·67 | 2·66 | 72 | 70·93 | 8·71 | 122 | 120·2 | 14·76 | 172 | 169·4 | 20·81 |
| 23 | 22·66 | 2·78 | 73 | 71·92 | 8·83 | 123 | 121·2 | 14·88 | 173 | 170·4 | 20·93 |
| 24 | 23·64 | 2·90 | 74 | 72·90 | 8·95 | 124 | 122·2 | 15·00 | 174 | 171·4 | 21·05 |
| 25 | 24·63 | 3·02 | 75 | 73·89 | 9·07 | 125 | 123·1 | 15·12 | 175 | 172·4 | 21·17 |
| 26 | 25·61 | 3·14 | 76 | 74·87 | 9·19 | 126 | 124·1 | 15·24 | 176 | 173·4 | 21·29 |
| 27 | 26·60 | 3·27 | 77 | 75·86 | 9·31 | 127 | 125·1 | 15·36 | 177 | 174·4 | 21·41 |
| 28 | 27·58 | 3·39 | 78 | 76·84 | 9·43 | 128 | 126·1 | 15·48 | 178 | 175·4 | 21·53 |
| 29 | 28·57 | 3·51 | 79 | 77·83 | 9·56 | 129 | 127·1 | 15·60 | 179 | 176·3 | 21·65 |
| 30 | 29·55 | 3·63 | 80 | 78·81 | 9·68 | 130 | 128·1 | 15·72 | 180 | 177·3 | 21·77 |
| 31 | 30·54 | 3·75 | 81 | 79·80 | 9·80 | 131 | 129·1 | 15·85 | 181 | 178·3 | 21·89 |
| 32 | 31·52 | 3·87 | 82 | 80·78 | 9·92 | 132 | 130·0 | 15·97 | 182 | 179·3 | 22·01 |
| 33 | 32·51 | 3·99 | 83 | 81·77 | 10·04 | 133 | 131·0 | 16·09 | 183 | 180·3 | 22·14 |
| 34 | 33·49 | 4·11 | 84 | 82·75 | 10·16 | 134 | 132·0 | 16·21 | 184 | 181·3 | 22·26 |
| 35 | 34·48 | 4·23 | 85 | 83·74 | 10·28 | 135 | 133·0 | 16·33 | 185 | 182·3 | 22·38 |
| 36 | 35·47 | 4·35 | 86 | 84·72 | 10·40 | 136 | 134·0 | 16·45 | 186 | 183·2 | 22·50 |
| 37 | 36·45 | 4·48 | 87 | 85·71 | 10·52 | 137 | 135·0 | 16·57 | 187 | 184·2 | 22·62 |
| 38 | 37·44 | 4·60 | 88 | 86·69 | 10·64 | 138 | 136·0 | 16·69 | 188 | 185·2 | 22·74 |
| 39 | 38·42 | 4·72 | 89 | 87·68 | 10·77 | 139 | 136·9 | 16·81 | 189 | 186·2 | 22·86 |
| 40 | 39·41 | 4·84 | 90 | 88·66 | 10·89 | 140 | 137·9 | 16·93 | 190 | 187·2 | 22·98 |
| 41 | 40·39 | 4·96 | 91 | 89·65 | 11·01 | 141 | 138·9 | 17·06 | 191 | 188·2 | 23·10 |
| 42 | 41·38 | 5·08 | 92 | 90·63 | 11·13 | 142 | 139·9 | 17·18 | 192 | 189·1 | 23·22 |
| 43 | 42·36 | 5·20 | 93 | 91·62 | 11·25 | 143 | 140·9 | 17·30 | 193 | 190·1 | 23·35 |
| 44 | 43·35 | 5·32 | 94 | 92·60 | 11·37 | 144 | 141·9 | 17·42 | 194 | 191·1 | 23·47 |
| 45 | 44·33 | 5·44 | 95 | 93·59 | 11·49 | 145 | 142·8 | 17·54 | 195 | 192·1 | 23·59 |
| 46 | 45·32 | 5·56 | 96 | 94·57 | 11·61 | 146 | 143·8 | 17·66 | 196 | 193·1 | 23·71 |
| 47 | 46·30 | 5·69 | 97 | 95·56 | 11·73 | 147 | 144·8 | 17·78 | 197 | 194·1 | 23·83 |
| 48 | 47·29 | 5·81 | 98 | 96·54 | 11·85 | 148 | 145·8 | 17·90 | 198 | 195·1 | 23·95 |
| 49 | 48·27 | 5·93 | 99 | 97·53 | 11·98 | 149 | 146·8 | 18·02 | 199 | 196·0 | 24·07 |
| 50 | 49·26 | 6·05 | 100 | 98·51 | 12·10 | 150 | 147·8 | 18·14 | 200 | 197·0 | 24·19 |
| 51 | 50·24 | 6·17 | 101 | 99·50 | 12·22 | 151 | 148·8 | 18·26 | 201 | 198·0 | 24·31 |
| 52 | 51·23 | 6·29 | 102 | 100·5 | 12·34 | 152 | 149·7 | 18·39 | 202 | 199·0 | 24·43 |
| 53 | 52·21 | 6·41 | 103 | 101·5 | 12·46 | 153 | 150·7 | 18·51 | 203 | 200·0 | 24·55 |
| 54 | 53·20 | 6·53 | 104 | 102·5 | 12·58 | 154 | 151·7 | 18·63 | 204 | 201·0 | 24·68 |
| 55 | 54·18 | 6·65 | 105 | 103·4 | 12·70 | 155 | 152·7 | 18·75 | 205 | 202·0 | 24·80 |
| 56 | 55·17 | 6·77 | 106 | 104·4 | 12·82 | 156 | 153·7 | 18·87 | 206 | 202·9 | 24·92 |
| 57 | 56·15 | 6·89 | 107 | 105·4 | 12·94 | 157 | 154·7 | 18·99 | 207 | 203·9 | 25·04 |
| 58 | 57·14 | 7·02 | 108 | 106·4 | 13·06 | 158 | 155·7 | 19·11 | 208 | 204·9 | 25·16 |
| 59 | 58·12 | 7·14 | 109 | 107·4 | 13·18 | 159 | 156·6 | 19·23 | 209 | 205·9 | 25·28 |
| 60 | 59·11 | 7·26 | 110 | 108·4 | 13·31 | 160 | 157·6 | 19·35 | 210 | 206·9 | 25·40 |

TABLE I

# 7° 10'

| G | D | H | G | D | H | G | D | H | G | D | H |
|---|---|---|---|---|---|---|---|---|---|---|---|
| 10 | 9·84 | 1·24 | 60 | 59·07 | 7·43 | 110 | 108·3 | 13·62 | 160 | 157·5 | 19·80 |
| 11 | 10·83 | 1·36 | 61 | 60·05 | 7·55 | 111 | 109·3 | 13·74 | 161 | 158·5 | 19·93 |
| 12 | 11·81 | 1·49 | 62 | 61·03 | 7·67 | 112 | 110·3 | 13·86 | 162 | 159·5 | 20·05 |
| 13 | 12·80 | 1·61 | 63 | 62·02 | 7·80 | 113 | 111·2 | 13·99 | 163 | 160·5 | 20·18 |
| 14 | 13·78 | 1·73 | 64 | 63·00 | 7·92 | 114 | 112·2 | 14·11 | 164 | 161·4 | 20·30 |
| 15 | 14·77 | 1·86 | 65 | 63·99 | 8·05 | 115 | 113·2 | 14·23 | 165 | 162·4 | 20·42 |
| 16 | 15·75 | 1·98 | 66 | 64·97 | 8·17 | 116 | 114·2 | 14·36 | 166 | 163·4 | 20·55 |
| 17 | 16·74 | 2·10 | 67 | 65·96 | 8·29 | 117 | 115·2 | 14·48 | 167 | 164·4 | 20·67 |
| 18 | 17·72 | 2·23 | 68 | 66·94 | 8·42 | 118 | 116·2 | 14·61 | 168 | 165·4 | 20·80 |
| 19 | 18·70 | 2·35 | 69 | 67·93 | 8·54 | 119 | 117·1 | 14·73 | 169 | 166·4 | 20·92 |
| 20 | 19·69 | 2·48 | 70 | 68·91 | 8·66 | 120 | 118·1 | 14·85 | 170 | 167·4 | 21·04 |
| 21 | 20·67 | 2·60 | 71 | 69·89 | 8·79 | 121 | 119·1 | 14·98 | 171 | 168·3 | 21·17 |
| 22 | 21·66 | 2·72 | 72 | 70·88 | 8·91 | 122 | 120·1 | 15·10 | 172 | 169·3 | 21·29 |
| 23 | 22·64 | 2·85 | 73 | 71·86 | 9·04 | 123 | 121·1 | 15·23 | 173 | 170·3 | 21·41 |
| 24 | 23·63 | 2·97 | 74 | 72·85 | 9·16 | 124 | 122·1 | 15·35 | 174 | 171·3 | 21·54 |
| 25 | 24·61 | 3·09 | 75 | 73·83 | 9·28 | 125 | 123·1 | 15·47 | 175 | 172·3 | 21·66 |
| 26 | 25·60 | 3·22 | 76 | 74·82 | 9·41 | 126 | 124·0 | 15·60 | 176 | 173·3 | 21·79 |
| 27 | 26·58 | 3·34 | 77 | 75·80 | 9·53 | 127 | 125·0 | 15·72 | 177 | 174·2 | 21·91 |
| 28 | 27·56 | 3·47 | 78 | 76·79 | 9·65 | 128 | 126·0 | 15·84 | 178 | 175·2 | 22·03 |
| 29 | 28·55 | 3·59 | 79 | 77·77 | 9·78 | 129 | 127·0 | 15·97 | 179 | 176·2 | 22·16 |
| 30 | 29·53 | 3·71 | 80 | 78·75 | 9·90 | 130 | 128·0 | 16·09 | 180 | 177·2 | 22·28 |
| 31 | 30·52 | 3·84 | 81 | 79·74 | 10·03 | 131 | 129·0 | 16·22 | 181 | 178·2 | 22·40 |
| 32 | 31·50 | 3·96 | 82 | 80·72 | 10·15 | 132 | 129·9 | 16·34 | 182 | 179·2 | 22·53 |
| 33 | 32·49 | 4·08 | 83 | 81·71 | 10·27 | 133 | 130·9 | 16·46 | 183 | 180·2 | 22·65 |
| 34 | 33·47 | 4·21 | 84 | 82·69 | 10·40 | 134 | 131·9 | 16·59 | 184 | 181·1 | 22·78 |
| 35 | 34·46 | 4·33 | 85 | 83·68 | 10·52 | 135 | 132·9 | 16·71 | 185 | 182·1 | 22·90 |
| 36 | 35·44 | 4·46 | 86 | 84·66 | 10·65 | 136 | 133·9 | 16·83 | 186 | 183·1 | 23·02 |
| 37 | 36·42 | 4·58 | 87 | 85·65 | 10·77 | 137 | 134·9 | 16·96 | 187 | 184·1 | 23·15 |
| 38 | 37·41 | 4·70 | 88 | 86·63 | 10·89 | 138 | 135·9 | 17·08 | 188 | 185·1 | 23·27 |
| 39 | 38·39 | 4·83 | 89 | 87·61 | 11·02 | 139 | 136·8 | 17·21 | 189 | 186·1 | 23·39 |
| 40 | 39·38 | 4·95 | 90 | 88·60 | 11·14 | 140 | 137·8 | 17·33 | 190 | 187·0 | 23·52 |
| 41 | 40·36 | 5·08 | 91 | 89·58 | 11·26 | 141 | 138·8 | 17·45 | 191 | 188·0 | 23·64 |
| 42 | 41·35 | 5·20 | 92 | 90·57 | 11·39 | 142 | 139·8 | 17·58 | 192 | 189·0 | 23·77 |
| 43 | 42·33 | 5·32 | 93 | 91·55 | 11·51 | 143 | 140·8 | 17·70 | 193 | 190·0 | 23·89 |
| 44 | 43·32 | 5·45 | 94 | 92·54 | 11·64 | 144 | 141·8 | 17·82 | 194 | 191·0 | 24·01 |
| 45 | 44·30 | 5·57 | 95 | 93·52 | 11·76 | 145 | 142·7 | 17·95 | 195 | 192·0 | 24·14 |
| 46 | 45·28 | 5·69 | 96 | 94·51 | 11·88 | 146 | 143·7 | 18·07 | 196 | 192·9 | 24·26 |
| 47 | 46·27 | 5·82 | 97 | 95·49 | 12·01 | 147 | 144·7 | 18·20 | 197 | 193·9 | 24·38 |
| 48 | 47·25 | 5·94 | 98 | 96·47 | 12·13 | 148 | 145·7 | 18·32 | 198 | 194·9 | 24·51 |
| 49 | 48·24 | 6·07 | 99 | 97·46 | 12·25 | 149 | 146·7 | 18·44 | 199 | 195·9 | 24·63 |
| 50 | 49·22 | 6·19 | 100 | 98·44 | 12·38 | 150 | 147·7 | 18·57 | 200 | 196·9 | 24·76 |
| 51 | 50·21 | 6·31 | 101 | 99·43 | 12·50 | 151 | 148·6 | 18·69 | 201 | 197·9 | 24·88 |
| 52 | 51·19 | 6·44 | 102 | 100·4 | 12·63 | 152 | 149·6 | 18·81 | 202 | 198·9 | 25·00 |
| 53 | 52·18 | 6·56 | 103 | 101·4 | 12·75 | 153 | 150·6 | 18·94 | 203 | 199·8 | 25·13 |
| 54 | 53·16 | 6·68 | 104 | 102·4 | 12·87 | 154 | 151·6 | 19·06 | 204 | 200·8 | 25·25 |
| 55 | 54·14 | 6·81 | 105 | 103·4 | 13·00 | 155 | 152·6 | 19·19 | 205 | 201·8 | 25·38 |
| 56 | 55·13 | 6·93 | 106 | 104·4 | 13·12 | 156 | 153·6 | 19·31 | 206 | 202·8 | 25·50 |
| 57 | 56·11 | 7·06 | 107 | 105·3 | 13·24 | 157 | 154·6 | 19·43 | 207 | 203·8 | 25·62 |
| 58 | 57·10 | 7·18 | 108 | 106·3 | 13·37 | 158 | 155·5 | 19·56 | 208 | 204·8 | 25·75 |
| 59 | 58·08 | 7·30 | 109 | 107·3 | 13·49 | 159 | 156·5 | 19·68 | 209 | 205·7 | 25·87 |
| 60 | 59·07 | 7·43 | 110 | 108·3 | 13·62 | 160 | 157·5 | 19·80 | 210 | 206·7 | 25·99 |

| G | D | H | G | D | H | G | D | H | G | D | H |
|---|---|---|---|---|---|---|---|---|---|---|---|
| 10 | 9·84 | 1·27 | 60 | 59·02 | 7·60 | 110 | 108·2 | 13·93 | 160 | 157·4 | 20·26 |
| 11 | 10·82 | 1·39 | 61 | 60·01 | 7·72 | 111 | 109·2 | 14·05 | 161 | 158·4 | 20·38 |
| 12 | 11·80 | 1·52 | 62 | 60·99 | 7·85 | 112 | 110·2 | 14·18 | 162 | 159·4 | 20·51 |
| 13 | 12·79 | 1·65 | 63 | 61·97 | 7·98 | 113 | 111·2 | 14·31 | 163 | 160·3 | 20·64 |
| 14 | 13·77 | 1·77 | 64 | 62·96 | 8·10 | 114 | 112·1 | 14·43 | 164 | 161·3 | 20·76 |
| 15 | 14·76 | 1·90 | 65 | 63·94 | 8·23 | 115 | 113·1 | 14·56 | 165 | 162·3 | 20·89 |
| 16 | 15·74 | 2·03 | 66 | 64·92 | 8·36 | 116 | 114·1 | 14·69 | 166 | 163·3 | 21·02 |
| 17 | 16·72 | 2·15 | 67 | 65·91 | 8·48 | 117 | 115·1 | 14·81 | 167 | 164·3 | 21·14 |
| 18 | 17·71 | 2·28 | 68 | 66·89 | 8·61 | 118 | 116·1 | 14·94 | 168 | 165·3 | 21·27 |
| 19 | 18·69 | 2·41 | 69 | 67·88 | 8·74 | 119 | 117·1 | 15·07 | 169 | 166·2 | 21·39 |
| 20 | 19·67 | 2·53 | 70 | 68·86 | 8·86 | 120 | 118·0 | 15·19 | 170 | 167·2 | 21·52 |
| 21 | 20·66 | 2·66 | 71 | 69·84 | 8·99 | 121 | 119·0 | 15·32 | 171 | 168·2 | 21·65 |
| 22 | 21·64 | 2·79 | 72 | 70·83 | 9·11 | 122 | 120·0 | 15·44 | 172 | 169·2 | 21·77 |
| 23 | 22·63 | 2·91 | 73 | 71·81 | 9·24 | 123 | 121·0 | 15·57 | 173 | 170·2 | 21·90 |
| 24 | 23·61 | 3·04 | 74 | 72·79 | 9·37 | 124 | 122·0 | 15·70 | 174 | 171·2 | 22·03 |
| 25 | 24·59 | 3·16 | 75 | 73·78 | 9·49 | 125 | 123·0 | 15·82 | 175 | 172·1 | 22·15 |
| 26 | 25·58 | 3·29 | 76 | 74·76 | 9·62 | 126 | 123·9 | 15·95 | 176 | 173·1 | 22·28 |
| 27 | 26·56 | 3·42 | 77 | 75·75 | 9·75 | 127 | 124·9 | 16·08 | 177 | 174·1 | 22·41 |
| 28 | 27·54 | 3·54 | 78 | 76·73 | 9·87 | 128 | 125·9 | 16·20 | 178 | 175·1 | 22·53 |
| 29 | 28·53 | 3·67 | 79 | 77·71 | 10·00 | 129 | 126·9 | 16·33 | 179 | 176·1 | 22·66 |
| 30 | 29·51 | 3·80 | 80 | 78·70 | 10·13 | 130 | 127·9 | 16·46 | 180 | 177·1 | 22·79 |
| 31 | 30·49 | 3·92 | 81 | 79·68 | 10·25 | 131 | 128·9 | 16·58 | 181 | 178·1 | 22·91 |
| 32 | 31·48 | 4·05 | 82 | 80·66 | 10·38 | 132 | 129·8 | 16·71 | 182 | 179·0 | 23·04 |
| 33 | 32·46 | 4·18 | 83 | 81·65 | 10·51 | 133 | 130·8 | 16·84 | 183 | 180·0 | 23·17 |
| 34 | 33·45 | 4·30 | 84 | 82·63 | 10·63 | 134 | 131·8 | 16·96 | 184 | 181·0 | 23·29 |
| 35 | 34·43 | 4·43 | 85 | 83·62 | 10·76 | 135 | 132·8 | 17·09 | 185 | 182·0 | 23·42 |
| 36 | 35·41 | 4·56 | 86 | 84·60 | 10·89 | 136 | 133·8 | 17·22 | 186 | 183·0 | 23·55 |
| 37 | 36·40 | 4·68 | 87 | 85·58 | 11·01 | 137 | 134·8 | 17·34 | 187 | 184·0 | 23·67 |
| 38 | 37·38 | 4·81 | 88 | 86·57 | 11·14 | 138 | 135·8 | 17·47 | 188 | 184·9 | 23·80 |
| 39 | 38·36 | 4·94 | 89 | 87·55 | 11·27 | 139 | 136·7 | 17·60 | 189 | 185·9 | 23·93 |
| 40 | 39·35 | 5·06 | 90 | 88·53 | 11·39 | 140 | 137·7 | 17·72 | 190 | 186·9 | 24·05 |
| 41 | 40·33 | 5·19 | 91 | 89·52 | 11·52 | 141 | 138·7 | 17·85 | 191 | 187·9 | 24·18 |
| 42 | 41·32 | 5·32 | 92 | 90·50 | 11·65 | 142 | 139·7 | 17·98 | 192 | 188·9 | 24·31 |
| 43 | 42·30 | 5·44 | 93 | 91·48 | 11·77 | 143 | 140·7 | 18·10 | 193 | 189·9 | 24·43 |
| 44 | 43·28 | 5·57 | 94 | 92·47 | 11·90 | 144 | 141·7 | 18·23 | 194 | 190·8 | 24·56 |
| 45 | 44·27 | 5·70 | 95 | 93·45 | 12·03 | 145 | 142·6 | 18·36 | 195 | 191·8 | 24·69 |
| 46 | 45·25 | 5·82 | 96 | 94·44 | 12·15 | 146 | 143·6 | 18·48 | 196 | 192·8 | 24·81 |
| 47 | 46·23 | 5·95 | 97 | 95·42 | 12·28 | 147 | 144·6 | 18·61 | 197 | 193·8 | 24·94 |
| 48 | 47·22 | 6·08 | 98 | 96·40 | 12·41 | 148 | 145·6 | 18·74 | 198 | 194·8 | 25·07 |
| 49 | 48·20 | 6·20 | 99 | 97·39 | 12·53 | 149 | 146·6 | 18·86 | 199 | 195·8 | 25·19 |
| 50 | 49·19 | 6·33 | 100 | 98·37 | 12·66 | 150 | 147·6 | 18·99 | 200 | 196·7 | 25·32 |
| 51 | 50·17 | 6·46 | 101 | 99·35 | 12·79 | 151 | 148·5 | 19·12 | 201 | 197·7 | 25·45 |
| 52 | 51·15 | 6·58 | 102 | 100·3 | 12·91 | 152 | 149·5 | 19·24 | 202 | 198·7 | 25·57 |
| 53 | 52·14 | 6·71 | 103 | 101·3 | 13·04 | 153 | 150·5 | 19·37 | 203 | 199·7 | 25·70 |
| 54 | 53·12 | 6·84 | 104 | 102·3 | 13·17 | 154 | 151·5 | 19·50 | 204 | 200·7 | 25·83 |
| 55 | 54·10 | 6·96 | 105 | 103·3 | 13·29 | 155 | 152·5 | 19·62 | 205 | 201·7 | 25·95 |
| 56 | 55·09 | 7·09 | 106 | 104·3 | 13·42 | 156 | 153·5 | 19·75 | 206 | 202·6 | 26·08 |
| 57 | 56·07 | 7·22 | 107 | 105·3 | 13·55 | 157 | 154·4 | 19·88 | 207 | 203·6 | 26·21 |
| 58 | 57·05 | 7·34 | 108 | 106·2 | 13·67 | 158 | 155·4 | 20·00 | 208 | 204·6 | 26·33 |
| 59 | 58·04 | 7·47 | 109 | 107·2 | 13·80 | 159 | 156·4 | 20·13 | 209 | 205·6 | 26·46 |
| 60 | 59·02 | 7·60 | 110 | 108·2 | 13·93 | 160 | 157·4 | 20·26 | 210 | 206·6 | 26·59 |

TABLE I

# 7° 30′

| G | D | H | G | D | H | G | D | H | G | D | H |
|---|---|---|---|---|---|---|---|---|---|---|---|
| 10 | 9·83 | 1·29 | 60 | 58·98 | 7·76 | 110 | 108·1 | 14·23 | 160 | 157·3 | 20·71 |
| 11 | 10·81 | 1·42 | 61 | 59·96 | 7·89 | 111 | 109·1 | 14·36 | 161 | 158·3 | 20·83 |
| 12 | 11·80 | 1·55 | 62 | 60·94 | 8·02 | 112 | 110·1 | 14·49 | 162 | 159·2 | 20·96 |
| 13 | 12·78 | 1·68 | 63 | 61·93 | 8·15 | 113 | 111·1 | 14·62 | 163 | 160·2 | 21·09 |
| 14 | 13·76 | 1·81 | 64 | 62·91 | 8·28 | 114 | 112·1 | 14·75 | 164 | 161·2 | 21·22 |
| 15 | 14·74 | 1·94 | 65 | 63·89 | 8·41 | 115 | 113·0 | 14·88 | 165 | 162·2 | 21·35 |
| 16 | 15·73 | 2·07 | 66 | 64·88 | 8·54 | 116 | 114·0 | 15·01 | 166 | 163·2 | 21·48 |
| 17 | 16·71 | 2·20 | 67 | 65·86 | 8·67 | 117 | 115·0 | 15·14 | 167 | 164·2 | 21·61 |
| 18 | 17·69 | 2·33 | 68 | 66·84 | 8·80 | 118 | 116·0 | 15·27 | 168 | 165·1 | 21·74 |
| 19 | 18·68 | 2·46 | 69 | 67·82 | 8·93 | 119 | 117·0 | 15·40 | 169 | 166·1 | 21·87 |
| 20 | 19·66 | 2·59 | 70 | 68·81 | 9·06 | 120 | 118·0 | 15·53 | 170 | 167·1 | 22·00 |
| 21 | 20·64 | 2·72 | 71 | 69·79 | 9·19 | 121 | 118·9 | 15·66 | 171 | 168·1 | 22·13 |
| 22 | 21·63 | 2·85 | 72 | 70·77 | 9·32 | 122 | 119·9 | 15·79 | 172 | 169·1 | 22·26 |
| 23 | 22·61 | 2·98 | 73 | 71·76 | 9·45 | 123 | 120·9 | 15·92 | 173 | 170·1 | 22·39 |
| 24 | 23·59 | 3·11 | 74 | 72·74 | 9·58 | 124 | 121·9 | 16·05 | 174 | 171·0 | 22·52 |
| 25 | 24·57 | 3·24 | 75 | 73·72 | 9·71 | 125 | 122·9 | 16·18 | 175 | 172·0 | 22·65 |
| 26 | 25·56 | 3·36 | 76 | 74·71 | 9·84 | 126 | 123·9 | 16·31 | 176 | 173·0 | 22·78 |
| 27 | 26·54 | 3·49 | 77 | 75·69 | 9·96 | 127 | 124·8 | 16·43 | 177 | 174·0 | 22·91 |
| 28 | 27·52 | 3·62 | 78 | 76·67 | 10·09 | 128 | 125·8 | 16·56 | 178 | 175·0 | 23·03 |
| 29 | 28·51 | 3·75 | 79 | 77·65 | 10·22 | 129 | 126·8 | 16·69 | 179 | 176·0 | 23·16 |
| 30 | 29·49 | 3·88 | 80 | 78·64 | 10·35 | 130 | 127·8 | 16·82 | 180 | 176·9 | 23·29 |
| 31 | 30·47 | 4·01 | 81 | 79·62 | 10·48 | 131 | 128·8 | 16·95 | 181 | 177·9 | 23·42 |
| 32 | 31·45 | 4·14 | 82 | 80·60 | 10·61 | 132 | 129·8 | 17·08 | 182 | 178·9 | 23·55 |
| 33 | 32·44 | 4·27 | 83 | 81·59 | 10·74 | 133 | 130·7 | 17·21 | 183 | 179·9 | 23·68 |
| 34 | 33·42 | 4·40 | 84 | 82·57 | 10·87 | 134 | 131·7 | 17·34 | 184 | 180·9 | 23·81 |
| 35 | 34·40 | 4·53 | 85 | 83·55 | 11·00 | 135 | 132·7 | 17·47 | 185 | 181·8 | 23·94 |
| 36 | 35·39 | 4·66 | 86 | 84·53 | 11·13 | 136 | 133·7 | 17·60 | 186 | 182·8 | 24·07 |
| 37 | 36·37 | 4·79 | 87 | 85·52 | 11·26 | 137 | 134·7 | 17·73 | 187 | 183·8 | 24·20 |
| 38 | 37·35 | 4·92 | 88 | 86·50 | 11·39 | 138 | 135·6 | 17·86 | 188 | 184·8 | 24·33 |
| 39 | 38·34 | 5·05 | 89 | 87·48 | 11·52 | 139 | 136·6 | 17·99 | 189 | 185·8 | 24·46 |
| 40 | 39·32 | 5·18 | 90 | 88·47 | 11·65 | 140 | 137·6 | 18·12 | 190 | 186·8 | 24·59 |
| 41 | 40·30 | 5·31 | 91 | 89·45 | 11·78 | 141 | 138·6 | 18·25 | 191 | 187·7 | 24·72 |
| 42 | 41·28 | 5·44 | 92 | 90·43 | 11·91 | 142 | 139·6 | 18·38 | 192 | 188·7 | 24·85 |
| 43 | 42·27 | 5·56 | 93 | 91·42 | 12·04 | 143 | 140·6 | 18·51 | 193 | 189·7 | 24·98 |
| 44 | 43·25 | 5·69 | 94 | 92·40 | 12·16 | 144 | 141·5 | 18·63 | 194 | 190·7 | 25·11 |
| 45 | 44·23 | 5·82 | 95 | 93·38 | 12·29 | 145 | 142·5 | 18·76 | 195 | 191·7 | 25·23 |
| 46 | 45·22 | 5·95 | 96 | 94·36 | 12·42 | 146 | 143·5 | 18·89 | 196 | 192·7 | 25·36 |
| 47 | 46·20 | 6·08 | 97 | 95·35 | 12·55 | 147 | 144·5 | 19·02 | 197 | 193·6 | 25·49 |
| 48 | 47·18 | 6·21 | 98 | 96·33 | 12·68 | 148 | 145·5 | 19·15 | 198 | 194·6 | 25·62 |
| 49 | 48·17 | 6·34 | 99 | 97·31 | 12·81 | 149 | 146·5 | 19·28 | 199 | 195·6 | 25·75 |
| 50 | 49·15 | 6·47 | 100 | 98·30 | 12·94 | 150 | 147·4 | 19·41 | 200 | 196·6 | 25·88 |
| 51 | 50·13 | 6·60 | 101 | 99·28 | 13·07 | 151 | 148·4 | 19·54 | 201 | 197·6 | 26·01 |
| 52 | 51·11 | 6·73 | 102 | 100·3 | 13·20 | 152 | 149·4 | 19·67 | 202 | 198·6 | 26·14 |
| 53 | 52·10 | 6·86 | 103 | 101·2 | 13·33 | 153 | 150·4 | 19·80 | 203 | 199·5 | 26·27 |
| 54 | 53·08 | 6·99 | 104 | 102·2 | 13·46 | 154 | 151·4 | 19·93 | 204 | 200·5 | 26·40 |
| 55 | 54·06 | 7·12 | 105 | 103·2 | 13·59 | 155 | 152·4 | 20·06 | 205 | 201·5 | 26·53 |
| 56 | 55·05 | 7·25 | 106 | 104·2 | 13·72 | 156 | 153·3 | 20·19 | 206 | 202·5 | 26·66 |
| 57 | 56·03 | 7·38 | 107 | 105·2 | 13·85 | 157 | 154·3 | 20·32 | 207 | 203·5 | 26·79 |
| 58 | 57·01 | 7·51 | 108 | 106·2 | 13·98 | 158 | 155·3 | 20·45 | 208 | 204·5 | 26·92 |
| 59 | 57·99 | 7·64 | 109 | 107·1 | 14·11 | 159 | 156·3 | 20·58 | 209 | 205·4 | 27·05 |
| 60 | 58·98 | 7·76 | 110 | 108·1 | 14·23 | 160 | 157·3 | 20·71 | 210 | 206·4 | 27·18 |

# 7° 40′

TABLE I

| G | D | H | G | D | H | G | D | H | G | D | H |
|---|---|---|---|---|---|---|---|---|---|---|---|
| 10 | 9·82 | 1·32 | 60 | 58·93 | 7·93 | 110 | 108·0 | 14·54 | 160 | 157·2 | 21·15 |
| 11 | 10·80 | 1·45 | 61 | 59·91 | 8·07 | 111 | 109·0 | 14·68 | 161 | 158·1 | 21·29 |
| 12 | 11·79 | 1·59 | 62 | 60·90 | 8·20 | 112 | 110·0 | 14·81 | 162 | 159·1 | 21·42 |
| 13 | 12·77 | 1·72 | 63 | 61·88 | 8·33 | 113 | 111·0 | 14·94 | 163 | 160·1 | 21·55 |
| 14 | 13·75 | 1·85 | 64 | 62·86 | 8·46 | 114 | 112·0 | 15·07 | 164 | 161·1 | 21·68 |
| 15 | 14·73 | 1·98 | 65 | 63·84 | 8·59 | 115 | 113·0 | 15·20 | 165 | 162·1 | 21·82 |
| 16 | 15·72 | 2·12 | 66 | 64·83 | 8·73 | 116 | 113·9 | 15·34 | 166 | 163·0 | 21·95 |
| 17 | 16·70 | 2·25 | 67 | 65·81 | 8·86 | 117 | 114·9 | 15·47 | 167 | 164·0 | 22·08 |
| 18 | 17·68 | 2·38 | 68 | 66·79 | 8·99 | 118 | 115·9 | 15·60 | 168 | 165·0 | 22·21 |
| 19 | 18·66 | 2·51 | 69 | 67·77 | 9·12 | 119 | 116·9 | 15·73 | 169 | 166·0 | 22·34 |
| 20 | 19·64 | 2·64 | 70 | 68·75 | 9·26 | 120 | 117·9 | 15·87 | 170 | 167·0 | 22·48 |
| 21 | 20·63 | 2·78 | 71 | 69·74 | 9·39 | 121 | 118·8 | 16·00 | 171 | 168·0 | 22·61 |
| 22 | 21·61 | 2·91 | 72 | 70·72 | 9·52 | 122 | 119·8 | 16·13 | 172 | 168·9 | 22·74 |
| 23 | 22·59 | 3·04 | 73 | 71·70 | 9·65 | 123 | 120·8 | 16·26 | 173 | 169·9 | 22·87 |
| 24 | 23·57 | 3·17 | 74 | 72·68 | 9·78 | 124 | 121·8 | 16·39 | 174 | 170·9 | 23·01 |
| 25 | 24·55 | 3·31 | 75 | 73·66 | 9·92 | 125 | 122·8 | 16·53 | 175 | 171·9 | 23·14 |
| 26 | 25·54 | 3·44 | 76 | 74·65 | 10·05 | 126 | 123·8 | 16·66 | 176 | 172·9 | 23·27 |
| 27 | 26·52 | 3·57 | 77 | 75·63 | 10·18 | 127 | 124·7 | 16·79 | 177 | 173·8 | 23·40 |
| 28 | 27·50 | 3·70 | 78 | 76·61 | 10·31 | 128 | 125·7 | 16·92 | 178 | 174·8 | 23·53 |
| 29 | 28·48 | 3·83 | 79 | 77·59 | 10·45 | 129 | 126·7 | 17·06 | 179 | 175·8 | 23·67 |
| 30 | 29·47 | 3·97 | 80 | 78·58 | 10·58 | 130 | 127·7 | 17·19 | 180 | 176·8 | 23·80 |
| 31 | 30·45 | 4·10 | 81 | 79·56 | 10·71 | 131 | 128·7 | 17·32 | 181 | 177·8 | 23·93 |
| 32 | 31·43 | 4·23 | 82 | 80·54 | 10·84 | 132 | 129·7 | 17·45 | 182 | 178·8 | 24·06 |
| 33 | 32·41 | 4·36 | 83 | 81·52 | 10·97 | 133 | 130·6 | 17·58 | 183 | 179·7 | 24·20 |
| 34 | 33·39 | 4·50 | 84 | 82·50 | 11·11 | 134 | 131·6 | 17·72 | 184 | 180·7 | 24·33 |
| 35 | 34·38 | 4·63 | 85 | 83·49 | 11·24 | 135 | 132·6 | 17·85 | 185 | 181·7 | 24·46 |
| 36 | 35·36 | 4·76 | 86 | 84·47 | 11·37 | 136 | 133·6 | 17·98 | 186 | 182·7 | 24·59 |
| 37 | 36·34 | 4·89 | 87 | 85·45 | 11·50 | 137 | 134·6 | 18·11 | 187 | 183·7 | 24·72 |
| 38 | 37·32 | 5·02 | 88 | 86·43 | 11·64 | 138 | 135·5 | 18·25 | 188 | 184·7 | 24·86 |
| 39 | 38·31 | 5·16 | 89 | 87·42 | 11·77 | 139 | 136·5 | 18·38 | 189 | 185·6 | 24·99 |
| 40 | 39·29 | 5·29 | 90 | 88·40 | 11·90 | 140 | 137·5 | 18·51 | 190 | 186·6 | 25·12 |
| 41 | 40·27 | 5·42 | 91 | 89·38 | 12·03 | 141 | 138·5 | 18·64 | 191 | 187·6 | 25·25 |
| 42 | 41·25 | 5·55 | 92 | 90·36 | 12·16 | 142 | 139·5 | 18·77 | 192 | 188·6 | 25·39 |
| 43 | 42·23 | 5·69 | 93 | 91·34 | 12·30 | 143 | 140·5 | 18·91 | 193 | 189·6 | 25·52 |
| 44 | 43·22 | 5·82 | 94 | 92·33 | 12·43 | 144 | 141·4 | 19·04 | 194 | 190·5 | 25·65 |
| 45 | 44·20 | 5·95 | 95 | 93·31 | 12·56 | 145 | 142·4 | 19·17 | 195 | 191·5 | 25·78 |
| 46 | 45·18 | 6·08 | 96 | 94·29 | 12·69 | 146 | 143·4 | 19·30 | 196 | 192·5 | 25·91 |
| 47 | 46·16 | 6·21 | 97 | 95·27 | 12·82 | 147 | 144·4 | 19·44 | 197 | 193·5 | 26·05 |
| 48 | 47·15 | 6·35 | 98 | 96·26 | 12·96 | 148 | 145·4 | 19·57 | 198 | 194·5 | 26·18 |
| 49 | 48·13 | 6·48 | 99 | 97·24 | 13·09 | 149 | 146·3 | 19·70 | 199 | 195·5 | 26·31 |
| 50 | 49·11 | 6·61 | 100 | 98·22 | 13·22 | 150 | 147·3 | 19·83 | 200 | 196·4 | 26·44 |
| 51 | 50·09 | 6·74 | 101 | 99·20 | 13·35 | 151 | 148·3 | 19·96 | 201 | 197·4 | 26·58 |
| 52 | 51·07 | 6·88 | 102 | 100·2 | 13·49 | 152 | 149·3 | 20·10 | 202 | 198·4 | 26·71 |
| 53 | 52·06 | 7·01 | 103 | 101·2 | 13·62 | 153 | 150·3 | 20·23 | 203 | 199·4 | 26·84 |
| 54 | 53·04 | 7·14 | 104 | 102·1 | 13·75 | 154 | 151·3 | 20·36 | 204 | 200·4 | 26·97 |
| 55 | 54·02 | 7·27 | 105 | 103·1 | 13·88 | 155 | 152·2 | 20·49 | 205 | 201·4 | 27·10 |
| 56 | 55·00 | 7·40 | 106 | 104·1 | 14·01 | 156 | 153·2 | 20·63 | 206 | 202·3 | 27·24 |
| 57 | 55·99 | 7·54 | 107 | 105·1 | 14·15 | 157 | 154·2 | 20·76 | 207 | 203·3 | 27·37 |
| 58 | 56·97 | 7·67 | 108 | 106·1 | 14·28 | 158 | 155·2 | 20·89 | 208 | 204·3 | 27·50 |
| 59 | 57·95 | 7·80 | 109 | 107·1 | 14·41 | 159 | 156·2 | 21·02 | 209 | 205·3 | 27·63 |
| 60 | 58·93 | 7·93 | 110 | 108·0 | 14·54 | 160 | 157·2 | 21·15 | 210 | 206·3 | 27·77 |

TABLE I

# 7° 50'

| G | D | H | G | D | H | G | D | H | G | D | H |
|---|---|---|---|---|---|---|---|---|---|---|---|
| 10 | 9·81 | 1·35 | 60 | 58·89 | 8·10 | 110 | 108·0 | 14·85 | 160 | 157·0 | 21·60 |
| 11 | 10·80 | 1·49 | 61 | 59·87 | 8·24 | 111 | 108·9 | 14·99 | 161 | 158·0 | 21·74 |
| 12 | 11·78 | 1·62 | 62 | 60·85 | 8·37 | 112 | 109·9 | 15·12 | 162 | 159·0 | 21·87 |
| 13 | 12·76 | 1·76 | 63 | 61·83 | 8·51 | 113 | 110·9 | 15·26 | 163 | 160·0 | 22·01 |
| 14 | 13·74 | 1·89 | 64 | 62·81 | 8·64 | 114 | 111·9 | 15·39 | 164 | 161·0 | 22·14 |
| 15 | 14·72 | 2·03 | 65 | 63·79 | 8·78 | 115 | 112·9 | 15·53 | 165 | 161·9 | 22·28 |
| 16 | 15·70 | 2·16 | 66 | 64·77 | 8·91 | 116 | 113·8 | 15·66 | 166 | 162·9 | 22·41 |
| 17 | 16·68 | 2·30 | 67 | 65·76 | 9·05 | 117 | 114·8 | 15·80 | 167 | 163·9 | 22·55 |
| 18 | 17·67 | 2·43 | 68 | 66·74 | 9·18 | 118 | 115·8 | 15·93 | 168 | 164·9 | 22·68 |
| 19 | 18·65 | 2·57 | 69 | 67·72 | 9·32 | 119 | 116·8 | 16·07 | 169 | 165·9 | 22·82 |
| 20 | 19·63 | 2·70 | 70 | 68·70 | 9·45 | 120 | 117·8 | 16·20 | 170 | 166·8 | 22·95 |
| 21 | 20·61 | 2·84 | 71 | 69·68 | 9·59 | 121 | 118·8 | 16·34 | 171 | 167·8 | 23·09 |
| 22 | 21·59 | 2·97 | 72 | 70·66 | 9·72 | 122 | 119·7 | 16·47 | 172 | 168·8 | 23·22 |
| 23 | 22·57 | 3·11 | 73 | 71·64 | 9·86 | 123 | 120·7 | 16·61 | 173 | 169·8 | 23·36 |
| 24 | 23·55 | 3·24 | 74 | 72·63 | 9·99 | 124 | 121·7 | 16·74 | 174 | 170·8 | 23·49 |
| 25 | 24·54 | 3·38 | 75 | 73·61 | 10·13 | 125 | 122·7 | 16·88 | 175 | 171·7 | 23·63 |
| 26 | 25·52 | 3·51 | 76 | 74·59 | 10·26 | 126 | 123·7 | 17·01 | 176 | 172·7 | 23·76 |
| 27 | 26·50 | 3·65 | 77 | 75·57 | 10·40 | 127 | 124·6 | 17·15 | 177 | 173·7 | 23·90 |
| 28 | 27·48 | 3·78 | 78 | 76·55 | 10·53 | 128 | 125·6 | 17·28 | 178 | 174·7 | 24·03 |
| 29 | 28·46 | 3·92 | 79 | 77·53 | 10·67 | 129 | 126·6 | 17·42 | 179 | 175·7 | 24·17 |
| 30 | 29·44 | 4·05 | 80 | 78·51 | 10·80 | 130 | 127·6 | 17·55 | 180 | 176·7 | 24·30 |
| 31 | 30·42 | 4·19 | 81 | 79·50 | 10·94 | 131 | 128·6 | 17·69 | 181 | 177·6 | 24·44 |
| 32 | 31·41 | 4·32 | 82 | 80·48 | 11·07 | 132 | 129·5 | 17·82 | 182 | 178·6 | 24·57 |
| 33 | 32·39 | 4·46 | 83 | 81·46 | 11·21 | 133 | 130·5 | 17·96 | 183 | 179·6 | 24·71 |
| 34 | 33·37 | 4·59 | 84 | 82·44 | 11·34 | 134 | 131·5 | 18·09 | 184 | 180·6 | 24·84 |
| 35 | 34·35 | 4·73 | 85 | 83·42 | 11·48 | 135 | 132·5 | 18·23 | 185 | 181·6 | 24·98 |
| 36 | 35·33 | 4·86 | 86 | 84·40 | 11·61 | 136 | 133·5 | 18·36 | 186 | 182·5 | 25·11 |
| 37 | 36·31 | 5·00 | 87 | 85·38 | 11·75 | 137 | 134·5 | 18·50 | 187 | 183·5 | 25·25 |
| 38 | 37·29 | 5·13 | 88 | 86·37 | 11·88 | 138 | 135·4 | 18·63 | 188 | 184·5 | 25·38 |
| 39 | 38·28 | 5·27 | 89 | 87·35 | 12·02 | 139 | 136·4 | 18·77 | 189 | 185·5 | 25·52 |
| 40 | 39·26 | 5·40 | 90 | 88·33 | 12·15 | 140 | 137·4 | 18·90 | 190 | 186·5 | 25·65 |
| 41 | 40·24 | 5·54 | 91 | 89·31 | 12·29 | 141 | 138·4 | 19·04 | 191 | 187·5 | 25·79 |
| 42 | 41·22 | 5·67 | 92 | 90·29 | 12·42 | 142 | 139·4 | 19·17 | 192 | 188·4 | 25·92 |
| 43 | 42·20 | 5·81 | 93 | 91·27 | 12·56 | 143 | 140·3 | 19·31 | 193 | 189·4 | 26·06 |
| 44 | 43·18 | 5·94 | 94 | 92·25 | 12·69 | 144 | 141·3 | 19·44 | 194 | 190·4 | 26·19 |
| 45 | 44·16 | 6·08 | 95 | 93·24 | 12·83 | 145 | 142·3 | 19·58 | 195 | 191·4 | 26·33 |
| 46 | 45·15 | 6·21 | 96 | 94·22 | 12·96 | 146 | 143·3 | 19·71 | 196 | 192·4 | 26·46 |
| 47 | 46·13 | 6·35 | 97 | 95·20 | 13·10 | 147 | 144·3 | 19·85 | 197 | 193·3 | 26·60 |
| 48 | 47·11 | 6·48 | 98 | 96·18 | 13·23 | 148 | 145·3 | 19·98 | 198 | 194·3 | 26·73 |
| 49 | 48·09 | 6·62 | 99 | 97·16 | 13·37 | 149 | 146·2 | 20·12 | 199 | 195·3 | 26·87 |
| 50 | 49·07 | 6·75 | 100 | 98·14 | 13·50 | 150 | 147·2 | 20·25 | 200 | 196·3 | 27·00 |
| 51 | 50·05 | 6·89 | 101 | 99·12 | 13·64 | 151 | 148·2 | 20·39 | 201 | 197·3 | 27·14 |
| 52 | 51·03 | 7·02 | 102 | 100·1 | 13·77 | 152 | 149·2 | 20·52 | 202 | 198·2 | 27·27 |
| 53 | 52·02 | 7·16 | 103 | 101·1 | 13·91 | 153 | 150·2 | 20·66 | 203 | 199·2 | 27·41 |
| 54 | 53·00 | 7·29 | 104 | 102·1 | 14·04 | 154 | 151·1 | 20·79 | 204 | 200·2 | 27·54 |
| 55 | 53·98 | 7·43 | 105 | 103·0 | 14·18 | 155 | 152·1 | 20·93 | 205 | 201·2 | 27·68 |
| 56 | 54·96 | 7·56 | 106 | 104·0 | 14·31 | 156 | 153·1 | 21·06 | 206 | 202·2 | 27·81 |
| 57 | 55·94 | 7·70 | 107 | 105·0 | 14·45 | 157 | 154·1 | 21·20 | 207 | 203·2 | 27·95 |
| 58 | 56·92 | 7·83 | 108 | 106·0 | 14·58 | 158 | 155·1 | 21·33 | 208 | 204·1 | 28·08 |
| 59 | 57·90 | 7·97 | 109 | 107·0 | 14·72 | 159 | 156·0 | 21·47 | 209 | 205·1 | 28·22 |
| 60 | 58·89 | 8·10 | 110 | 108·0 | 14·85 | 160 | 157·0 | 21·60 | 210 | 206·1 | 28·35 |

| G | D | H | G | D | H | G | D | H | G | D | H |
|---|---|---|---|---|---|---|---|---|---|---|---|
| 10 | 9·81 | 1·38 | 60 | 58·84 | 8·27 | 110 | 107·9 | 15·16 | 160 | 156·9 | 22·05 |
| 11 | 10·79 | 1·52 | 61 | 59·82 | 8·41 | 111 | 108·8 | 15·30 | 161 | 157·9 | 22·19 |
| 12 | 11·77 | 1·65 | 62 | 60·80 | 8·54 | 112 | 109·8 | 15·44 | 162 | 158·9 | 22·33 |
| 13 | 12·75 | 1·79 | 63 | 61·78 | 8·68 | 113 | 110·8 | 15·57 | 163 | 159·8 | 22·46 |
| 14 | 13·73 | 1·93 | 64 | 62·76 | 8·82 | 114 | 111·8 | 15·71 | 164 | 160·8 | 22·60 |
| 15 | 14·71 | 2·07 | 65 | 63·74 | 8·96 | 115 | 112·8 | 15·85 | 165 | 161·8 | 22·74 |
| 16 | 15·69 | 2·21 | 66 | 64·72 | 9·10 | 116 | 113·8 | 15·99 | 166 | 162·8 | 22·88 |
| 17 | 16·67 | 2·34 | 67 | 65·70 | 9·23 | 117 | 114·7 | 16·12 | 167 | 163·8 | 23·02 |
| 18 | 17·65 | 2·48 | 68 | 66·68 | 9·37 | 118 | 115·7 | 16·26 | 168 | 164·7 | 23·15 |
| 19 | 18·63 | 2·62 | 69 | 67·66 | 9·51 | 119 | 116·7 | 16·40 | 169 | 165·7 | 23·29 |
| 20 | 19·61 | 2·76 | 70 | 68·64 | 9·65 | 120 | 117·7 | 16·54 | 170 | 166·7 | 23·43 |
| 21 | 20·59 | 2·89 | 71 | 69·62 | 9·79 | 121 | 118·7 | 16·68 | 171 | 167·7 | 23·57 |
| 22 | 21·57 | 3·03 | 72 | 70·61 | 9·92 | 122 | 119·6 | 16·81 | 172 | 168·7 | 23·70 |
| 23 | 22·55 | 3·17 | 73 | 71·59 | 10·06 | 123 | 120·6 | 16·95 | 173 | 169·6 | 23·84 |
| 24 | 23·54 | 3·31 | 74 | 72·57 | 10·20 | 124 | 121·6 | 17·09 | 174 | 170·6 | 23·98 |
| 25 | 24·52 | 3·45 | 75 | 73·55 | 10·34 | 125 | 122·6 | 17·23 | 175 | 171·6 | 24·12 |
| 26 | 25·50 | 3·58 | 76 | 74·53 | 10·47 | 126 | 123·6 | 17·37 | 176 | 172·6 | 24·26 |
| 27 | 26·48 | 3·72 | 77 | 75·51 | 10·61 | 127 | 124·5 | 17·50 | 177 | 173·6 | 24·39 |
| 28 | 27·46 | 3·86 | 78 | 76·49 | 10·75 | 128 | 125·5 | 17·64 | 178 | 174·6 | 24·53 |
| 29 | 28·44 | 4·00 | 79 | 77·47 | 10·89 | 129 | 126·5 | 17·78 | 179 | 175·5 | 24·67 |
| 30 | 29·42 | 4·13 | 80 | 78·45 | 11·03 | 130 | 127·5 | 17·92 | 180 | 176·5 | 24·81 |
| 31 | 30·40 | 4·27 | 81 | 79·43 | 11·16 | 131 | 128·5 | 18·05 | 181 | 177·5 | 24·95 |
| 32 | 31·38 | 4·41 | 82 | 80·41 | 11·30 | 132 | 129·4 | 18·19 | 182 | 178·5 | 25·08 |
| 33 | 32·36 | 4·55 | 83 | 81·39 | 11·44 | 133 | 130·4 | 18·33 | 183 | 179·5 | 25·22 |
| 34 | 33·34 | 4·69 | 84 | 82·37 | 11·58 | 134 | 131·4 | 18·47 | 184 | 180·4 | 25·36 |
| 35 | 34·32 | 4·82 | 85 | 83·35 | 11·71 | 135 | 132·4 | 18·61 | 185 | 181·4 | 25·50 |
| 36 | 35·30 | 4·96 | 86 | 84·33 | 11·85 | 136 | 133·4 | 18·74 | 186 | 182·4 | 25·63 |
| 37 | 36·28 | 5·10 | 87 | 85·31 | 11·99 | 137 | 134·3 | 18·88 | 187 | 183·4 | 25·77 |
| 38 | 37·26 | 5·24 | 88 | 86·30 | 12·13 | 138 | 135·3 | 19·02 | 188 | 184·4 | 25·91 |
| 39 | 38·24 | 5·37 | 89 | 87·28 | 12·27 | 139 | 136·3 | 19·16 | 189 | 185·3 | 26·05 |
| 40 | 39·23 | 5·51 | 90 | 88·26 | 12·40 | 140 | 137·3 | 19·29 | 190 | 186·3 | 26·19 |
| 41 | 40·21 | 5·65 | 91 | 89·24 | 12·54 | 141 | 138·3 | 19·43 | 191 | 187·3 | 26·32 |
| 42 | 41·19 | 5·79 | 92 | 90·22 | 12·68 | 142 | 139·2 | 19·57 | 192 | 188·3 | 26·46 |
| 43 | 42·17 | 5·93 | 93 | 91·20 | 12·82 | 143 | 140·2 | 19·71 | 193 | 189·3 | 26·60 |
| 44 | 43·15 | 6·06 | 94 | 92·18 | 12·95 | 144 | 141·2 | 19·85 | 194 | 190·2 | 26·74 |
| 45 | 44·13 | 6·20 | 95 | 93·16 | 13·09 | 145 | 142·2 | 19·98 | 195 | 191·2 | 26·87 |
| 46 | 45·11 | 6·34 | 96 | 94·14 | 13·23 | 146 | 143·2 | 20·12 | 196 | 192·2 | 27·01 |
| 47 | 46·09 | 6·48 | 97 | 95·12 | 13·37 | 147 | 144·2 | 20·26 | 197 | 193·2 | 27·15 |
| 48 | 47·07 | 6·62 | 98 | 96·10 | 13·51 | 148 | 145·1 | 20·40 | 198 | 194·2 | 27·29 |
| 49 | 48·05 | 6·75 | 99 | 97·08 | 13·64 | 149 | 146·1 | 20·53 | 199 | 195·1 | 27·43 |
| 50 | 49·03 | 6·89 | 100 | 98·06 | 13·78 | 150 | 147·1 | 20·67 | 200 | 196·1 | 27·56 |
| 51 | 50·01 | 7·03 | 101 | 99·04 | 13·92 | 151 | 148·1 | 20·81 | 201 | 197·1 | 27·70 |
| 52 | 50·99 | 7·17 | 102 | 100·0 | 14·06 | 152 | 149·1 | 20·95 | 202 | 198·1 | 27·84 |
| 53 | 51·97 | 7·30 | 103 | 101·0 | 14·20 | 153 | 150·0 | 21·09 | 203 | 199·1 | 27·98 |
| 54 | 52·95 | 7·44 | 104 | 102·0 | 14·33 | 154 | 151·0 | 21·22 | 204 | 200·0 | 28·11 |
| 55 | 53·93 | 7·58 | 105 | 103·0 | 14·47 | 155 | 152·0 | 21·36 | 205 | 201·0 | 28·25 |
| 56 | 54·92 | 7·72 | 106 | 103·9 | 14·61 | 156 | 153·0 | 21·50 | 206 | 202·0 | 28·39 |
| 57 | 55·90 | 7·86 | 107 | 104·9 | 14·75 | 157 | 154·0 | 21·64 | 207 | 203·0 | 28·53 |
| 58 | 56·88 | 7·99 | 108 | 105·9 | 14·88 | 158 | 154·9 | 21·78 | 208 | 204·0 | 28·67 |
| 59 | 57·86 | 8·13 | 109 | 106·9 | 15·02 | 159 | 155·9 | 21·91 | 209 | 205·0 | 28·80 |
| 60 | 58·84 | 8·27 | 110 | 107·9 | 15·16 | 160 | 156·9 | 22·05 | 210 | 205·9 | 28·94 |

TABLE I

**8° 10′**

| G | D | H | G | D | H | G | D | H | G | D | H |
|---|---|---|---|---|---|---|---|---|---|---|---|
| 10 | 9·80 | 1·41 | 60 | 58·79 | 8·44 | 110 | 107·8 | 15·47 | 160 | 156·8 | 22·50 |
| 11 | 10·78 | 1·55 | 61 | 59·77 | 8·58 | 111 | 108·8 | 15·61 | 161 | 157·8 | 22·64 |
| 12 | 11·76 | 1·69 | 62 | 60·75 | 8·72 | 112 | 109·7 | 15·75 | 162 | 158·7 | 22·78 |
| 13 | 12·74 | 1·83 | 63 | 61·73 | 8·86 | 113 | 110·7 | 15·89 | 163 | 159·7 | 22·92 |
| 14 | 13·72 | 1·97 | 64 | 62·71 | 9·00 | 114 | 111·7 | 16·03 | 164 | 160·7 | 23·06 |
| 15 | 14·70 | 2·11 | 65 | 63·69 | 9·14 | 115 | 112·7 | 16·17 | 165 | 161·7 | 23·20 |
| 16 | 15·68 | 2·25 | 66 | 64·67 | 9·28 | 116 | 113·7 | 16·31 | 166 | 162·7 | 23·34 |
| 17 | 16·66 | 2·39 | 67 | 65·65 | 9·42 | 117 | 114·6 | 16·45 | 167 | 163·6 | 23·48 |
| 18 | 17·64 | 2·53 | 68 | 66·63 | 9·56 | 118 | 115·6 | 16·59 | 168 | 164·6 | 23·62 |
| 19 | 18·62 | 2·67 | 69 | 67·61 | 9·70 | 119 | 116·6 | 16·73 | 169 | 165·6 | 23·76 |
| 20 | 19·60 | 2·81 | 70 | 68·59 | 9·84 | 120 | 117·6 | 16·87 | 170 | 166·6 | 23·90 |
| 21 | 20·58 | 2·95 | 71 | 69·57 | 9·98 | 121 | 118·6 | 17·01 | 171 | 167·5 | 24·04 |
| 22 | 21·56 | 3·09 | 72 | 70·55 | 10·12 | 122 | 119·5 | 17·15 | 172 | 168·5 | 24·19 |
| 23 | 22·54 | 3·23 | 73 | 71·53 | 10·26 | 123 | 120·5 | 17·30 | 173 | 169·5 | 24·33 |
| 24 | 23·52 | 3·37 | 74 | 72·51 | 10·41 | 124 | 121·5 | 17·44 | 174 | 170·5 | 24·47 |
| 25 | 24·50 | 3·52 | 75 | 73·49 | 10·55 | 125 | 122·5 | 17·58 | 175 | 171·5 | 24·61 |
| 26 | 25·48 | 3·66 | 76 | 74·47 | 10·69 | 126 | 123·5 | 17·72 | 176 | 172·4 | 24·75 |
| 27 | 26·46 | 3·80 | 77 | 75·45 | 10·83 | 127 | 124·4 | 17·86 | 177 | 173·4 | 24·89 |
| 28 | 27·43 | 3·94 | 78 | 76·43 | 10·97 | 128 | 125·4 | 18·00 | 178 | 174·4 | 25·03 |
| 29 | 28·41 | 4·08 | 79 | 77·41 | 11·11 | 129 | 126·4 | 18·14 | 179 | 175·4 | 25·17 |
| 30 | 29·39 | 4·22 | 80 | 78·39 | 11·25 | 130 | 127·4 | 18·28 | 180 | 176·4 | 25·31 |
| 31 | 30·37 | 4·36 | 81 | 79·37 | 11·39 | 131 | 128·4 | 18·42 | 181 | 177·3 | 25·45 |
| 32 | 31·35 | 4·50 | 82 | 80·35 | 11·53 | 132 | 129·3 | 18·56 | 182 | 178·3 | 25·59 |
| 33 | 32·33 | 4·64 | 83 | 81·33 | 11·67 | 133 | 130·3 | 18·70 | 183 | 179·3 | 25·73 |
| 34 | 33·31 | 4·78 | 84 | 82·30 | 11·81 | 134 | 131·3 | 18·84 | 184 | 180·3 | 25·87 |
| 35 | 34·29 | 4·92 | 85 | 83·28 | 11·95 | 135 | 132·3 | 18·98 | 185 | 181·3 | 26·01 |
| 36 | 35·27 | 5·06 | 86 | 84·26 | 12·09 | 136 | 133·3 | 19·12 | 186 | 182·2 | 26·15 |
| 37 | 36·25 | 5·20 | 87 | 85·24 | 12·23 | 137 | 134·2 | 19·26 | 187 | 183·2 | 26·29 |
| 38 | 37·23 | 5·34 | 88 | 86·22 | 12·37 | 138 | 135·2 | 19·40 | 188 | 184·2 | 26·44 |
| 39 | 38·21 | 5·48 | 89 | 87·20 | 12·51 | 139 | 136·2 | 19·55 | 189 | 185·2 | 26·58 |
| 40 | 39·19 | 5·62 | 90 | 88·18 | 12·66 | 140 | 137·2 | 19·69 | 190 | 186·2 | 26·72 |
| 41 | 40·17 | 5·77 | 91 | 89·16 | 12·80 | 141 | 138·2 | 19·83 | 191 | 187·1 | 26·86 |
| 42 | 41·15 | 5·91 | 92 | 90·14 | 12·94 | 142 | 139·1 | 19·97 | 192 | 188·1 | 27·00 |
| 43 | 42·13 | 6·05 | 93 | 91·12 | 13·08 | 143 | 140·1 | 20·11 | 193 | 189·1 | 27·14 |
| 44 | 43·11 | 6·19 | 94 | 92·10 | 13·22 | 144 | 141·1 | 20·25 | 194 | 190·1 | 27·28 |
| 45 | 44·09 | 6·33 | 95 | 93·08 | 13·36 | 145 | 142·1 | 20·39 | 195 | 191·1 | 27·42 |
| 46 | 45·07 | 6·47 | 96 | 94·06 | 13·50 | 146 | 143·1 | 20·53 | 196 | 192·0 | 27·56 |
| 47 | 46·05 | 6·61 | 97 | 95·04 | 13·64 | 147 | 144·0 | 20·67 | 197 | 193·0 | 27·70 |
| 48 | 47·03 | 6·75 | 98 | 96·02 | 13·78 | 148 | 145·0 | 20·81 | 198 | 194·0 | 27·84 |
| 49 | 48·01 | 6·89 | 99 | 97·00 | 13·92 | 149 | 146·0 | 20·95 | 199 | 195·0 | 27·98 |
| 50 | 48·99 | 7·03 | 100 | 97·98 | 14·06 | 150 | 147·0 | 21·09 | 200 | 196·0 | 28·12 |
| 51 | 49·97 | 7·17 | 101 | 98·96 | 14·20 | 151 | 148·0 | 21·23 | 201 | 196·9 | 28·26 |
| 52 | 50·95 | 7·31 | 102 | 99·94 | 14·34 | 152 | 148·9 | 21·37 | 202 | 197·9 | 28·40 |
| 53 | 51·93 | 7·45 | 103 | 100·9 | 14·48 | 153 | 149·9 | 21·51 | 203 | 198·9 | 28·54 |
| 54 | 52·91 | 7·59 | 104 | 101·9 | 14·62 | 154 | 150·9 | 21·65 | 204 | 199·9 | 28·68 |
| 55 | 53·89 | 7·73 | 105 | 102·9 | 14·76 | 155 | 151·9 | 21·79 | 205 | 200·9 | 28·83 |
| 56 | 54·87 | 7·87 | 106 | 103·9 | 14·90 | 156 | 152·9 | 21·94 | 206 | 201·8 | 28·97 |
| 57 | 55·85 | 8·01 | 107 | 104·8 | 15·05 | 157 | 153·8 | 22·08 | 207 | 202·8 | 29·11 |
| 58 | 56·83 | 8·16 | 108 | 105·8 | 15·19 | 158 | 154·8 | 22·22 | 208 | 203·8 | 29·25 |
| 59 | 57·81 | 8·30 | 109 | 106·8 | 15·33 | 159 | 155·8 | 22·36 | 209 | 204·8 | 29·39 |
| 60 | 58·79 | 8·44 | 110 | 107·8 | 15·47 | 160 | 156·8 | 22·50 | 210 | 205·8 | 29·53 |

| G | D | H | G | D | H | G | D | H | G | D | H |
|---|---|---|---|---|---|---|---|---|---|---|---|
| 10 | 9·79 | 1·43 | 60 | 58·74 | 8·60 | 110 | 107·7 | 15·77 | 160 | 156·6 | 22·94 |
| 11 | 10·77 | 1·58 | 61 | 59·72 | 8·75 | 111 | 108·7 | 15·92 | 161 | 157·6 | 23·09 |
| 12 | 11·75 | 1·72 | 62 | 60·70 | 8·89 | 112 | 109·6 | 16·06 | 162 | 158·6 | 23·23 |
| 13 | 12·73 | 1·86 | 63 | 61·68 | 9·03 | 113 | 110·6 | 16·20 | 163 | 159·6 | 23·37 |
| 14 | 13·71 | 2·01 | 64 | 62·66 | 9·18 | 114 | 111·6 | 16·35 | 164 | 160·6 | 23·52 |
| 15 | 14·68 | 2·15 | 65 | 63·63 | 9·32 | 115 | 112·6 | 16·49 | 165 | 161·5 | 23·66 |
| 16 | 15·66 | 2·29 | 66 | 64·61 | 9·46 | 116 | 113·6 | 16·63 | 166 | 162·5 | 23·80 |
| 17 | 16·64 | 2·44 | 67 | 65·59 | 9·61 | 117 | 114·5 | 16·78 | 167 | 163·5 | 23·95 |
| 18 | 17·62 | 2·58 | 68 | 66·57 | 9·75 | 118 | 115·5 | 16·92 | 168 | 164·5 | 24·09 |
| 19 | 18·60 | 2·72 | 69 | 67·55 | 9·89 | 119 | 116·5 | 17·06 | 169 | 165·4 | 24·23 |
| 20 | 19·58 | 2·87 | 70 | 68·53 | 10·04 | 120 | 117·5 | 17·21 | 170 | 166·4 | 24·38 |
| 21 | 20·56 | 3·01 | 71 | 69·51 | 10·18 | 121 | 118·5 | 17·35 | 171 | 167·4 | 24·52 |
| 22 | 21·54 | 3·15 | 72 | 70·49 | 10·32 | 122 | 119·4 | 17·49 | 172 | 168·4 | 24·66 |
| 23 | 22·52 | 3·30 | 73 | 71·47 | 10·47 | 123 | 120·4 | 17·64 | 173 | 169·4 | 24·81 |
| 24 | 23·50 | 3·44 | 74 | 72·45 | 10·61 | 124 | 121·4 | 17·78 | 174 | 170·3 | 24·95 |
| 25 | 24·47 | 3·59 | 75 | 73·42 | 10·76 | 125 | 122·4 | 17·93 | 175 | 171·3 | 25·10 |
| 26 | 25·45 | 3·73 | 76 | 74·40 | 10·90 | 126 | 123·4 | 18·07 | 176 | 172·3 | 25·24 |
| 27 | 26·43 | 3·87 | 77 | 75·38 | 11·04 | 127 | 124·3 | 18·21 | 177 | 173·3 | 25·38 |
| 28 | 27·41 | 4·02 | 78 | 76·36 | 11·19 | 128 | 125·3 | 18·36 | 178 | 174·3 | 25·53 |
| 29 | 28·39 | 4·16 | 79 | 77·34 | 11·33 | 129 | 126·3 | 18·50 | 179 | 175·2 | 25·67 |
| 30 | 29·37 | 4·30 | 80 | 78·32 | 11·47 | 130 | 127·3 | 18·64 | 180 | 176·2 | 25·81 |
| 31 | 30·35 | 4·45 | 81 | 79·30 | 11·62 | 131 | 128·2 | 18·79 | 181 | 177·2 | 25·96 |
| 32 | 31·33 | 4·59 | 82 | 80·28 | 11·76 | 132 | 129·2 | 18·93 | 182 | 178·2 | 26·10 |
| 33 | 32·31 | 4·73 | 83 | 81·26 | 11·90 | 133 | 130·2 | 19·07 | 183 | 179·2 | 26·24 |
| 34 | 33·29 | 4·88 | 84 | 82·24 | 12·05 | 134 | 131·2 | 19·22 | 184 | 180·1 | 26·39 |
| 35 | 34·26 | 5·02 | 85 | 83·21 | 12·19 | 135 | 132·2 | 19·36 | 185 | 181·1 | 26·53 |
| 36 | 35·24 | 5·16 | 86 | 84·19 | 12·33 | 136 | 133·1 | 19·50 | 186 | 182·1 | 26·67 |
| 37 | 36·22 | 5·31 | 87 | 85·17 | 12·48 | 137 | 134·1 | 19·65 | 187 | 183·1 | 26·82 |
| 38 | 37·20 | 5·45 | 88 | 86·15 | 12·62 | 138 | 135·1 | 19·79 | 188 | 184·1 | 26·96 |
| 39 | 38·18 | 5·59 | 89 | 87·13 | 12·76 | 139 | 136·1 | 19·93 | 189 | 185·0 | 27·10 |
| 40 | 39·16 | 5·74 | 90 | 88·11 | 12·91 | 140 | 137·1 | 20·08 | 190 | 186·0 | 27·25 |
| 41 | 40·14 | 5·88 | 91 | 89·09 | 13·05 | 141 | 138·0 | 20·22 | 191 | 187·0 | 27·39 |
| 42 | 41·12 | 6·02 | 92 | 90·07 | 13·19 | 142 | 139·0 | 20·36 | 192 | 188·0 | 27·53 |
| 43 | 42·10 | 6·17 | 93 | 91·05 | 13·34 | 143 | 140·0 | 20·51 | 193 | 188·9 | 27·68 |
| 44 | 43·08 | 6·31 | 94 | 92·03 | 13·48 | 144 | 141·0 | 20·65 | 194 | 189·9 | 27·82 |
| 45 | 44·05 | 6·45 | 95 | 93·00 | 13·62 | 145 | 142·0 | 20·79 | 195 | 190·9 | 27·96 |
| 46 | 45·03 | 6·60 | 96 | 93·98 | 13·77 | 146 | 142·9 | 20·94 | 196 | 191·9 | 28·11 |
| 47 | 46·01 | 6·74 | 97 | 94·96 | 13·91 | 147 | 143·9 | 21·08 | 197 | 192·9 | 28·25 |
| 48 | 46·99 | 6·88 | 98 | 95·94 | 14·05 | 148 | 144·9 | 21·22 | 198 | 193·8 | 28·39 |
| 49 | 47·97 | 7·03 | 99 | 96·92 | 14·20 | 149 | 145·9 | 21·37 | 199 | 194·8 | 28·54 |
| 50 | 48·95 | 7·17 | 100 | 97·90 | 14·34 | 150 | 146·8 | 21·51 | 200 | 195·8 | 28·68 |
| 51 | 49·93 | 7·31 | 101 | 98·88 | 14·48 | 151 | 147·8 | 21·65 | 201 | 196·8 | 28·82 |
| 52 | 50·91 | 7·46 | 102 | 99·86 | 14·63 | 152 | 148·8 | 21·80 | 202 | 197·8 | 28·97 |
| 53 | 51·89 | 7·60 | 103 | 100·8 | 14·77 | 153 | 149·8 | 21·94 | 203 | 198·7 | 29·11 |
| 54 | 52·87 | 7·74 | 104 | 101·8 | 14·91 | 154 | 150·8 | 22·08 | 204 | 199·7 | 29·25 |
| 55 | 53·84 | 7·89 | 105 | 102·8 | 15·06 | 155 | 151·7 | 22·23 | 205 | 200·7 | 29·40 |
| 56 | 54·82 | 8·03 | 106 | 103·8 | 15·20 | 156 | 152·7 | 22·37 | 206 | 201·7 | 29·54 |
| 57 | 55·80 | 8·17 | 107 | 104·8 | 15·34 | 157 | 153·7 | 22·51 | 207 | 202·7 | 29·68 |
| 58 | 56·78 | 8·32 | 108 | 105·7 | 15·49 | 158 | 154·7 | 22·66 | 208 | 203·6 | 29·83 |
| 59 | 57·76 | 8·46 | 109 | 106·7 | 15·63 | 159 | 155·7 | 22·80 | 209 | 204·6 | 29·97 |
| 60 | 58·74 | 8·60 | 110 | 107·7 | 15·77 | 160 | 156·6 | 22·94 | 210 | 205·6 | 30·11 |

TABLE I

# 8° 30′

| G | D | H | G | D | H | G | D | H | G | D | H |
|---|---|---|---|---|---|---|---|---|---|---|---|
| 10 | 9.78 | 1.46 | 60 | 58.69 | 8.77 | 110 | 107.6 | 16.08 | 160 | 156.5 | 23.39 |
| 11 | 10.76 | 1.61 | 61 | 59.67 | 8.92 | 111 | 108.6 | 16.23 | 161 | 157.5 | 23.54 |
| 12 | 11.74 | 1.75 | 62 | 60.65 | 9.06 | 112 | 109.6 | 16.37 | 162 | 158.5 | 23.68 |
| 13 | 12.72 | 1.90 | 63 | 61.62 | 9.21 | 113 | 110.5 | 16.52 | 163 | 159.4 | 23.83 |
| 14 | 13.69 | 2.05 | 64 | 62.60 | 9.36 | 114 | 111.5 | 16.67 | 164 | 160.4 | 23.97 |
| 15 | 14.67 | 2.19 | 65 | 63.58 | 9.50 | 115 | 112.5 | 16.81 | 165 | 161.4 | 24.12 |
| 16 | 15.65 | 2.34 | 66 | 64.56 | 9.65 | 116 | 113.5 | 16.96 | 166 | 162.4 | 24.27 |
| 17 | 16.63 | 2.49 | 67 | 65.54 | 9.79 | 117 | 114.4 | 17.10 | 167 | 163.4 | 24.41 |
| 18 | 17.61 | 2.63 | 68 | 66.51 | 9.94 | 118 | 115.4 | 17.25 | 168 | 164.3 | 24.56 |
| 19 | 18.58 | 2.78 | 69 | 67.49 | 10.09 | 119 | 116.4 | 17.40 | 169 | 165.3 | 24.71 |
| 20 | 19.56 | 2.92 | 70 | 68.47 | 10.23 | 120 | 117.4 | 17.54 | 170 | 166.3 | 24.85 |
| 21 | 20.54 | 3.07 | 71 | 69.45 | 10.38 | 121 | 118.4 | 17.69 | 171 | 167.3 | 25.00 |
| 22 | 21.52 | 3.22 | 72 | 70.43 | 10.53 | 122 | 119.3 | 17.83 | 172 | 168.2 | 25.14 |
| 23 | 22.50 | 3.36 | 73 | 71.40 | 10.67 | 123 | 120.3 | 17.98 | 173 | 169.2 | 25.29 |
| 24 | 23.48 | 3.51 | 74 | 72.38 | 10.82 | 124 | 121.3 | 18.13 | 174 | 170.2 | 25.44 |
| 25 | 24.45 | 3.65 | 75 | 73.36 | 10.96 | 125 | 122.3 | 18.27 | 175 | 171.2 | 25.58 |
| 26 | 25.43 | 3.80 | 76 | 74.34 | 11.11 | 126 | 123.2 | 18.42 | 176 | 172.2 | 25.73 |
| 27 | 26.41 | 3.95 | 77 | 75.32 | 11.26 | 127 | 124.2 | 18.57 | 177 | 173.1 | 25.87 |
| 28 | 27.39 | 4.09 | 78 | 76.30 | 11.40 | 128 | 125.2 | 18.71 | 178 | 174.1 | 26.02 |
| 29 | 28.37 | 4.24 | 79 | 77.27 | 11.55 | 129 | 126.2 | 18.86 | 179 | 175.1 | 26.17 |
| 30 | 29.34 | 4.39 | 80 | 78.25 | 11.69 | 130 | 127.2 | 19.00 | 180 | 176.1 | 26.31 |
| 31 | 30.32 | 4.53 | 81 | 79.23 | 11.84 | 131 | 128.1 | 19.15 | 181 | 177.0 | 26.46 |
| 32 | 31.30 | 4.68 | 82 | 80.21 | 11.99 | 132 | 129.1 | 19.30 | 182 | 178.0 | 26.61 |
| 33 | 32.28 | 4.82 | 83 | 81.19 | 12.13 | 133 | 130.1 | 19.44 | 183 | 179.0 | 26.75 |
| 34 | 33.26 | 4.97 | 84 | 82.16 | 12.28 | 134 | 131.1 | 19.59 | 184 | 180.0 | 26.90 |
| 35 | 34.24 | 5.12 | 85 | 83.14 | 12.43 | 135 | 132.1 | 19.73 | 185 | 181.0 | 27.04 |
| 36 | 35.21 | 5.26 | 86 | 84.12 | 12.57 | 136 | 133.0 | 19.88 | 186 | 181.9 | 27.19 |
| 37 | 36.19 | 5.41 | 87 | 85.10 | 12.72 | 137 | 134.0 | 20.03 | 187 | 182.9 | 27.34 |
| 38 | 37.17 | 5.56 | 88 | 86.08 | 12.86 | 138 | 135.0 | 20.17 | 188 | 183.9 | 27.48 |
| 39 | 38.15 | 5.70 | 89 | 87.06 | 13.01 | 139 | 136.0 | 20.32 | 189 | 184.9 | 27.63 |
| 40 | 39.13 | 5.85 | 90 | 88.03 | 13.16 | 140 | 136.9 | 20.47 | 190 | 185.8 | 27.78 |
| 41 | 40.10 | 5.99 | 91 | 89.01 | 13.30 | 141 | 137.9 | 20.61 | 191 | 186.8 | 27.92 |
| 42 | 41.08 | 6.14 | 92 | 89.99 | 13.45 | 142 | 138.9 | 20.76 | 192 | 187.8 | 28.07 |
| 43 | 42.06 | 6.29 | 93 | 90.97 | 13.60 | 143 | 139.9 | 20.90 | 193 | 188.8 | 28.21 |
| 44 | 43.04 | 6.43 | 94 | 91.95 | 13.74 | 144 | 140.9 | 21.05 | 194 | 189.8 | 28.36 |
| 45 | 44.02 | 6.58 | 95 | 92.92 | 13.89 | 145 | 141.8 | 21.20 | 195 | 190.7 | 28.51 |
| 46 | 44.99 | 6.72 | 96 | 93.90 | 14.03 | 146 | 142.8 | 21.34 | 196 | 191.7 | 28.65 |
| 47 | 45.97 | 6.87 | 97 | 94.88 | 14.18 | 147 | 143.8 | 21.49 | 197 | 192.7 | 28.80 |
| 48 | 46.95 | 7.02 | 98 | 95.86 | 14.33 | 148 | 144.8 | 21.64 | 198 | 193.7 | 28.94 |
| 49 | 47.93 | 7.16 | 99 | 96.84 | 14.47 | 149 | 145.7 | 21.78 | 199 | 194.7 | 29.09 |
| 50 | 48.91 | 7.31 | 100 | 97.82 | 14.62 | 150 | 146.7 | 21.93 | 200 | 195.6 | 29.24 |
| 51 | 49.89 | 7.46 | 101 | 98.79 | 14.76 | 151 | 147.7 | 22.07 | 201 | 196.6 | 29.38 |
| 52 | 50.86 | 7.60 | 102 | 99.77 | 14.91 | 152 | 148.7 | 22.22 | 202 | 197.6 | 29.53 |
| 53 | 51.84 | 7.75 | 103 | 100.7 | 15.06 | 153 | 149.7 | 22.37 | 203 | 198.6 | 29.68 |
| 54 | 52.82 | 7.89 | 104 | 101.7 | 15.20 | 154 | 150.6 | 22.51 | 204 | 199.5 | 29.82 |
| 55 | 53.80 | 8.04 | 105 | 102.7 | 15.35 | 155 | 151.6 | 22.66 | 205 | 200.5 | 29.97 |
| 56 | 54.78 | 8.19 | 106 | 103.7 | 15.50 | 156 | 152.6 | 22.80 | 206 | 201.5 | 30.11 |
| 57 | 55.75 | 8.33 | 107 | 104.7 | 15.64 | 157 | 153.6 | 22.95 | 207 | 202.5 | 30.26 |
| 58 | 56.73 | 8.48 | 108 | 105.6 | 15.79 | 158 | 154.5 | 23.10 | 208 | 203.5 | 30.41 |
| 59 | 57.71 | 8.62 | 109 | 106.6 | 15.93 | 159 | 155.5 | 23.24 | 209 | 204.4 | 30.55 |
| 60 | 58.69 | 8.77 | 110 | 107.6 | 16.08 | 160 | 156.5 | 23.39 | 210 | 205.4 | 30.70 |

| G | D | H | G | D | H | G | D | H | G | D | H |
|---|---|---|---|---|---|---|---|---|---|---|---|
| 10 | 9·77 | 1·49 | 60 | 58·64 | 8·94 | 110 | 107·5 | 16·39 | 160 | 156·4 | 23·83 |
| 11 | 10·75 | 1·64 | 61 | 59·61 | 9·09 | 111 | 108·5 | 16·54 | 161 | 157·3 | 23·98 |
| 12 | 11·73 | 1·79 | 62 | 60·59 | 9·24 | 112 | 109·5 | 16·68 | 162 | 158·3 | 24·13 |
| 13 | 12·70 | 1·94 | 63 | 61·57 | 9·38 | 113 | 110·4 | 16·83 | 163 | 159·3 | 24·28 |
| 14 | 13·68 | 2·09 | 64 | 62·55 | 9·53 | 114 | 111·4 | 16·98 | 164 | 160·3 | 24·43 |
| 15 | 14·66 | 2·23 | 65 | 63·52 | 9·68 | 115 | 112·4 | 17·13 | 165 | 161·3 | 24·58 |
| 16 | 15·64 | 2·38 | 66 | 64·50 | 9·83 | 116 | 113·4 | 17·28 | 166 | 162·2 | 24·73 |
| 17 | 16·61 | 2·53 | 67 | 65·48 | 9·98 | 117 | 114·3 | 17·43 | 167 | 163·2 | 24·88 |
| 18 | 17·59 | 2·68 | 68 | 66·46 | 10·13 | 118 | 115·3 | 17·58 | 168 | 164·2 | 25·03 |
| 19 | 18·57 | 2·83 | 69 | 67·43 | 10·28 | 119 | 116·3 | 17·73 | 169 | 165·2 | 25·18 |
| 20 | 19·55 | 2·98 | 70 | 68·41 | 10·43 | 120 | 117·3 | 17·88 | 170 | 166·1 | 25·32 |
| 21 | 20·52 | 3·13 | 71 | 69·39 | 10·58 | 121 | 118·3 | 18·02 | 171 | 167·1 | 25·47 |
| 22 | 21·50 | 3·28 | 72 | 70·37 | 10·73 | 122 | 119·2 | 18·17 | 172 | 168·1 | 25·62 |
| 23 | 22·48 | 3·43 | 73 | 71·34 | 10·87 | 123 | 120·2 | 18·32 | 173 | 169·1 | 25·77 |
| 24 | 23·46 | 3·58 | 74 | 72·32 | 11·02 | 124 | 121·2 | 18·47 | 174 | 170·0 | 25·92 |
| 25 | 24·43 | 3·72 | 75 | 73·30 | 11·17 | 125 | 122·2 | 18·62 | 175 | 171·0 | 26·07 |
| 26 | 25·41 | 3·87 | 76 | 74·27 | 11·32 | 126 | 123·1 | 18·77 | 176 | 172·0 | 26·22 |
| 27 | 26·39 | 4·02 | 77 | 75·25 | 11·47 | 127 | 124·1 | 18·92 | 177 | 173·0 | 26·37 |
| 28 | 27·36 | 4·17 | 78 | 76·23 | 11·62 | 128 | 125·1 | 19·07 | 178 | 174·0 | 26·52 |
| 29 | 28·34 | 4·32 | 79 | 77·21 | 11·77 | 129 | 126·1 | 19·22 | 179 | 174·9 | 26·66 |
| 30 | 29·32 | 4·47 | 80 | 78·18 | 11·92 | 130 | 127·0 | 19·37 | 180 | 175·9 | 26·81 |
| 31 | 30·30 | 4·62 | 81 | 79·16 | 12·07 | 131 | 128·0 | 19·51 | 181 | 176·9 | 26·96 |
| 32 | 31·27 | 4·77 | 82 | 80·14 | 12·22 | 132 | 129·0 | 19·66 | 182 | 177·9 | 27·11 |
| 33 | 32·25 | 4·92 | 83 | 81·12 | 12·36 | 133 | 130·0 | 19·81 | 183 | 178·8 | 27·26 |
| 34 | 33·23 | 5·06 | 84 | 82·09 | 12·51 | 134 | 131·0 | 19·96 | 184 | 179·8 | 27·41 |
| 35 | 34·21 | 5·21 | 85 | 83·07 | 12·66 | 135 | 131·9 | 20·11 | 185 | 180·8 | 27·56 |
| 36 | 35·18 | 5·36 | 86 | 84·05 | 12·81 | 136 | 132·9 | 20·26 | 186 | 181·8 | 27·71 |
| 37 | 36·16 | 5·51 | 87 | 85·02 | 12·96 | 137 | 133·9 | 20·41 | 187 | 182·8 | 27·86 |
| 38 | 37·14 | 5·66 | 88 | 86·00 | 13·11 | 138 | 134·9 | 20·56 | 188 | 183·7 | 28·01 |
| 39 | 38·11 | 5·81 | 89 | 86·98 | 13·26 | 139 | 135·8 | 20·71 | 189 | 184·7 | 28·15 |
| 40 | 39·09 | 5·96 | 90 | 87·96 | 13·41 | 140 | 136·8 | 20·86 | 190 | 185·7 | 28·30 |
| 41 | 40·07 | 6·11 | 91 | 88·93 | 13·56 | 141 | 137·8 | 21·00 | 191 | 186·7 | 28·45 |
| 42 | 41·05 | 6·26 | 92 | 89·91 | 13·70 | 142 | 138·8 | 21·15 | 192 | 187·6 | 28·60 |
| 43 | 42·02 | 6·41 | 93 | 90·89 | 13·85 | 143 | 139·8 | 21·30 | 193 | 188·6 | 28·75 |
| 44 | 43·00 | 6·55 | 94 | 91·87 | 14·00 | 144 | 140·7 | 21·45 | 194 | 189·6 | 28·90 |
| 45 | 43·98 | 6·70 | 95 | 92·84 | 14·15 | 145 | 141·7 | 21·60 | 195 | 190·6 | 29·05 |
| 46 | 44·96 | 6·85 | 96 | 93·82 | 14·30 | 146 | 142·7 | 21·75 | 196 | 191·5 | 29·20 |
| 47 | 45·93 | 7·00 | 97 | 94·80 | 14·45 | 147 | 143·7 | 21·90 | 197 | 192·5 | 29·35 |
| 48 | 46·91 | 7·15 | 98 | 95·77 | 14·60 | 148 | 144·6 | 22·05 | 198 | 193·5 | 29·50 |
| 49 | 47·89 | 7·30 | 99 | 96·75 | 14·75 | 149 | 145·6 | 22·20 | 199 | 194·5 | 29·64 |
| 50 | 48·86 | 7·45 | 100 | 97·73 | 14·90 | 150 | 146·6 | 22·34 | 200 | 195·5 | 29·79 |
| 51 | 49·84 | 7·60 | 101 | 98·71 | 15·05 | 151 | 147·6 | 22·49 | 201 | 196·4 | 29·94 |
| 52 | 50·82 | 7·75 | 102 | 99·68 | 15·19 | 152 | 148·5 | 22·64 | 202 | 197·4 | 30·09 |
| 53 | 51·80 | 7·90 | 103 | 100·7 | 15·34 | 153 | 149·5 | 22·79 | 203 | 198·4 | 30·24 |
| 54 | 52·77 | 8·04 | 104 | 101·6 | 15·49 | 154 | 150·5 | 22·94 | 204 | 199·4 | 30·39 |
| 55 | 53·75 | 8·19 | 105 | 102·6 | 15·64 | 155 | 151·5 | 23·09 | 205 | 200·3 | 30·54 |
| 56 | 54·73 | 8·34 | 106 | 103·6 | 15·79 | 156 | 152·5 | 23·24 | 206 | 201·3 | 30·69 |
| 57 | 55·71 | 8·49 | 107 | 104·6 | 15·94 | 157 | 153·4 | 23·39 | 207 | 202·3 | 30·84 |
| 58 | 56·68 | 8·64 | 108 | 105·5 | 16·09 | 158 | 154·4 | 23·54 | 208 | 203·3 | 30·98 |
| 59 | 57·66 | 8·79 | 109 | 106·5 | 16·24 | 159 | 155·4 | 23·69 | 209 | 204·3 | 31·13 |
| 60 | 58·64 | 8·94 | 110 | 107·5 | 16·39 | 160 | 156·4 | 23·83 | 210 | 205·2 | 31·28 |

TABLE I

# 8° 50′

| G | D | H | G | D | H | G | D | H | G | D | H |
|---|---|---|---|---|---|---|---|---|---|---|---|
| 10 | 9·76 | 1·52 | 60 | 58·59 | 9·10 | 110 | 107·4 | 16·69 | 160 | 156·2 | 24·28 |
| 11 | 10·74 | 1·67 | 61 | 59·56 | 9·26 | 111 | 108·4 | 16·84 | 161 | 157·2 | 24·43 |
| 12 | 11·72 | 1·82 | 62 | 60·54 | 9·41 | 112 | 109·4 | 16·99 | 162 | 158·2 | 24·58 |
| 13 | 12·69 | 1·97 | 63 | 61·51 | 9·56 | 113 | 110·3 | 17·15 | 163 | 159·2 | 24·73 |
| 14 | 13·67 | 2·12 | 64 | 62·49 | 9·71 | 114 | 111·3 | 17·30 | 164 | 160·1 | 24·89 |
| 15 | 14·65 | 2·28 | 65 | 63·47 | 9·86 | 115 | 112·3 | 17·45 | 165 | 161·1 | 25·04 |
| 16 | 15·62 | 2·43 | 66 | 64·44 | 10·01 | 116 | 113·3 | 17·60 | 166 | 162·1 | 25·19 |
| 17 | 16·60 | 2·58 | 67 | 65·42 | 10·17 | 117 | 114·2 | 17·75 | 167 | 163·1 | 25·34 |
| 18 | 17·58 | 2·73 | 68 | 66·40 | 10·32 | 118 | 115·2 | 17·91 | 168 | 164·0 | 25·49 |
| 19 | 18·55 | 2·88 | 69 | 67·37 | 10·47 | 119 | 116·2 | 18·06 | 169 | 165·0 | 25·64 |
| 20 | 19·53 | 3·03 | 70 | 68·35 | 10·62 | 120 | 117·2 | 18·21 | 170 | 166·0 | 25·80 |
| 21 | 20·50 | 3·19 | 71 | 69·33 | 10·77 | 121 | 118·1 | 18·36 | 171 | 167·0 | 25·95 |
| 22 | 21·48 | 3·34 | 72 | 70·30 | 10·93 | 122 | 119·1 | 18·51 | 172 | 167·9 | 26·10 |
| 23 | 22·46 | 3·49 | 73 | 71·28 | 11·08 | 123 | 120·1 | 18·66 | 173 | 168·9 | 26·25 |
| 24 | 23·43 | 3·64 | 74 | 72·25 | 11·23 | 124 | 121·1 | 18·82 | 174 | 169·9 | 26·40 |
| 25 | 24·41 | 3·79 | 75 | 73·23 | 11·38 | 125 | 122·1 | 18·97 | 175 | 170·9 | 26·55 |
| 26 | 25·39 | 3·95 | 76 | 74·21 | 11·53 | 126 | 123·0 | 19·12 | 176 | 171·8 | 26·71 |
| 27 | 26·36 | 4·10 | 77 | 75·18 | 11·68 | 127 | 124·0 | 19·27 | 177 | 172·8 | 26·86 |
| 28 | 27·34 | 4·25 | 78 | 76·16 | 11·84 | 128 | 125·0 | 19·42 | 178 | 173·8 | 27·01 |
| 29 | 28·32 | 4·40 | 79 | 77·14 | 11·99 | 129 | 126·0 | 19·57 | 179 | 174·8 | 27·16 |
| 30 | 29·29 | 4·55 | 80 | 78·11 | 12·14 | 130 | 126·9 | 19·73 | 180 | 175·8 | 27·31 |
| 31 | 30·27 | 4·70 | 81 | 79·09 | 12·29 | 131 | 127·9 | 19·88 | 181 | 176·7 | 27·46 |
| 32 | 31·25 | 4·86 | 82 | 80·07 | 12·44 | 132 | 128·9 | 20·03 | 182 | 177·7 | 27·62 |
| 33 | 32·22 | 5·01 | 83 | 81·04 | 12·59 | 133 | 129·9 | 20·18 | 183 | 178·7 | 27·77 |
| 34 | 33·20 | 5·16 | 84 | 82·02 | 12·75 | 134 | 130·8 | 20·33 | 184 | 179·7 | 27·92 |
| 35 | 34·17 | 5·31 | 85 | 83·00 | 12·90 | 135 | 131·8 | 20·48 | 185 | 180·6 | 28·07 |
| 36 | 35·15 | 5·46 | 86 | 83·97 | 13·05 | 136 | 132·8 | 20·64 | 186 | 181·6 | 28·22 |
| 37 | 36·13 | 5·61 | 87 | 84·95 | 13·20 | 137 | 133·8 | 20·79 | 187 | 182·6 | 28·38 |
| 38 | 37·10 | 5·77 | 88 | 85·92 | 13·35 | 138 | 134·7 | 20·94 | 188 | 183·6 | 28·53 |
| 39 | 38·08 | 5·92 | 89 | 86·90 | 13·50 | 139 | 135·7 | 21·09 | 189 | 184·5 | 28·68 |
| 40 | 39·06 | 6·07 | 90 | 87·88 | 13·66 | 140 | 136·7 | 21·24 | 190 | 185·5 | 28·83 |
| 41 | 40·03 | 6·22 | 91 | 88·85 | 13·81 | 141 | 137·7 | 21·40 | 191 | 186·5 | 28·98 |
| 42 | 41·01 | 6·37 | 92 | 89·83 | 13·96 | 142 | 138·7 | 21·55 | 192 | 187·5 | 29·13 |
| 43 | 41·99 | 6·52 | 93 | 90·81 | 14·11 | 143 | 139·6 | 21·70 | 193 | 188·4 | 29·29 |
| 44 | 42·96 | 6·68 | 94 | 91·78 | 14·26 | 144 | 140·6 | 21·85 | 194 | 189·4 | 29·44 |
| 45 | 43·94 | 6·83 | 95 | 92·76 | 14·42 | 145 | 141·6 | 22·00 | 195 | 190·4 | 29·59 |
| 46 | 44·92 | 6·98 | 96 | 93·74 | 14·57 | 146 | 142·6 | 22·15 | 196 | 191·4 | 29·74 |
| 47 | 45·89 | 7·13 | 97 | 94·71 | 14·72 | 147 | 143·5 | 22·31 | 197 | 192·4 | 29·89 |
| 48 | 46·87 | 7·28 | 98 | 95·69 | 14·87 | 148 | 144·5 | 22·46 | 198 | 193·3 | 30·04 |
| 49 | 47·84 | 7·44 | 99 | 96·67 | 15·02 | 149 | 145·5 | 22·61 | 199 | 194·3 | 30·20 |
| 50 | 48·82 | 7·59 | 100 | 97·64 | 15·17 | 150 | 146·5 | 22·76 | 200 | 195·3 | 30·35 |
| 51 | 49·80 | 7·74 | 101 | 98·62 | 15·33 | 151 | 147·4 | 22·91 | 201 | 196·3 | 30·50 |
| 52 | 50·77 | 7·89 | 102 | 99·59 | 15·48 | 152 | 148·4 | 23·06 | 202 | 197·2 | 30·65 |
| 53 | 51·75 | 8·04 | 103 | 100·6 | 15·63 | 153 | 149·4 | 23·22 | 203 | 198·2 | 30·80 |
| 54 | 52·73 | 8·19 | 104 | 101·5 | 15·78 | 154 | 150·4 | 23·37 | 204 | 199·2 | 30·95 |
| 55 | 53·70 | 8·35 | 105 | 102·5 | 15·93 | 155 | 151·3 | 23·52 | 205 | 200·2 | 31·11 |
| 56 | 54·68 | 8·50 | 106 | 103·5 | 16·08 | 156 | 152·3 | 23·67 | 206 | 201·1 | 31·26 |
| 57 | 55·66 | 8·65 | 107 | 104·5 | 16·24 | 157 | 153·3 | 23·82 | 207 | 202·1 | 31·41 |
| 58 | 56·63 | 8·80 | 108 | 105·5 | 16·39 | 158 | 154·3 | 23·97 | 208 | 203·1 | 31·56 |
| 59 | 57·61 | 8·95 | 109 | 106·4 | 16·54 | 159 | 155·3 | 24·13 | 209 | 204·1 | 31·71 |
| 60 | 58·59 | 9·10 | 110 | 107·4 | 16·69 | 160 | 156·2 | 24·28 | 210 | 205·0 | 31·87 |

| G | D | H | G | D | H | G | D | H | G | D | H |
|---|---|---|---|---|---|---|---|---|---|---|---|
| 10 | 9·76 | 1·55 | 60 | 58·53 | 9·27 | 110 | 107·3 | 17·00 | 160 | 156·1 | 24·72 |
| 11 | 10·73 | 1·70 | 61 | 59·51 | 9·42 | 111 | 108·3 | 17·15 | 161 | 157·1 | 24·88 |
| 12 | 11·71 | 1·85 | 62 | 60·48 | 9·58 | 112 | 109·3 | 17·30 | 162 | 158·0 | 25·03 |
| 13 | 12·68 | 2·01 | 63 | 61·46 | 9·73 | 113 | 110·2 | 17·46 | 163 | 159·0 | 25·18 |
| 14 | 13·66 | 2·16 | 64 | 62·43 | 9·89 | 114 | 111·2 | 17·61 | 164 | 160·0 | 25·34 |
| 15 | 14·63 | 2·32 | 65 | 63·41 | 10·04 | 115 | 112·2 | 17·77 | 165 | 161·0 | 25·49 |
| 16 | 15·61 | 2·47 | 66 | 64·38 | 10·20 | 116 | 113·2 | 17·92 | 166 | 161·9 | 25·65 |
| 17 | 16·58 | 2·63 | 67 | 65·36 | 10·35 | 117 | 114·1 | 18·08 | 167 | 162·9 | 25·80 |
| 18 | 17·56 | 2·78 | 68 | 66·34 | 10·51 | 118 | 115·1 | 18·23 | 168 | 163·9 | 25·96 |
| 19 | 18·54 | 2·94 | 69 | 67·31 | 10·66 | 119 | 116·1 | 18·39 | 169 | 164·9 | 26·11 |
| 20 | 19·51 | 3·09 | 70 | 68·29 | 10·82 | 120 | 117·1 | 18·54 | 170 | 165·8 | 26·27 |
| 21 | 20·49 | 3·24 | 71 | 69·26 | 10·97 | 121 | 118·0 | 18·70 | 171 | 166·8 | 26·42 |
| 22 | 21·46 | 3·40 | 72 | 70·24 | 11·12 | 122 | 119·0 | 18·85 | 172 | 167·8 | 26·58 |
| 23 | 22·44 | 3·55 | 73 | 71·21 | 11·28 | 123 | 120·0 | 19·00 | 173 | 168·8 | 26·73 |
| 24 | 23·41 | 3·71 | 74 | 72·19 | 11·43 | 124 | 121·0 | 19·16 | 174 | 169·7 | 26·88 |
| 25 | 24·39 | 3·86 | 75 | 73·16 | 11·59 | 125 | 121·9 | 19·31 | 175 | 170·7 | 27·04 |
| 26 | 25·36 | 4·02 | 76 | 74·14 | 11·74 | 126 | 122·9 | 19·47 | 176 | 171·7 | 27·19 |
| 27 | 26·34 | 4·17 | 77 | 75·12 | 11·90 | 127 | 123·9 | 19·62 | 177 | 172·7 | 27·35 |
| 28 | 27·31 | 4·33 | 78 | 76·09 | 12·05 | 128 | 124·9 | 19·78 | 178 | 173·6 | 27·50 |
| 29 | 28·29 | 4·48 | 79 | 77·07 | 12·21 | 129 | 125·8 | 19·93 | 179 | 174·6 | 27·66 |
| 30 | 29·27 | 4·64 | 80 | 78·04 | 12·36 | 130 | 126·8 | 20·09 | 180 | 175·6 | 27·81 |
| 31 | 30·24 | 4·79 | 81 | 79·02 | 12·52 | 131 | 127·8 | 20·24 | 181 | 176·6 | 27·97 |
| 32 | 31·22 | 4·94 | 82 | 79·99 | 12·67 | 132 | 128·8 | 20·40 | 182 | 177·5 | 28·12 |
| 33 | 32·19 | 5·10 | 83 | 80·97 | 12·82 | 133 | 129·7 | 20·55 | 183 | 178·5 | 28·27 |
| 34 | 33·17 | 5·25 | 84 | 81·94 | 12·98 | 134 | 130·7 | 20·70 | 184 | 179·5 | 28·43 |
| 35 | 34·14 | 5·41 | 85 | 82·92 | 13·13 | 135 | 131·7 | 20·86 | 185 | 180·5 | 28·58 |
| 36 | 35·12 | 5·56 | 86 | 83·90 | 13·29 | 136 | 132·7 | 21·01 | 186 | 181·4 | 28·74 |
| 37 | 36·09 | 5·72 | 87 | 84·87 | 13·44 | 137 | 133·6 | 21·17 | 187 | 182·4 | 28·89 |
| 38 | 37·07 | 5·87 | 88 | 85·85 | 13·60 | 138 | 134·6 | 21·32 | 188 | 183·4 | 29·05 |
| 39 | 38·05 | 6·03 | 89 | 86·82 | 13·75 | 139 | 135·6 | 21·48 | 189 | 184·4 | 29·20 |
| 40 | 39·02 | 6·18 | 90 | 87·80 | 13·91 | 140 | 136·6 | 21·63 | 190 | 185·4 | 29·36 |
| 41 | 40·00 | 6·33 | 91 | 88·77 | 14·06 | 141 | 137·5 | 21·79 | 191 | 186·3 | 29·51 |
| 42 | 40·97 | 6·49 | 92 | 89·75 | 14·21 | 142 | 138·5 | 21·94 | 192 | 187·3 | 29·67 |
| 43 | 41·95 | 6·64 | 93 | 90·72 | 14·37 | 143 | 139·5 | 22·09 | 193 | 188·3 | 29·82 |
| 44 | 42·92 | 6·80 | 94 | 91·70 | 14·52 | 144 | 140·5 | 22·25 | 194 | 189·3 | 29·97 |
| 45 | 43·90 | 6·95 | 95 | 92·68 | 14·68 | 145 | 141·5 | 22·40 | 195 | 190·2 | 30·13 |
| 46 | 44·87 | 7·11 | 96 | 93·65 | 14·83 | 146 | 142·4 | 22·56 | 196 | 191·2 | 30·28 |
| 47 | 45·85 | 7·26 | 97 | 94·63 | 14·99 | 147 | 143·4 | 22·71 | 197 | 192·2 | 30·44 |
| 48 | 46·83 | 7·42 | 98 | 95·60 | 15·14 | 148 | 144·4 | 22·87 | 198 | 193·2 | 30·59 |
| 49 | 47·80 | 7·57 | 99 | 96·58 | 15·30 | 149 | 145·4 | 23·02 | 199 | 194·1 | 30·75 |
| 50 | 48·78 | 7·73 | 100 | 97·55 | 15·45 | 150 | 146·3 | 23·18 | 200 | 195·1 | 30·90 |
| 51 | 49·75 | 7·88 | 101 | 98·53 | 15·61 | 151 | 147·3 | 23·33 | 201 | 196·1 | 31·06 |
| 52 | 50·73 | 8·03 | 102 | 99·50 | 15·76 | 152 | 148·3 | 23·49 | 202 | 197·1 | 31·21 |
| 53 | 51·70 | 8·19 | 103 | 100·5 | 15·91 | 153 | 149·3 | 23·64 | 203 | 198·0 | 31·37 |
| 54 | 52·68 | 8·34 | 104 | 101·5 | 16·07 | 154 | 150·2 | 23·79 | 204 | 199·0 | 31·52 |
| 55 | 53·65 | 8·50 | 105 | 102·4 | 16·22 | 155 | 151·2 | 23·95 | 205 | 200·0 | 31·67 |
| 56 | 54·63 | 8·65 | 106 | 103·4 | 16·38 | 156 | 152·2 | 24·10 | 206 | 201·0 | 31·83 |
| 57 | 55·61 | 8·81 | 107 | 104·4 | 16·53 | 157 | 153·2 | 24·26 | 207 | 201·9 | 31·98 |
| 58 | 56·58 | 8·96 | 108 | 105·4 | 16·69 | 158 | 154·1 | 24·41 | 208 | 202·9 | 32·14 |
| 59 | 57·56 | 9·12 | 109 | 106·3 | 16·84 | 159 | 155·1 | 24·57 | 209 | 203·9 | 32·29 |
| 60 | 58·53 | 9·27 | 110 | 107·3 | 17·00 | 160 | 156·1 | 24·72 | 210 | 204·9 | 32·45 |

TABLE I 9° 10′

| G | D | H | G | D | H | G | D | H | G | D | H |
|---|---|---|---|---|---|---|---|---|---|---|---|
| 10 | 9·75 | 1·57 | 60 | 58·48 | 9·44 | 110 | 107·2 | 17·30 | 160 | 155·9 | 25·16 |
| 11 | 10·72 | 1·73 | 61 | 59·45 | 9·59 | 111 | 108·2 | 17·46 | 161 | 156·9 | 25·32 |
| 12 | 11·70 | 1·89 | 62 | 60·43 | 9·75 | 112 | 109·2 | 17·61 | 162 | 157·9 | 25·48 |
| 13 | 12·67 | 2·04 | 63 | 61·40 | 9·91 | 113 | 110·1 | 17·77 | 163 | 158·9 | 25·64 |
| 14 | 13·64 | 2·20 | 64 | 62·38 | 10·07 | 114 | 111·1 | 17·93 | 164 | 159·8 | 25·79 |
| 15 | 14·62 | 2·36 | 65 | 63·35 | 10·22 | 115 | 112·1 | 18·09 | 165 | 160·8 | 25·95 |
| 16 | 15·59 | 2·52 | 66 | 64·32 | 10·38 | 116 | 113·1 | 18·24 | 166 | 161·8 | 26·11 |
| 17 | 16·57 | 2·67 | 67 | 65·30 | 10·54 | 117 | 114·0 | 18·40 | 167 | 162·8 | 26·26 |
| 18 | 17·54 | 2·83 | 68 | 66·27 | 10·69 | 118 | 115·0 | 18·56 | 168 | 163·7 | 26·42 |
| 19 | 18·52 | 2·99 | 69 | 67·25 | 10·85 | 119 | 116·0 | 18·72 | 169 | 164·7 | 26·58 |
| 20 | 19·49 | 3·15 | 70 | 68·22 | 11·01 | 120 | 117·0 | 18·87 | 170 | 165·7 | 26·74 |
| 21 | 20·47 | 3·30 | 71 | 69·20 | 11·17 | 121 | 117·9 | 19·03 | 171 | 166·7 | 26·89 |
| 22 | 21·44 | 3·46 | 72 | 70·17 | 11·32 | 122 | 118·9 | 19·19 | 172 | 167·6 | 27·05 |
| 23 | 22·42 | 3·62 | 73 | 71·15 | 11·48 | 123 | 119·9 | 19·34 | 173 | 168·6 | 27·21 |
| 24 | 23·39 | 3·77 | 74 | 72·12 | 11·64 | 124 | 120·9 | 19·50 | 174 | 169·6 | 27·37 |
| 25 | 24·37 | 3·93 | 75 | 73·10 | 11·80 | 125 | 121·8 | 19·66 | 175 | 170·6 | 27·52 |
| 26 | 25·34 | 4·09 | 76 | 74·07 | 11·95 | 126 | 122·8 | 19·82 | 176 | 171·5 | 27·68 |
| 27 | 26·31 | 4·25 | 77 | 75·05 | 12·11 | 127 | 123·8 | 19·97 | 177 | 172·5 | 27·84 |
| 28 | 27·29 | 4·40 | 78 | 76·02 | 12·27 | 128 | 124·8 | 20·13 | 178 | 173·5 | 27·99 |
| 29 | 28·26 | 4·56 | 79 | 77·00 | 12·42 | 129 | 125·7 | 20·29 | 179 | 174·5 | 28·15 |
| 30 | 29·24 | 4·72 | 80 | 77·97 | 12·58 | 130 | 126·7 | 20·45 | 180 | 175·4 | 28·31 |
| 31 | 30·21 | 4·88 | 81 | 78·94 | 12·74 | 131 | 127·7 | 20·60 | 181 | 176·4 | 28·47 |
| 32 | 31·19 | 5·03 | 82 | 79·92 | 12·90 | 132 | 128·6 | 20·76 | 182 | 177·4 | 28·62 |
| 33 | 32·16 | 5·19 | 83 | 80·89 | 13·05 | 133 | 129·6 | 20·92 | 183 | 178·4 | 28·78 |
| 34 | 33·14 | 5·35 | 84 | 81·87 | 13·21 | 134 | 130·6 | 21·07 | 184 | 179·3 | 28·94 |
| 35 | 34·11 | 5·50 | 85 | 82·84 | 13·37 | 135 | 131·6 | 21·23 | 185 | 180·3 | 29·10 |
| 36 | 35·09 | 5·66 | 86 | 83·82 | 13·53 | 136 | 132·5 | 21·39 | 186 | 181·3 | 29·25 |
| 37 | 36·06 | 5·82 | 87 | 84·79 | 13·68 | 137 | 133·5 | 21·55 | 187 | 182·3 | 29·41 |
| 38 | 37·04 | 5·98 | 88 | 85·77 | 13·84 | 138 | 134·5 | 21·70 | 188 | 183·2 | 29·57 |
| 39 | 38·01 | 6·13 | 89 | 86·74 | 14·00 | 139 | 135·5 | 21·86 | 189 | 184·2 | 29·72 |
| 40 | 38·98 | 6·29 | 90 | 87·72 | 14·15 | 140 | 136·4 | 22·02 | 190 | 185·2 | 29·88 |
| 41 | 39·96 | 6·45 | 91 | 88·69 | 14·31 | 141 | 137·4 | 22·18 | 191 | 186·2 | 30·04 |
| 42 | 40·93 | 6·61 | 92 | 89·67 | 14·47 | 142 | 138·4 | 22·33 | 192 | 187·1 | 30·20 |
| 43 | 41·91 | 6·76 | 93 | 90·64 | 14·63 | 143 | 139·4 | 22·49 | 193 | 188·1 | 30·35 |
| 44 | 42·88 | 6·92 | 94 | 91·61 | 14·78 | 144 | 140·3 | 22·65 | 194 | 189·1 | 30·51 |
| 45 | 43·86 | 7·08 | 95 | 92·59 | 14·94 | 145 | 141·3 | 22·80 | 195 | 190·1 | 30·67 |
| 46 | 44·83 | 7·23 | 96 | 93·56 | 15·10 | 146 | 142·3 | 22·96 | 196 | 191·0 | 30·83 |
| 47 | 45·81 | 7·39 | 97 | 94·54 | 15·26 | 147 | 143·3 | 23·12 | 197 | 192·0 | 30·98 |
| 48 | 46·78 | 7·55 | 98 | 95·51 | 15·41 | 148 | 144·2 | 23·28 | 198 | 193·0 | 31·14 |
| 49 | 47·76 | 7·71 | 99 | 96·49 | 15·57 | 149 | 145·2 | 23·43 | 199 | 193·9 | 31·30 |
| 50 | 48·73 | 7·86 | 100 | 97·46 | 15·73 | 150 | 146·2 | 23·59 | 200 | 194·9 | 31·45 |
| 51 | 49·71 | 8·02 | 101 | 98·44 | 15·88 | 151 | 147·2 | 23·75 | 201 | 195·9 | 31·61 |
| 52 | 50·68 | 8·18 | 102 | 99·41 | 16·04 | 152 | 148·1 | 23·91 | 202 | 196·9 | 31·77 |
| 53 | 51·65 | 8·34 | 103 | 100·4 | 16·20 | 153 | 149·1 | 24·06 | 203 | 197·8 | 31·93 |
| 54 | 52·63 | 8·49 | 104 | 101·4 | 16·36 | 154 | 150·1 | 24·22 | 204 | 198·8 | 32·08 |
| 55 | 53·60 | 8·65 | 105 | 102·3 | 16·51 | 155 | 151·1 | 24·38 | 205 | 199·8 | 32·24 |
| 56 | 54·58 | 8·81 | 106 | 103·3 | 16·67 | 156 | 152·0 | 24·53 | 206 | 200·8 | 32·40 |
| 57 | 55·55 | 8·96 | 107 | 104·3 | 16·83 | 157 | 153·0 | 24·69 | 207 | 201·7 | 32·56 |
| 58 | 56·53 | 9·12 | 108 | 105·3 | 16·99 | 158 | 154·0 | 24·85 | 208 | 202·7 | 32·71 |
| 59 | 57·50 | 9·28 | 109 | 106·2 | 17·14 | 159 | 155·0 | 25·01 | 209 | 203·7 | 32·87 |
| 60 | 58·48 | 9·44 | 110 | 107·2 | 17·30 | 160 | 155·9 | 25·16 | 210 | 204·7 | 33·03 |

| G | D | H | G | D | H | G | D | H | G | D | H |
|---|---|---|---|---|---|---|---|---|---|---|---|
| 10 | 9·74 | 1·60 | 60 | 58·42 | 9·60 | 110 | 107·1 | 17·60 | 160 | 155·8 | 25·60 |
| 11 | 10·71 | 1·76 | 61 | 59·40 | 9·76 | 111 | 108·1 | 17·76 | 161 | 156·8 | 25·76 |
| 12 | 11·68 | 1·92 | 62 | 60·37 | 9·92 | 112 | 109·1 | 17·92 | 162 | 157·7 | 25·92 |
| 13 | 12·66 | 2·08 | 63 | 61·34 | 10·08 | 113 | 110·0 | 18·08 | 163 | 158·7 | 26·08 |
| 14 | 13·63 | 2·24 | 64 | 62·32 | 10·24 | 114 | 111·0 | 18·24 | 164 | 159·7 | 26·24 |
| 15 | 14·61 | 2·40 | 65 | 63·29 | 10·40 | 115 | 112·0 | 18·40 | 165 | 160·7 | 26·40 |
| 16 | 15·58 | 2·56 | 66 | 64·26 | 10·56 | 116 | 112·9 | 18·56 | 166 | 161·6 | 26·56 |
| 17 | 16·55 | 2·72 | 67 | 65·24 | 10·72 | 117 | 113·9 | 18·72 | 167 | 162·6 | 26·73 |
| 18 | 17·53 | 2·88 | 68 | 66·21 | 10·88 | 118 | 114·9 | 18·88 | 168 | 163·6 | 26·89 |
| 19 | 18·50 | 3·04 | 69 | 67·19 | 11·04 | 119 | 115·9 | 19·04 | 169 | 164·6 | 27·05 |
| 20 | 19·47 | 3·20 | 70 | 68·16 | 11·20 | 120 | 116·8 | 19·20 | 170 | 165·5 | 27·21 |
| 21 | 20·45 | 3·36 | 71 | 69·13 | 11·36 | 121 | 117·8 | 19·36 | 171 | 166·5 | 27·37 |
| 22 | 21·42 | 3·52 | 72 | 70·11 | 11·52 | 122 | 118·8 | 19·52 | 172 | 167·5 | 27·53 |
| 23 | 22·40 | 3·68 | 73 | 71·08 | 11·68 | 123 | 119·8 | 19·68 | 173 | 168·4 | 27·69 |
| 24 | 23·37 | 3·84 | 74 | 72·05 | 11·84 | 124 | 120·7 | 19·84 | 174 | 169·4 | 27·85 |
| 25 | 24·34 | 4·00 | 75 | 73·03 | 12·00 | 125 | 121·7 | 20·00 | 175 | 170·4 | 28·01 |
| 26 | 25·32 | 4·16 | 76 | 74·00 | 12·16 | 126 | 122·7 | 20·16 | 176 | 171·4 | 28·17 |
| 27 | 26·29 | 4·32 | 77 | 74·97 | 12·32 | 127 | 123·7 | 20·32 | 177 | 172·3 | 28·33 |
| 28 | 27·26 | 4·48 | 78 | 75·95 | 12·48 | 128 | 124·6 | 20·48 | 178 | 173·3 | 28·49 |
| 29 | 28·24 | 4·64 | 79 | 76·92 | 12·64 | 129 | 125·6 | 20·64 | 179 | 174·3 | 28·65 |
| 30 | 29·21 | 4·80 | 80 | 77·90 | 12·80 | 130 | 126·6 | 20·80 | 180 | 175·3 | 28·81 |
| 31 | 30·18 | 4·96 | 81 | 78·87 | 12·96 | 131 | 127·6 | 20·96 | 181 | 176·2 | 28·97 |
| 32 | 31·16 | 5·12 | 82 | 79·84 | 13·12 | 132 | 128·5 | 21·12 | 182 | 177·2 | 29·13 |
| 33 | 32·13 | 5·28 | 83 | 80·82 | 13·28 | 133 | 129·5 | 21·28 | 183 | 178·2 | 29·29 |
| 34 | 33·11 | 5·44 | 84 | 81·79 | 13·44 | 134 | 130·5 | 21·44 | 184 | 179·2 | 29·45 |
| 35 | 34·08 | 5·60 | 85 | 82·76 | 13·60 | 135 | 131·4 | 21·60 | 185 | 180·1 | 29·61 |
| 36 | 35·05 | 5·76 | 86 | 83·74 | 13·76 | 136 | 132·4 | 21·76 | 186 | 181·1 | 29·77 |
| 37 | 36·03 | 5·92 | 87 | 84·71 | 13·92 | 137 | 133·4 | 21·92 | 187 | 182·1 | 29·93 |
| 38 | 37·00 | 6·08 | 88 | 85·69 | 14·08 | 138 | 134·4 | 22·08 | 188 | 183·1 | 30·09 |
| 39 | 37·97 | 6·24 | 89 | 86·66 | 14·24 | 139 | 135·3 | 22·24 | 189 | 184·0 | 30·25 |
| 40 | 38·95 | 6·40 | 90 | 87·63 | 14·40 | 140 | 136·3 | 22·40 | 190 | 185·0 | 30·41 |
| 41 | 39·92 | 6·56 | 91 | 88·61 | 14·56 | 141 | 137·3 | 22·56 | 191 | 186·0 | 30·57 |
| 42 | 40·90 | 6·72 | 92 | 89·58 | 14·72 | 142 | 138·3 | 22·72 | 192 | 186·9 | 30·73 |
| 43 | 41·87 | 6·88 | 93 | 90·55 | 14·88 | 143 | 139·2 | 22·88 | 193 | 187·9 | 30·89 |
| 44 | 42·84 | 7·04 | 94 | 91·53 | 15·04 | 144 | 140·2 | 23·04 | 194 | 188·9 | 31·05 |
| 45 | 43·82 | 7·20 | 95 | 92·50 | 15·20 | 145 | 141·2 | 23·20 | 195 | 189·9 | 31·21 |
| 46 | 44·79 | 7·36 | 96 | 93·47 | 15·36 | 146 | 142·2 | 23·36 | 196 | 190·8 | 31·37 |
| 47 | 45·76 | 7·52 | 97 | 94·45 | 15·52 | 147 | 143·1 | 23·52 | 197 | 191·8 | 31·53 |
| 48 | 46·74 | 7·68 | 98 | 95·42 | 15·68 | 148 | 144·1 | 23·68 | 198 | 192·8 | 31·69 |
| 49 | 47·71 | 7·84 | 99 | 96·40 | 15·84 | 149 | 145·1 | 23·84 | 199 | 193·8 | 31·85 |
| 50 | 48·68 | 8·00 | 100 | 97·37 | 16·00 | 150 | 146·1 | 24·00 | 200 | 194·7 | 32·01 |
| 51 | 49·66 | 8·16 | 101 | 98·34 | 16·16 | 151 | 147·0 | 24·16 | 201 | 195·7 | 32·17 |
| 52 | 50·63 | 8·32 | 102 | 99·32 | 16·32 | 152 | 148·0 | 24·32 | 202 | 196·7 | 32·33 |
| 53 | 51·61 | 8·48 | 103 | 100·3 | 16·48 | 153 | 149·0 | 24·48 | 203 | 197·7 | 32·49 |
| 54 | 52·58 | 8·64 | 104 | 101·3 | 16·64 | 154 | 149·9 | 24·64 | 204 | 198·6 | 32·65 |
| 55 | 53·55 | 8·80 | 105 | 102·2 | 16·80 | 155 | 150·9 | 24·80 | 205 | 199·6 | 32·81 |
| 56 | 54·53 | 8·96 | 106 | 103·2 | 16·96 | 156 | 151·9 | 24·96 | 206 | 200·6 | 32·97 |
| 57 | 55·50 | 9·12 | 107 | 104·2 | 17·12 | 157 | 152·9 | 25·12 | 207 | 201·6 | 33·13 |
| 58 | 56·47 | 9·28 | 108 | 105·2 | 17·28 | 158 | 153·8 | 25·28 | 208 | 202·5 | 33·29 |
| 59 | 57·45 | 9·44 | 109 | 106·1 | 17·44 | 159 | 154·8 | 25·44 | 209 | 203·5 | 33·45 |
| 60 | 58·42 | 9·60 | 110 | 107·1 | 17·60 | 160 | 155·8 | 25·60 | 210 | 204·5 | 33·61 |

TABLE I

# 9° 30′

| G | D | H | G | D | H | G | D | H | G | D | H |
|---|---|---|---|---|---|---|---|---|---|---|---|
| 10 | 9·73 | 1·63 | 60 | 58·37 | 9·77 | 110 | 107·0 | 17·91 | 160 | 155·6 | 26·05 |
| 11 | 10·70 | 1·79 | 61 | 59·34 | 9·93 | 111 | 108·0 | 18·07 | 161 | 156·6 | 26·21 |
| 12 | 11·67 | 1·95 | 62 | 60·31 | 10·09 | 112 | 108·9 | 18·23 | 162 | 157·6 | 26·37 |
| 13 | 12·65 | 2·12 | 63 | 61·28 | 10·26 | 113 | 109·9 | 18·39 | 163 | 158·6 | 26·53 |
| 14 | 13·62 | 2·28 | 64 | 62·26 | 10·42 | 114 | 110·9 | 18·56 | 164 | 159·5 | 26·70 |
| 15 | 14·59 | 2·44 | 65 | 63·23 | 10·58 | 115 | 111·9 | 18·72 | 165 | 160·5 | 26·86 |
| 16 | 15·56 | 2·60 | 66 | 64·20 | 10·74 | 116 | 112·8 | 18·88 | 166 | 161·5 | 27·02 |
| 17 | 16·54 | 2·77 | 67 | 65·17 | 10·91 | 117 | 113·8 | 19·05 | 167 | 162·5 | 27·18 |
| 18 | 17·51 | 2·93 | 68 | 66·15 | 11·07 | 118 | 114·8 | 19·21 | 168 | 163·4 | 27·35 |
| 19 | 18·48 | 3·09 | 69 | 67·12 | 11·23 | 119 | 115·8 | 19·37 | 169 | 164·4 | 27·51 |
| 20 | 19·46 | 3·26 | 70 | 68·09 | 11·39 | 120 | 116·7 | 19·53 | 170 | 165·4 | 27·67 |
| 21 | 20·43 | 3·42 | 71 | 69·07 | 11·56 | 121 | 117·7 | 19·70 | 171 | 166·3 | 27·84 |
| 22 | 21·40 | 3·58 | 72 | 70·04 | 11·72 | 122 | 118·7 | 19·86 | 172 | 167·3 | 28·00 |
| 23 | 22·37 | 3·74 | 73 | 71·01 | 11·88 | 123 | 119·6 | 20·02 | 173 | 168·3 | 28·16 |
| 24 | 23·35 | 3·91 | 74 | 71·98 | 12·05 | 124 | 120·6 | 20·19 | 174 | 169·3 | 28·32 |
| 25 | 24·32 | 4·07 | 75 | 72·96 | 12·21 | 125 | 121·6 | 20·35 | 175 | 170·2 | 28·49 |
| 26 | 25·29 | 4·23 | 76 | 73·93 | 12·37 | 126 | 122·6 | 20·51 | 176 | 171·2 | 28·65 |
| 27 | 26·26 | 4·40 | 77 | 74·90 | 12·53 | 127 | 123·5 | 20·67 | 177 | 172·2 | 28·81 |
| 28 | 27·24 | 4·56 | 78 | 75·88 | 12·70 | 128 | 124·5 | 20·84 | 178 | 173·2 | 28·98 |
| 29 | 28·21 | 4·72 | 79 | 76·85 | 12·86 | 129 | 125·5 | 21·00 | 179 | 174·1 | 29·14 |
| 30 | 29·18 | 4·88 | 80 | 77·82 | 13·02 | 130 | 126·5 | 21·16 | 180 | 175·1 | 29·30 |
| 31 | 30·16 | 5·05 | 81 | 78·79 | 13·19 | 131 | 127·4 | 21·32 | 181 | 176·1 | 29·46 |
| 32 | 31·13 | 5·21 | 82 | 79·77 | 13·35 | 132 | 128·4 | 21·49 | 182 | 177·0 | 29·63 |
| 33 | 32·10 | 5·37 | 83 | 80·74 | 13·51 | 133 | 129·4 | 21·65 | 183 | 178·0 | 29·79 |
| 34 | 33·07 | 5·53 | 84 | 81·71 | 13·67 | 134 | 130·3 | 21·81 | 184 | 179·0 | 29·95 |
| 35 | 34·05 | 5·70 | 85 | 82·68 | 13·84 | 135 | 131·3 | 21·98 | 185 | 180·0 | 30·11 |
| 36 | 35·02 | 5·86 | 86 | 83·66 | 14·00 | 136 | 132·3 | 22·14 | 186 | 180·9 | 30·28 |
| 37 | 35·99 | 6·02 | 87 | 84·63 | 14·16 | 137 | 133·3 | 22·30 | 187 | 181·9 | 30·44 |
| 38 | 36·96 | 6·19 | 88 | 85·60 | 14·32 | 138 | 134·2 | 22·46 | 188 | 182·9 | 30·60 |
| 39 | 37·94 | 6·35 | 89 | 86·58 | 14·49 | 139 | 135·2 | 22·63 | 189 | 183·9 | 30·77 |
| 40 | 38·91 | 6·51 | 90 | 87·55 | 14·65 | 140 | 136·2 | 22·79 | 190 | 184·8 | 30·93 |
| 41 | 39·88 | 6·67 | 91 | 88·52 | 14·81 | 141 | 137·2 | 22·95 | 191 | 185·8 | 31·09 |
| 42 | 40·86 | 6·84 | 92 | 89·49 | 14·98 | 142 | 138·1 | 23·12 | 192 | 186·8 | 31·25 |
| 43 | 41·83 | 7·00 | 93 | 90·47 | 15·14 | 143 | 139·1 | 23·28 | 193 | 187·7 | 31·42 |
| 44 | 42·80 | 7·16 | 94 | 91·44 | 15·30 | 144 | 140·1 | 23·44 | 194 | 188·7 | 31·58 |
| 45 | 43·77 | 7·33 | 95 | 92·41 | 15·46 | 145 | 141·0 | 23·60 | 195 | 189·7 | 31·74 |
| 46 | 44·75 | 7·49 | 96 | 93·38 | 15·63 | 146 | 142·0 | 23·77 | 196 | 190·7 | 31·91 |
| 47 | 45·72 | 7·65 | 97 | 94·36 | 15·79 | 147 | 143·0 | 23·93 | 197 | 191·6 | 32·07 |
| 48 | 46·69 | 7·81 | 98 | 95·33 | 15·95 | 148 | 144·0 | 24·09 | 198 | 192·6 | 32·23 |
| 49 | 47·67 | 7·98 | 99 | 96·30 | 16·12 | 149 | 144·9 | 24·25 | 199 | 193·6 | 32·39 |
| 50 | 48·64 | 8·14 | 100 | 97·28 | 16·28 | 150 | 145·9 | 24·42 | 200 | 194·6 | 32·56 |
| 51 | 49·61 | 8·30 | 101 | 98·25 | 16·44 | 151 | 146·9 | 24·58 | 201 | 195·5 | 32·72 |
| 52 | 50·58 | 8·46 | 102 | 99·22 | 16·60 | 152 | 147·9 | 24·74 | 202 | 196·5 | 32·88 |
| 53 | 51·56 | 8·63 | 103 | 100·2 | 16·77 | 153 | 148·8 | 24·91 | 203 | 197·5 | 33·04 |
| 54 | 52·53 | 8·79 | 104 | 101·2 | 16·93 | 154 | 149·8 | 25·07 | 204 | 198·4 | 33·21 |
| 55 | 53·50 | 8·95 | 105 | 102·1 | 17·09 | 155 | 150·8 | 25·23 | 205 | 199·4 | 33·37 |
| 56 | 54·47 | 9·12 | 106 | 103·1 | 17·25 | 156 | 151·8 | 25·39 | 206 | 200·4 | 33·53 |
| 57 | 55·45 | 9·28 | 107 | 104·1 | 17·42 | 157 | 152·7 | 25·56 | 207 | 201·4 | 33·70 |
| 58 | 56·42 | 9·44 | 108 | 105·1 | 17·58 | 158 | 153·7 | 25·72 | 208 | 202·3 | 33·86 |
| 59 | 57·39 | 9·60 | 109 | 106·0 | 17·74 | 159 | 154·7 | 25·88 | 209 | 203·3 | 34·02 |
| 60 | 58·37 | 9·77 | 110 | 107·0 | 17·91 | 160 | 155·6 | 26·05 | 210 | 204·3 | 34·18 |

| G | D | H | G | D | H | G | D | H | G | D | H |
|---|---|---|---|---|---|---|---|---|---|---|---|
| 10 | 9.72 | 1.66 | 60 | 58.31 | 9.93 | 110 | 106.9 | 18.21 | 160 | 155.5 | 26.48 |
| 11 | 10.69 | 1.82 | 61 | 59.28 | 10.10 | 111 | 107.9 | 18.37 | 161 | 156.5 | 26.65 |
| 12 | 11.66 | 1.99 | 62 | 60.25 | 10.26 | 112 | 108.8 | 18.54 | 162 | 157.4 | 26.82 |
| 13 | 12.63 | 2.15 | 63 | 61.22 | 10.43 | 113 | 109.8 | 18.71 | 163 | 158.4 | 26.98 |
| 14 | 13.61 | 2.32 | 64 | 62.20 | 10.59 | 114 | 110.8 | 18.87 | 164 | 159.4 | 27.15 |
| 15 | 14.58 | 2.48 | 65 | 63.17 | 10.76 | 115 | 111.8 | 19.04 | 165 | 160.3 | 27.31 |
| 16 | 15.55 | 2.65 | 66 | 64.14 | 10.93 | 116 | 112.7 | 19.20 | 166 | 161.3 | 27.48 |
| 17 | 16.52 | 2.81 | 67 | 65.11 | 11.09 | 117 | 113.7 | 19.37 | 167 | 162.3 | 27.64 |
| 18 | 17.49 | 2.98 | 68 | 66.08 | 11.26 | 118 | 114.7 | 19.53 | 168 | 163.3 | 27.81 |
| 19 | 18.46 | 3.15 | 69 | 67.05 | 11.42 | 119 | 115.6 | 19.70 | 169 | 164.2 | 27.97 |
| 20 | 19.44 | 3.31 | 70 | 68.03 | 11.59 | 120 | 116.6 | 19.86 | 170 | 165.2 | 28.14 |
| 21 | 20.41 | 3.48 | 71 | 69.00 | 11.75 | 121 | 117.6 | 20.03 | 171 | 166.2 | 28.31 |
| 22 | 21.38 | 3.64 | 72 | 69.97 | 11.92 | 122 | 118.6 | 20.19 | 172 | 167.2 | 28.47 |
| 23 | 22.35 | 3.81 | 73 | 70.94 | 12.08 | 123 | 119.5 | 20.36 | 173 | 168.1 | 28.64 |
| 24 | 23.32 | 3.97 | 74 | 71.91 | 12.25 | 124 | 120.5 | 20.53 | 174 | 169.1 | 28.80 |
| 25 | 24.30 | 4.14 | 75 | 72.89 | 12.41 | 125 | 121.5 | 20.69 | 175 | 170.1 | 28.97 |
| 26 | 25.27 | 4.30 | 76 | 73.86 | 12.58 | 126 | 122.4 | 20.86 | 176 | 171.0 | 29.13 |
| 27 | 26.24 | 4.47 | 77 | 74.83 | 12.75 | 127 | 123.4 | 21.02 | 177 | 172.0 | 29.30 |
| 28 | 27.21 | 4.63 | 78 | 75.80 | 12.91 | 128 | 124.4 | 21.19 | 178 | 173.0 | 29.46 |
| 29 | 28.18 | 4.80 | 79 | 76.77 | 13.08 | 129 | 125.4 | 21.35 | 179 | 174.0 | 29.63 |
| 30 | 29.15 | 4.97 | 80 | 77.74 | 13.24 | 130 | 126.3 | 21.52 | 180 | 174.9 | 29.80 |
| 31 | 30.13 | 5.13 | 81 | 78.72 | 13.41 | 131 | 127.3 | 21.68 | 181 | 175.9 | 29.96 |
| 32 | 31.10 | 5.30 | 82 | 79.69 | 13.57 | 132 | 128.3 | 21.85 | 182 | 176.9 | 30.13 |
| 33 | 32.07 | 5.46 | 83 | 80.66 | 13.74 | 133 | 129.2 | 22.02 | 183 | 177.8 | 30.29 |
| 34 | 33.04 | 5.63 | 84 | 81.63 | 13.90 | 134 | 130.2 | 22.18 | 184 | 178.8 | 30.46 |
| 35 | 34.01 | 5.79 | 85 | 82.60 | 14.07 | 135 | 131.2 | 22.35 | 185 | 179.8 | 30.62 |
| 36 | 34.98 | 5.96 | 86 | 83.58 | 14.24 | 136 | 132.2 | 22.51 | 186 | 180.8 | 30.79 |
| 37 | 35.96 | 6.12 | 87 | 84.55 | 14.40 | 137 | 133.1 | 22.68 | 187 | 181.7 | 30.95 |
| 38 | 36.93 | 6.29 | 88 | 85.52 | 14.57 | 138 | 134.1 | 22.84 | 188 | 182.7 | 31.12 |
| 39 | 37.90 | 6.46 | 89 | 86.49 | 14.73 | 139 | 135.1 | 23.01 | 189 | 183.7 | 31.29 |
| 40 | 38.87 | 6.62 | 90 | 87.46 | 14.90 | 140 | 136.1 | 23.17 | 190 | 184.6 | 31.45 |
| 41 | 39.84 | 6.79 | 91 | 88.43 | 15.06 | 141 | 137.0 | 23.34 | 191 | 185.6 | 31.62 |
| 42 | 40.82 | 6.95 | 92 | 89.41 | 15.23 | 142 | 138.0 | 23.51 | 192 | 186.6 | 31.78 |
| 43 | 41.79 | 7.12 | 93 | 90.38 | 15.39 | 143 | 139.0 | 23.67 | 193 | 187.6 | 31.95 |
| 44 | 42.76 | 7.28 | 94 | 91.35 | 15.56 | 144 | 139.9 | 23.84 | 194 | 188.5 | 32.11 |
| 45 | 43.73 | 7.45 | 95 | 92.32 | 15.73 | 145 | 140.9 | 24.00 | 195 | 189.5 | 32.28 |
| 46 | 44.70 | 7.61 | 96 | 93.29 | 15.89 | 146 | 141.9 | 24.17 | 196 | 190.5 | 32.44 |
| 47 | 45.67 | 7.78 | 97 | 94.26 | 16.06 | 147 | 142.9 | 24.33 | 197 | 191.4 | 32.61 |
| 48 | 46.65 | 7.95 | 98 | 95.24 | 16.22 | 148 | 143.8 | 24.50 | 198 | 192.4 | 32.78 |
| 49 | 47.62 | 8.11 | 99 | 96.21 | 16.39 | 149 | 144.8 | 24.66 | 199 | 193.4 | 32.94 |
| 50 | 48.59 | 8.28 | 100 | 97.18 | 16.55 | 150 | 145.8 | 24.83 | 200 | 194.4 | 33.11 |
| 51 | 49.56 | 8.44 | 101 | 98.15 | 16.72 | 151 | 146.7 | 25.00 | 201 | 195.3 | 33.27 |
| 52 | 50.53 | 8.61 | 102 | 99.12 | 16.88 | 152 | 147.7 | 25.16 | 202 | 196.3 | 33.44 |
| 53 | 51.51 | 8.77 | 103 | 100.1 | 17.05 | 153 | 148.7 | 25.33 | 203 | 197.3 | 33.60 |
| 54 | 52.48 | 8.94 | 104 | 101.1 | 17.22 | 154 | 149.7 | 25.49 | 204 | 198.2 | 33.77 |
| 55 | 53.45 | 9.10 | 105 | 102.0 | 17.38 | 155 | 150.6 | 25.66 | 205 | 199.2 | 33.93 |
| 56 | 54.42 | 9.27 | 106 | 103.0 | 17.55 | 156 | 151.6 | 25.82 | 206 | 200.2 | 34.10 |
| 57 | 55.39 | 9.44 | 107 | 104.0 | 17.71 | 157 | 152.6 | 25.99 | 207 | 201.2 | 34.26 |
| 58 | 56.36 | 9.60 | 108 | 105.0 | 17.88 | 158 | 153.5 | 26.15 | 208 | 202.1 | 34.43 |
| 59 | 57.34 | 9.77 | 109 | 105.9 | 18.04 | 159 | 154.5 | 26.32 | 209 | 203.1 | 34.60 |
| 60 | 58.31 | 9.93 | 110 | 106.9 | 18.21 | 160 | 155.5 | 26.48 | 210 | 204.1 | 34.76 |

TABLE I 9° 50′

| G | D | H | G | D | H | G | D | H | G | D | H |
|---|---|---|---|---|---|---|---|---|---|---|---|
| 10 | 9·71 | 1·68 | 60 | 58·25 | 10·10 | 110 | 106·8 | 18·51 | 160 | 155·3 | 26·92 |
| 11 | 10·68 | 1·85 | 61 | 59·22 | 10·26 | 111 | 107·8 | 18·68 | 161 | 156·3 | 27·09 |
| 12 | 11·65 | 2·02 | 62 | 60·19 | 10·43 | 112 | 108·7 | 18·85 | 162 | 157·3 | 27·26 |
| 13 | 12·62 | 2·19 | 63 | 61·16 | 10·60 | 113 | 109·7 | 19·01 | 163 | 158·2 | 27·43 |
| 14 | 13·59 | 2·36 | 64 | 62·13 | 10·77 | 114 | 110·7 | 19·18 | 164 | 159·2 | 27·60 |
| 15 | 14·56 | 2·52 | 65 | 63·10 | 10·94 | 115 | 111·6 | 19·35 | 165 | 160·2 | 27·77 |
| 16 | 15·53 | 2·69 | 66 | 64·07 | 11·11 | 116 | 112·6 | 19·52 | 166 | 161·2 | 27·93 |
| 17 | 16·50 | 2·86 | 67 | 65·05 | 11·27 | 117 | 113·6 | 19·69 | 167 | 162·1 | 28·10 |
| 18 | 17·47 | 3·03 | 68 | 66·02 | 11·44 | 118 | 114·6 | 19·86 | 168 | 163·1 | 28·27 |
| 19 | 18·45 | 3·20 | 69 | 66·99 | 11·61 | 119 | 115·5 | 20·02 | 169 | 164·1 | 28·44 |
| 20 | 19·42 | 3·37 | 70 | 67·96 | 11·78 | 120 | 116·5 | 20·19 | 170 | 165·0 | 28·61 |
| 21 | 20·39 | 3·53 | 71 | 68·93 | 11·95 | 121 | 117·5 | 20·36 | 171 | 166·0 | 28·77 |
| 22 | 21·36 | 3·70 | 72 | 69·90 | 12·12 | 122 | 118·4 | 20·53 | 172 | 167·0 | 28·94 |
| 23 | 22·33 | 3·87 | 73 | 70·87 | 12·28 | 123 | 119·4 | 20·70 | 173 | 168·0 | 29·11 |
| 24 | 23·30 | 4·04 | 74 | 71·84 | 12·45 | 124 | 120·4 | 20·87 | 174 | 168·9 | 29·28 |
| 25 | 24·27 | 4·21 | 75 | 72·81 | 12·62 | 125 | 121·4 | 21·03 | 175 | 169·9 | 29·45 |
| 26 | 25·24 | 4·38 | 76 | 73·78 | 12·79 | 126 | 122·3 | 21·20 | 176 | 170·9 | 29·62 |
| 27 | 26·21 | 4·54 | 77 | 74·75 | 12·96 | 127 | 123·3 | 21·37 | 177 | 171·8 | 29·78 |
| 28 | 27·18 | 4·71 | 78 | 75·72 | 13·13 | 128 | 124·3 | 21·54 | 178 | 172·8 | 29·95 |
| 29 | 28·15 | 4·88 | 79 | 76·70 | 13·29 | 129 | 125·2 | 21·71 | 179 | 173·8 | 30·12 |
| 30 | 29·12 | 5·05 | 80 | 77·67 | 13·46 | 130 | 126·2 | 21·88 | 180 | 174·7 | 30·29 |
| 31 | 30·10 | 5·22 | 81 | 78·64 | 13·63 | 131 | 127·2 | 22·04 | 181 | 175·7 | 30·46 |
| 32 | 31·07 | 5·38 | 82 | 79·61 | 13·80 | 132 | 128·1 | 22·21 | 182 | 176·7 | 30·63 |
| 33 | 32·04 | 5·55 | 83 | 80·58 | 13·97 | 133 | 129·1 | 22·38 | 183 | 177·7 | 30·79 |
| 34 | 33·01 | 5·72 | 84 | 81·55 | 14·13 | 134 | 130·1 | 22·55 | 184 | 178·6 | 30·96 |
| 35 | 33·98 | 5·89 | 85 | 82·52 | 14·30 | 135 | 131·1 | 22·72 | 185 | 179·6 | 31·13 |
| 36 | 34·95 | 6·06 | 86 | 83·49 | 14·47 | 136 | 132·0 | 22·89 | 186 | 180·6 | 31·30 |
| 37 | 35·92 | 6·23 | 87 | 84·46 | 14·64 | 137 | 133·0 | 23·05 | 187 | 181·5 | 31·47 |
| 38 | 36·89 | 6·39 | 88 | 85·43 | 14·81 | 138 | 134·0 | 23·22 | 188 | 182·5 | 31·64 |
| 39 | 37·86 | 6·56 | 89 | 86·40 | 14·98 | 139 | 134·9 | 23·39 | 189 | 183·5 | 31·80 |
| 40 | 38·83 | 6·73 | 90 | 87·37 | 15·14 | 140 | 135·9 | 23·56 | 190 | 184·5 | 31·97 |
| 41 | 39·80 | 6·90 | 91 | 88·35 | 15·31 | 141 | 136·9 | 23·73 | 191 | 185·4 | 32·14 |
| 42 | 40·77 | 7·07 | 92 | 89·32 | 15·48 | 142 | 137·9 | 23·89 | 192 | 186·4 | 32·31 |
| 43 | 41·75 | 7·24 | 93 | 90·29 | 15·65 | 143 | 138·8 | 24·06 | 193 | 187·4 | 32·48 |
| 44 | 42·72 | 7·40 | 94 | 91·26 | 15·82 | 144 | 139·8 | 24·23 | 194 | 188·3 | 32·64 |
| 45 | 43·69 | 7·57 | 95 | 92·23 | 15·99 | 145 | 140·8 | 24·40 | 195 | 189·3 | 32·81 |
| 46 | 44·66 | 7·74 | 96 | 93·20 | 16·15 | 146 | 141·7 | 24·57 | 196 | 190·3 | 32·98 |
| 47 | 45·63 | 7·91 | 97 | 94·17 | 16·32 | 147 | 142·7 | 24·74 | 197 | 191·3 | 33·15 |
| 48 | 46·60 | 8·08 | 98 | 95·14 | 16·49 | 148 | 143·7 | 24·90 | 198 | 192·2 | 33·32 |
| 49 | 47·57 | 8·25 | 99 | 96·11 | 16·66 | 149 | 144·7 | 25·07 | 199 | 193·2 | 33·49 |
| 50 | 48·54 | 8·41 | 100 | 97·08 | 16·83 | 150 | 145·6 | 25·24 | 200 | 194·2 | 33·65 |
| 51 | 49·51 | 8·58 | 101 | 98·05 | 17·00 | 151 | 146·6 | 25·41 | 201 | 195·1 | 33·82 |
| 52 | 50·48 | 8·75 | 102 | 99·02 | 17·16 | 152 | 147·6 | 25·58 | 202 | 196·1 | 33·99 |
| 53 | 51·45 | 8·92 | 103 | 100·0 | 17·33 | 153 | 148·5 | 25·75 | 203 | 197·1 | 34·16 |
| 54 | 52·42 | 9·09 | 104 | 101·0 | 17·50 | 154 | 149·5 | 25·91 | 204 | 198·0 | 34·33 |
| 55 | 53·40 | 9·26 | 105 | 101·9 | 17·67 | 155 | 150·5 | 26·08 | 205 | 199·0 | 34·50 |
| 56 | 54·37 | 9·42 | 106 | 102·9 | 17·84 | 156 | 151·4 | 26·25 | 206 | 200·0 | 34·66 |
| 57 | 55·34 | 9·59 | 107 | 103·9 | 18·01 | 157 | 152·4 | 26·42 | 207 | 201·0 | 34·83 |
| 58 | 56·31 | 9·76 | 108 | 104·8 | 18·17 | 158 | 153·4 | 26·59 | 208 | 201·9 | 35·00 |
| 59 | 57·28 | 9·93 | 109 | 105·8 | 18·34 | 159 | 154·4 | 26·76 | 209 | 202·9 | 35·17 |
| 60 | 58·25 | 10·10 | 110 | 106·8 | 18·51 | 160 | 155·3 | 26·92 | 210 | 203·9 | 35·34 |

| G | D | H | G | D | H | G | D | H | G | D | H |
|---|---|---|---|---|---|---|---|---|---|---|---|
| 10 | 9.70 | 1.71 | 60 | 58.19 | 10.26 | 110 | 106.7 | 18.81 | 160 | 155.2 | 27.36 |
| 11 | 10.67 | 1.88 | 61 | 59.16 | 10.43 | 111 | 107.7 | 18.98 | 161 | 156.1 | 27.53 |
| 12 | 11.64 | 2.05 | 62 | 60.13 | 10.60 | 112 | 108.6 | 19.15 | 162 | 157.1 | 27.70 |
| 13 | 12.61 | 2.22 | 63 | 61.10 | 10.77 | 113 | 109.6 | 19.32 | 163 | 158.1 | 27.87 |
| 14 | 13.58 | 2.39 | 64 | 62.07 | 10.94 | 114 | 110.6 | 19.50 | 164 | 159.1 | 28.05 |
| 15 | 14.55 | 2.57 | 65 | 63.04 | 11.12 | 115 | 111.5 | 19.67 | 165 | 160.0 | 28.22 |
| 16 | 15.52 | 2.74 | 66 | 64.01 | 11.29 | 116 | 112.5 | 19.84 | 166 | 161.0 | 28.39 |
| 17 | 16.49 | 2.91 | 67 | 64.98 | 11.46 | 117 | 113.5 | 20.01 | 167 | 162.0 | 28.56 |
| 18 | 17.46 | 3.08 | 68 | 65.95 | 11.63 | 118 | 114.4 | 20.18 | 168 | 162.9 | 28.73 |
| 19 | 18.43 | 3.25 | 69 | 66.92 | 11.80 | 119 | 115.4 | 20.35 | 169 | 163.9 | 28.90 |
| 20 | 19.40 | 3.42 | 70 | 67.89 | 11.97 | 120 | 116.4 | 20.52 | 170 | 164.9 | 29.07 |
| 21 | 20.37 | 3.59 | 71 | 68.86 | 12.14 | 121 | 117.4 | 20.69 | 171 | 165.8 | 29.24 |
| 22 | 21.34 | 3.76 | 72 | 69.83 | 12.31 | 122 | 118.3 | 20.86 | 172 | 166.8 | 29.41 |
| 23 | 22.31 | 3.93 | 73 | 70.80 | 12.48 | 123 | 119.3 | 21.03 | 173 | 167.8 | 29.58 |
| 24 | 23.28 | 4.10 | 74 | 71.77 | 12.65 | 124 | 120.3 | 21.21 | 174 | 168.8 | 29.76 |
| 25 | 24.25 | 4.28 | 75 | 72.74 | 12.83 | 125 | 121.2 | 21.38 | 175 | 169.7 | 29.93 |
| 26 | 25.22 | 4.45 | 76 | 73.71 | 13.00 | 126 | 122.2 | 21.55 | 176 | 170.7 | 30.10 |
| 27 | 26.19 | 4.62 | 77 | 74.68 | 13.17 | 127 | 123.2 | 21.72 | 177 | 171.7 | 30.27 |
| 28 | 27.16 | 4.79 | 78 | 75.65 | 13.34 | 128 | 124.1 | 21.89 | 178 | 172.6 | 30.44 |
| 29 | 28.13 | 4.96 | 79 | 76.62 | 13.51 | 129 | 125.1 | 22.06 | 179 | 173.6 | 30.61 |
| 30 | 29.10 | 5.13 | 80 | 77.59 | 13.68 | 130 | 126.1 | 22.23 | 180 | 174.6 | 30.78 |
| 31 | 30.07 | 5.30 | 81 | 78.56 | 13.85 | 131 | 127.0 | 22.40 | 181 | 175.5 | 30.95 |
| 32 | 31.04 | 5.47 | 82 | 79.53 | 14.02 | 132 | 128.0 | 22.57 | 182 | 176.5 | 31.12 |
| 33 | 32.00 | 5.64 | 83 | 80.50 | 14.19 | 133 | 129.0 | 22.74 | 183 | 177.5 | 31.29 |
| 34 | 32.97 | 5.81 | 84 | 81.47 | 14.36 | 134 | 130.0 | 22.92 | 184 | 178.5 | 31.47 |
| 35 | 33.94 | 5.99 | 85 | 82.44 | 14.54 | 135 | 130.9 | 23.09 | 185 | 179.4 | 31.64 |
| 36 | 34.91 | 6.16 | 86 | 83.41 | 14.71 | 136 | 131.9 | 23.26 | 186 | 180.4 | 31.81 |
| 37 | 35.88 | 6.33 | 87 | 84.38 | 14.88 | 137 | 132.9 | 23.43 | 187 | 181.4 | 31.98 |
| 38 | 36.85 | 6.50 | 88 | 85.35 | 15.05 | 138 | 133.8 | 23.60 | 188 | 182.3 | 32.15 |
| 39 | 37.82 | 6.67 | 89 | 86.32 | 15.22 | 139 | 134.8 | 23.77 | 189 | 183.3 | 32.32 |
| 40 | 38.79 | 6.84 | 90 | 87.29 | 15.39 | 140 | 135.8 | 23.94 | 190 | 184.3 | 32.49 |
| 41 | 39.76 | 7.01 | 91 | 88.26 | 15.56 | 141 | 136.7 | 24.11 | 191 | 185.2 | 32.66 |
| 42 | 40.73 | 7.18 | 92 | 89.23 | 15.73 | 142 | 137.7 | 24.28 | 192 | 186.2 | 32.83 |
| 43 | 41.70 | 7.35 | 93 | 90.20 | 15.90 | 143 | 138.7 | 24.45 | 193 | 187.2 | 33.00 |
| 44 | 42.67 | 7.52 | 94 | 91.17 | 16.07 | 144 | 139.7 | 24.63 | 194 | 188.1 | 33.18 |
| 45 | 43.64 | 7.70 | 95 | 92.14 | 16.25 | 145 | 140.6 | 24.80 | 195 | 189.1 | 33.35 |
| 46 | 44.61 | 7.87 | 96 | 93.11 | 16.42 | 146 | 141.6 | 24.97 | 196 | 190.1 | 33.52 |
| 47 | 45.58 | 8.04 | 97 | 94.07 | 16.59 | 147 | 142.6 | 25.14 | 197 | 191.1 | 33.69 |
| 48 | 46.55 | 8.21 | 98 | 95.04 | 16.76 | 148 | 143.5 | 25.31 | 198 | 192.0 | 33.86 |
| 49 | 47.52 | 8.38 | 99 | 96.01 | 16.93 | 149 | 144.5 | 25.48 | 199 | 193.0 | 34.03 |
| 50 | 48.49 | 8.55 | 100 | 96.98 | 17.10 | 150 | 145.5 | 25.65 | 200 | 194.0 | 34.20 |
| 51 | 49.46 | 8.72 | 101 | 97.95 | 17.27 | 151 | 146.4 | 25.82 | 201 | 194.9 | 34.37 |
| 52 | 50.43 | 8.89 | 102 | 98.92 | 17.44 | 152 | 147.4 | 25.99 | 202 | 195.9 | 34.54 |
| 53 | 51.40 | 9.06 | 103 | 99.89 | 17.61 | 153 | 148.4 | 26.16 | 203 | 196.9 | 34.71 |
| 54 | 52.37 | 9.23 | 104 | 100.9 | 17.78 | 154 | 149.4 | 26.34 | 204 | 197.8 | 34.89 |
| 55 | 53.34 | 9.41 | 105 | 101.8 | 17.96 | 155 | 150.3 | 26.51 | 205 | 198.8 | 35.06 |
| 56 | 54.31 | 9.58 | 106 | 102.8 | 18.13 | 156 | 151.3 | 26.68 | 206 | 199.8 | 35.23 |
| 57 | 55.28 | 9.75 | 107 | 103.8 | 18.30 | 157 | 152.3 | 26.85 | 207 | 200.8 | 35.40 |
| 58 | 56.25 | 9.92 | 108 | 104.7 | 18.47 | 158 | 153.2 | 27.02 | 208 | 201.7 | 35.57 |
| 59 | 57.22 | 10.09 | 109 | 105.7 | 18.64 | 159 | 154.2 | 27.19 | 209 | 202.7 | 35.74 |
| 60 | 58.19 | 10.26 | 110 | 106.7 | 18.81 | 160 | 155.2 | 27.36 | 210 | 203.7 | 35.91 |

| G | D | H | G | D | H | G | D | H | G | D | H |
|---|---|---|---|---|---|---|---|---|---|---|---|
| 10 | 9·68 | 1·76 | 60 | 58·07 | 10·59 | 110 | 106·5 | 19·41 | 160 | 154·9 | 28·23 |
| 11 | 10·65 | 1·94 | 61 | 59·04 | 10·76 | 111 | 107·4 | 19·59 | 161 | 155·8 | 28·41 |
| 12 | 11·61 | 2·12 | 62 | 60·01 | 10·94 | 112 | 108·4 | 19·76 | 162 | 156·8 | 28·59 |
| 13 | 12·58 | 2·29 | 63 | 60·97 | 11·12 | 113 | 109·4 | 19·94 | 163 | 157·8 | 28·76 |
| 14 | 13·55 | 2·47 | 64 | 61·94 | 11·29 | 114 | 110·3 | 20·12 | 164 | 158·7 | 28·94 |
| 15 | 14·52 | 2·65 | 65 | 62·91 | 11·47 | 115 | 111·3 | 20·29 | 165 | 159·7 | 29·12 |
| 16 | 15·49 | 2·82 | 66 | 63·88 | 11·65 | 116 | 112·3 | 20·47 | 166 | 160·7 | 29·29 |
| 17 | 16·45 | 3·00 | 67 | 64·84 | 11·82 | 117 | 113·2 | 20·65 | 167 | 161·6 | 29·47 |
| 18 | 17·42 | 3·18 | 68 | 65·81 | 12·00 | 118 | 114·2 | 20·82 | 168 | 162·6 | 29·65 |
| 19 | 18·39 | 3·35 | 69 | 66·78 | 12·18 | 119 | 115·2 | 21·00 | 169 | 163·6 | 29·82 |
| 20 | 19·36 | 3·53 | 70 | 67·75 | 12·35 | 120 | 116·1 | 21·18 | 170 | 164·5 | 30·00 |
| 21 | 20·32 | 3·71 | 71 | 68·72 | 12·53 | 121 | 117·1 | 21·35 | 171 | 165·5 | 30·18 |
| 22 | 21·29 | 3·88 | 72 | 69·68 | 12·71 | 122 | 118·1 | 21·53 | 172 | 166·5 | 30·35 |
| 23 | 22·26 | 4·06 | 73 | 70·65 | 12·88 | 123 | 119·0 | 21·71 | 173 | 167·4 | 30·53 |
| 24 | 23·23 | 4·24 | 74 | 71·62 | 13·06 | 124 | 120·0 | 21·88 | 174 | 168·4 | 30·70 |
| 25 | 24·20 | 4·41 | 75 | 72·59 | 13·23 | 125 | 121·0 | 22·06 | 175 | 169·4 | 30·88 |
| 26 | 25·16 | 4·59 | 76 | 73·55 | 13·41 | 126 | 121·9 | 22·23 | 176 | 170·3 | 31·06 |
| 27 | 26·13 | 4·76 | 77 | 74·52 | 13·59 | 127 | 122·9 | 22·41 | 177 | 171·3 | 31·23 |
| 28 | 27·10 | 4·94 | 78 | 75·49 | 13·76 | 128 | 123·9 | 22·59 | 178 | 172·3 | 31·41 |
| 29 | 28·07 | 5·12 | 79 | 76·46 | 13·94 | 129 | 124·8 | 22·76 | 179 | 173·2 | 31·59 |
| 30 | 29·03 | 5·29 | 80 | 77·43 | 14·12 | 130 | 125·8 | 22·94 | 180 | 174·2 | 31·76 |
| 31 | 30·00 | 5·47 | 81 | 78·39 | 14·29 | 131 | 126·8 | 23·12 | 181 | 175·2 | 31·94 |
| 32 | 30·97 | 5·65 | 82 | 79·36 | 14·47 | 132 | 127·8 | 23·29 | 182 | 176·1 | 32·12 |
| 33 | 31·94 | 5·82 | 83 | 80·33 | 14·65 | 133 | 128·7 | 23·47 | 183 | 177·1 | 32·29 |
| 34 | 32·91 | 6·00 | 84 | 81·30 | 14·82 | 134 | 129·7 | 23·65 | 184 | 178·1 | 32·47 |
| 35 | 33·87 | 6·18 | 85 | 82·26 | 15·00 | 135 | 130·7 | 23·82 | 185 | 179·0 | 32·65 |
| 36 | 34·84 | 6·35 | 86 | 83·23 | 15·18 | 136 | 131·6 | 24·00 | 186 | 180·0 | 32·82 |
| 37 | 35·81 | 6·53 | 87 | 84·20 | 15·35 | 137 | 132·6 | 24·18 | 187 | 181·0 | 33·00 |
| 38 | 36·78 | 6·71 | 88 | 85·17 | 15·53 | 138 | 133·6 | 24·35 | 188 | 182·0 | 33·18 |
| 39 | 37·75 | 6·88 | 89 | 86·14 | 15·71 | 139 | 134·5 | 24·53 | 189 | 182·9 | 33·35 |
| 40 | 38·71 | 7·06 | 90 | 87·10 | 15·88 | 140 | 135·5 | 24·71 | 190 | 183·9 | 33·53 |
| 41 | 39·68 | 7·24 | 91 | 88·07 | 16·06 | 141 | 136·5 | 24·88 | 191 | 184·9 | 33·70 |
| 42 | 40·65 | 7·41 | 92 | 89·04 | 16·23 | 142 | 137·4 | 25·06 | 192 | 185·8 | 33·88 |
| 43 | 41·62 | 7·59 | 93 | 90·01 | 16·41 | 143 | 138·4 | 25·23 | 193 | 186·8 | 34·06 |
| 44 | 42·58 | 7·76 | 94 | 90·98 | 16·59 | 144 | 139·4 | 25·41 | 194 | 187·8 | 34·23 |
| 45 | 43·55 | 7·94 | 95 | 91·94 | 16·76 | 145 | 140·3 | 25·59 | 195 | 188·7 | 34·41 |
| 46 | 44·52 | 8·12 | 96 | 92·91 | 16·94 | 146 | 141·3 | 25·76 | 196 | 189·7 | 34·59 |
| 47 | 45·49 | 8·29 | 97 | 93·88 | 17·12 | 147 | 142·3 | 25·94 | 197 | 190·7 | 34·76 |
| 48 | 46·46 | 8·47 | 98 | 94·85 | 17·29 | 148 | 143·2 | 26·12 | 198 | 191·6 | 34·94 |
| 49 | 47·42 | 8·65 | 99 | 95·81 | 17·47 | 149 | 144·2 | 26·29 | 199 | 192·6 | 35·12 |
| 50 | 48·39 | 8·82 | 100 | 96·78 | 17·65 | 150 | 145·2 | 26·47 | 200 | 193·6 | 35·29 |
| 51 | 49·36 | 9·00 | 101 | 97·75 | 17·82 | 151 | 146·1 | 26·65 | 201 | 194·5 | 35·47 |
| 52 | 50·33 | 9·18 | 102 | 98·72 | 18·00 | 152 | 147·1 | 26·82 | 202 | 195·5 | 35·65 |
| 53 | 51·29 | 9·35 | 103 | 99·69 | 18·18 | 153 | 148·1 | 27·00 | 203 | 196·5 | 35·82 |
| 54 | 52·26 | 9·53 | 104 | 100·7 | 18·35 | 154 | 149·0 | 27·18 | 204 | 197·4 | 36·00 |
| 55 | 53·23 | 9·71 | 105 | 101·6 | 18·53 | 155 | 150·0 | 27·35 | 205 | 198·4 | 36·18 |
| 56 | 54·20 | 9·88 | 106 | 102·6 | 18·71 | 156 | 151·0 | 27·53 | 206 | 199·4 | 36·35 |
| 57 | 55·17 | 10·06 | 107 | 103·6 | 18·88 | 157 | 151·9 | 27·71 | 207 | 200·3 | 36·53 |
| 58 | 56·13 | 10·23 | 108 | 104·5 | 19·06 | 158 | 152·9 | 27·88 | 208 | 201·3 | 36·70 |
| 59 | 57·10 | 10·41 | 109 | 105·5 | 19·23 | 159 | 153·9 | 28·06 | 209 | 202·3 | 36·88 |
| 60 | 58·07 | 10·59 | 110 | 106·5 | 19·41 | 160 | 154·9 | 28·23 | 210 | 203·2 | 37·06 |

| G | D | H | G | D | H | G | D | H | G | D | H |
|---|---|---|---|---|---|---|---|---|---|---|---|
| 10 | 9.66 | 1.82 | 60 | 57.94 | 10.91 | 110 | 106.2 | 20.01 | 160 | 154.5 | 29.10 |
| 11 | 10.62 | 2.00 | 61 | 58.91 | 11.10 | 111 | 107.2 | 20.19 | 161 | 155.5 | 29.29 |
| 12 | 11.59 | 2.18 | 62 | 59.88 | 11.28 | 112 | 108.2 | 20.37 | 162 | 156.4 | 29.47 |
| 13 | 12.55 | 2.36 | 63 | 60.84 | 11.46 | 113 | 109.1 | 20.55 | 163 | 157.4 | 29.65 |
| 14 | 13.52 | 2.55 | 64 | 61.81 | 11.64 | 114 | 110.1 | 20.74 | 164 | 158.4 | 29.83 |
| 15 | 14.49 | 2.73 | 65 | 62.77 | 11.82 | 115 | 111.1 | 20.92 | 165 | 159.3 | 30.01 |
| 16 | 15.45 | 2.91 | 66 | 63.74 | 12.01 | 116 | 112.0 | 21.10 | 166 | 160.3 | 30.19 |
| 17 | 16.42 | 3.09 | 67 | 64.70 | 12.19 | 117 | 113.0 | 21.28 | 167 | 161.3 | 30.38 |
| 18 | 17.38 | 3.27 | 68 | 65.67 | 12.37 | 118 | 114.0 | 21.46 | 168 | 162.2 | 30.56 |
| 19 | 18.35 | 3.46 | 69 | 66.64 | 12.55 | 119 | 114.9 | 21.65 | 169 | 163.2 | 30.74 |
| 20 | 19.31 | 3.64 | 70 | 67.60 | 12.73 | 120 | 115.9 | 21.83 | 170 | 164.2 | 30.92 |
| 21 | 20.28 | 3.82 | 71 | 68.57 | 12.91 | 121 | 116.9 | 22.01 | 171 | 165.1 | 31.10 |
| 22 | 21.25 | 4.00 | 72 | 69.53 | 13.10 | 122 | 117.8 | 22.19 | 172 | 166.1 | 31.29 |
| 23 | 22.21 | 4.18 | 73 | 70.50 | 13.28 | 123 | 118.8 | 22.37 | 173 | 167.1 | 31.47 |
| 24 | 23.18 | 4.37 | 74 | 71.46 | 13.46 | 124 | 119.8 | 22.56 | 174 | 168.0 | 31.65 |
| 25 | 24.14 | 4.55 | 75 | 72.43 | 13.64 | 125 | 120.7 | 22.74 | 175 | 169.0 | 31.83 |
| 26 | 25.11 | 4.73 | 76 | 73.40 | 13.82 | 126 | 121.7 | 22.92 | 176 | 170.0 | 32.01 |
| 27 | 26.07 | 4.91 | 77 | 74.36 | 14.01 | 127 | 122.6 | 23.10 | 177 | 170.9 | 32.20 |
| 28 | 27.04 | 5.09 | 78 | 75.33 | 14.19 | 128 | 123.6 | 23.28 | 178 | 171.9 | 32.38 |
| 29 | 28.01 | 5.27 | 79 | 76.29 | 14.37 | 129 | 124.6 | 23.46 | 179 | 172.9 | 32.56 |
| 30 | 28.97 | 5.46 | 80 | 77.26 | 14.55 | 130 | 125.5 | 23.65 | 180 | 173.8 | 32.74 |
| 31 | 29.94 | 5.64 | 81 | 78.22 | 14.73 | 131 | 126.5 | 23.83 | 181 | 174.8 | 32.92 |
| 32 | 30.90 | 5.82 | 82 | 79.19 | 14.92 | 132 | 127.5 | 24.01 | 182 | 175.8 | 33.11 |
| 33 | 31.87 | 6.00 | 83 | 80.16 | 15.10 | 133 | 128.4 | 24.19 | 183 | 176.7 | 33.29 |
| 34 | 32.84 | 6.18 | 84 | 81.12 | 15.28 | 134 | 129.4 | 24.37 | 184 | 177.7 | 33.47 |
| 35 | 33.80 | 6.37 | 85 | 82.09 | 15.46 | 135 | 130.4 | 24.56 | 185 | 178.7 | 33.65 |
| 36 | 34.77 | 6.55 | 86 | 83.05 | 15.64 | 136 | 131.3 | 24.74 | 186 | 179.6 | 33.83 |
| 37 | 35.73 | 6.73 | 87 | 84.02 | 15.82 | 137 | 132.3 | 24.92 | 187 | 180.6 | 34.01 |
| 38 | 36.70 | 6.91 | 88 | 84.98 | 16.01 | 138 | 133.3 | 25.10 | 188 | 181.6 | 34.20 |
| 39 | 37.66 | 7.09 | 89 | 85.95 | 16.19 | 139 | 134.2 | 25.28 | 189 | 182.5 | 34.38 |
| 40 | 38.63 | 7.28 | 90 | 86.92 | 16.37 | 140 | 135.2 | 25.47 | 190 | 183.5 | 34.56 |
| 41 | 39.60 | 7.46 | 91 | 87.88 | 16.55 | 141 | 136.2 | 25.65 | 191 | 184.5 | 34.74 |
| 42 | 40.56 | 7.64 | 92 | 88.85 | 16.73 | 142 | 137.1 | 25.83 | 192 | 185.4 | 34.92 |
| 43 | 41.53 | 7.82 | 93 | 89.81 | 16.92 | 143 | 138.1 | 26.01 | 193 | 186.4 | 35.11 |
| 44 | 42.49 | 8.00 | 94 | 90.78 | 17.10 | 144 | 139.1 | 26.19 | 194 | 187.4 | 35.29 |
| 45 | 43.46 | 8.19 | 95 | 91.75 | 17.28 | 145 | 140.0 | 26.37 | 195 | 188.3 | 35.47 |
| 46 | 44.42 | 8.37 | 96 | 92.71 | 17.46 | 146 | 141.0 | 26.56 | 196 | 189.3 | 35.65 |
| 47 | 45.39 | 8.55 | 97 | 93.68 | 17.64 | 147 | 142.0 | 26.74 | 197 | 190.3 | 35.83 |
| 48 | 46.36 | 8.73 | 98 | 94.64 | 17.83 | 148 | 142.9 | 26.92 | 198 | 191.2 | 36.02 |
| 49 | 47.32 | 8.91 | 99 | 95.61 | 18.01 | 149 | 143.9 | 27.10 | 199 | 192.2 | 36.20 |
| 50 | 48.29 | 9.09 | 100 | 96.57 | 18.19 | 150 | 144.9 | 27.28 | 200 | 193.1 | 36.38 |
| 51 | 49.25 | 9.28 | 101 | 97.54 | 18.37 | 151 | 145.8 | 27.47 | 201 | 194.1 | 36.56 |
| 52 | 50.22 | 9.46 | 102 | 98.51 | 18.55 | 152 | 146.8 | 27.65 | 202 | 195.1 | 36.74 |
| 53 | 51.18 | 9.64 | 103 | 99.47 | 18.74 | 153 | 147.8 | 27.83 | 203 | 196.0 | 36.92 |
| 54 | 52.15 | 9.82 | 104 | 100.4 | 18.92 | 154 | 148.7 | 28.01 | 204 | 197.0 | 37.11 |
| 55 | 53.12 | 10.00 | 105 | 101.4 | 19.10 | 155 | 149.7 | 28.19 | 205 | 198.0 | 37.29 |
| 56 | 54.08 | 10.19 | 106 | 102.4 | 19.28 | 156 | 150.7 | 28.38 | 206 | 198.9 | 37.47 |
| 57 | 55.05 | 10.37 | 107 | 103.3 | 19.46 | 157 | 151.6 | 28.56 | 207 | 199.9 | 37.65 |
| 58 | 56.01 | 10.55 | 108 | 104.3 | 19.64 | 158 | 152.6 | 28.74 | 208 | 200.9 | 37.83 |
| 59 | 56.98 | 10.73 | 109 | 105.3 | 19.83 | 159 | 153.6 | 28.92 | 209 | 201.8 | 38.02 |
| 60 | 57.94 | 10.91 | 110 | 106.2 | 20.01 | 160 | 154.5 | 29.10 | 210 | 202.8 | 38.20 |

TABLE I

# 11° 00′

| G | D | H | G | D | H | G | D | H | G | D | H |
|---|---|---|---|---|---|---|---|---|---|---|---|
| 10 | 9·64 | 1·87 | 60 | 57·82 | 11·24 | 110 | 106·0 | 20·60 | 160 | 154·2 | 29·97 |
| 11 | 10·60 | 2·06 | 61 | 58·78 | 11·43 | 111 | 107·0 | 20·79 | 161 | 155·1 | 30·16 |
| 12 | 11·56 | 2·25 | 62 | 59·74 | 11·61 | 112 | 107·9 | 20·98 | 162 | 156·1 | 30·34 |
| 13 | 12·53 | 2·43 | 63 | 60·71 | 11·80 | 113 | 108·9 | 21·17 | 163 | 157·1 | 30·53 |
| 14 | 13·49 | 2·62 | 64 | 61·67 | 11·99 | 114 | 109·8 | 21·35 | 164 | 158·0 | 30·72 |
| 15 | 14·45 | 2·81 | 65 | 62·63 | 12·17 | 115 | 110·8 | 21·54 | 165 | 159·0 | 30·90 |
| 16 | 15·42 | 3·00 | 66 | 63·60 | 12·36 | 116 | 111·8 | 21·73 | 166 | 160·0 | 31·09 |
| 17 | 16·38 | 3·18 | 67 | 64·56 | 12·55 | 117 | 112·7 | 21·91 | 167 | 160·9 | 31·28 |
| 18 | 17·34 | 3·37 | 68 | 65·52 | 12·74 | 118 | 113·7 | 22·10 | 168 | 161·9 | 31·47 |
| 19 | 18·31 | 3·56 | 69 | 66·49 | 12·92 | 119 | 114·7 | 22·29 | 169 | 162·8 | 31·65 |
| 20 | 19·27 | 3·75 | 70 | 67·45 | 13·11 | 120 | 115·6 | 22·48 | 170 | 163·8 | 31·84 |
| 21 | 20·24 | 3·93 | 71 | 68·41 | 13·30 | 121 | 116·6 | 22·66 | 171 | 164·8 | 32·03 |
| 22 | 21·20 | 4·12 | 72 | 69·38 | 13·49 | 122 | 117·6 | 22·85 | 172 | 165·7 | 32·22 |
| 23 | 22·16 | 4·31 | 73 | 70·34 | 13·67 | 123 | 118·5 | 23·04 | 173 | 166·7 | 32·40 |
| 24 | 23·13 | 4·50 | 74 | 71·31 | 13·86 | 124 | 119·5 | 23·23 | 174 | 167·7 | 32·59 |
| 25 | 24·09 | 4·68 | 75 | 72·27 | 14·05 | 125 | 120·4 | 23·41 | 175 | 168·6 | 32·78 |
| 26 | 25·05 | 4·87 | 76 | 73·23 | 14·24 | 126 | 121·4 | 23·60 | 176 | 169·6 | 32·97 |
| 27 | 26·02 | 5·06 | 77 | 74·20 | 14·42 | 127 | 122·4 | 23·79 | 177 | 170·6 | 33·15 |
| 28 | 26·98 | 5·24 | 78 | 75·16 | 14·61 | 128 | 123·3 | 23·97 | 178 | 171·5 | 33·34 |
| 29 | 27·94 | 5·43 | 79 | 76·12 | 14·80 | 129 | 124·3 | 24·16 | 179 | 172·5 | 33·53 |
| 30 | 28·91 | 5·62 | 80 | 77·09 | 14·98 | 130 | 125·3 | 24·35 | 180 | 173·4 | 33·71 |
| 31 | 29·87 | 5·81 | 81 | 78·05 | 15·17 | 131 | 126·2 | 24·54 | 181 | 174·4 | 33·90 |
| 32 | 30·83 | 5·99 | 82 | 79·01 | 15·36 | 132 | 127·2 | 24·72 | 182 | 175·4 | 34·09 |
| 33 | 31·80 | 6·18 | 83 | 79·98 | 15·55 | 133 | 128·2 | 24·91 | 183 | 176·3 | 34·28 |
| 34 | 32·76 | 6·37 | 84 | 80·94 | 15·73 | 134 | 129·1 | 25·10 | 184 | 177·3 | 34·46 |
| 35 | 33·73 | 6·56 | 85 | 81·91 | 15·92 | 135 | 130·1 | 25·29 | 185 | 178·3 | 34·65 |
| 36 | 34·69 | 6·74 | 86 | 82·87 | 16·11 | 136 | 131·0 | 25·47 | 186 | 179·2 | 34·84 |
| 37 | 35·65 | 6·93 | 87 | 83·83 | 16·30 | 137 | 132·0 | 25·66 | 187 | 180·2 | 35·03 |
| 38 | 36·62 | 7·12 | 88 | 84·80 | 16·48 | 138 | 133·0 | 25·85 | 188 | 181·2 | 35·21 |
| 39 | 37·58 | 7·30 | 89 | 85·76 | 16·67 | 139 | 133·9 | 26·04 | 189 | 182·1 | 35·40 |
| 40 | 38·54 | 7·49 | 90 | 86·72 | 16·86 | 140 | 134·9 | 26·22 | 190 | 183·1 | 35·59 |
| 41 | 39·51 | 7·68 | 91 | 87·69 | 17·04 | 141 | 135·9 | 26·41 | 191 | 184·0 | 35·77 |
| 42 | 40·47 | 7·87 | 92 | 88·65 | 17·23 | 142 | 136·8 | 26·60 | 192 | 185·0 | 35·96 |
| 43 | 41·43 | 8·05 | 93 | 89·61 | 17·42 | 143 | 137·8 | 26·78 | 193 | 186·0 | 36·15 |
| 44 | 42·40 | 8·24 | 94 | 90·58 | 17·61 | 144 | 138·8 | 26·97 | 194 | 186·9 | 36·34 |
| 45 | 43·36 | 8·43 | 95 | 91·54 | 17·79 | 145 | 139·7 | 27·16 | 195 | 187·9 | 36·52 |
| 46 | 44·33 | 8·62 | 96 | 92·50 | 17·98 | 146 | 140·7 | 27·35 | 196 | 188·9 | 36·71 |
| 47 | 45·29 | 8·80 | 97 | 93·47 | 18·17 | 147 | 141·6 | 27·53 | 197 | 189·8 | 36·90 |
| 48 | 46·25 | 8·99 | 98 | 94·43 | 18·36 | 148 | 142·6 | 27·72 | 198 | 190·8 | 37·09 |
| 49 | 47·22 | 9·18 | 99 | 95·40 | 18·54 | 149 | 143·6 | 27·91 | 199 | 191·8 | 37·27 |
| 50 | 48·18 | 9·37 | 100 | 96·36 | 18·73 | 150 | 144·5 | 28·10 | 200 | 192·7 | 37·46 |
| 51 | 49·14 | 9·55 | 101 | 97·32 | 18·92 | 151 | 145·5 | 28·28 | 201 | 193·7 | 37·65 |
| 52 | 50·11 | 9·74 | 102 | 98·29 | 19·10 | 152 | 146·5 | 28·47 | 202 | 194·6 | 37·84 |
| 53 | 51·07 | 9·93 | 103 | 99·25 | 19·29 | 153 | 147·4 | 28·66 | 203 | 195·6 | 38·02 |
| 54 | 52·03 | 10·11 | 104 | 100·2 | 19·48 | 154 | 148·4 | 28·84 | 204 | 196·6 | 38·21 |
| 55 | 53·00 | 10·30 | 105 | 101·2 | 19·67 | 155 | 149·4 | 29·03 | 205 | 197·5 | 38·40 |
| 56 | 53·96 | 10·49 | 106 | 102·1 | 19·85 | 156 | 150·3 | 29·22 | 206 | 198·5 | 38·58 |
| 57 | 54·92 | 10·68 | 107 | 103·1 | 20·04 | 157 | 151·3 | 29·41 | 207 | 199·5 | 38·77 |
| 58 | 55·89 | 10·86 | 108 | 104·1 | 20·23 | 158 | 152·2 | 29·59 | 208 | 200·4 | 38·96 |
| 59 | 56·85 | 11·05 | 109 | 105·0 | 20·42 | 159 | 153·2 | 29·78 | 209 | 201·4 | 39·15 |
| 60 | 57·82 | 11·24 | 110 | 106·0 | 20·60 | 160 | 154·2 | 29·97 | 210 | 202·4 | 39·33 |

| G | D | H | G | D | H | G | D | H | G | D | H |
|---|---|---|---|---|---|---|---|---|---|---|---|
| 10 | 9·61 | 1·93 | 60 | 57·68 | 11·56 | 110 | 105·8 | 21·20 | 160 | 153·8 | 30·83 |
| 11 | 10·58 | 2·12 | 61 | 58·64 | 11·75 | 111 | 106·7 | 21·39 | 161 | 154·8 | 31·02 |
| 12 | 11·54 | 2·31 | 62 | 59·61 | 11·95 | 112 | 107·7 | 21·58 | 162 | 155·7 | 31·21 |
| 13 | 12·50 | 2·50 | 63 | 60·57 | 12·14 | 113 | 108·6 | 21·77 | 163 | 156·7 | 31·41 |
| 14 | 13·46 | 2·70 | 64 | 61·53 | 12·33 | 114 | 109·6 | 21·97 | 164 | 157·7 | 31·60 |
| 15 | 14·42 | 2·89 | 65 | 62·49 | 12·52 | 115 | 110·6 | 22·16 | 165 | 158·6 | 31·79 |
| 16 | 15·38 | 3·08 | 66 | 63·45 | 12·72 | 116 | 111·5 | 22·35 | 166 | 159·6 | 31·99 |
| 17 | 16·34 | 3·28 | 67 | 64·41 | 12·91 | 117 | 112·5 | 22·54 | 167 | 160·6 | 32·18 |
| 18 | 17·30 | 3·47 | 68 | 65·37 | 13·10 | 118 | 113·4 | 22·74 | 168 | 161·5 | 32·37 |
| 19 | 18·27 | 3·66 | 69 | 66·34 | 13·30 | 119 | 114·4 | 22·93 | 169 | 162·5 | 32·56 |
| 20 | 19·23 | 3·85 | 70 | 67·30 | 13·49 | 120 | 115·4 | 23·12 | 170 | 163·4 | 32·76 |
| 21 | 20·19 | 4·05 | 71 | 68·26 | 13·68 | 121 | 116·3 | 23·31 | 171 | 164·4 | 32·95 |
| 22 | 21·15 | 4·24 | 72 | 69·22 | 13·87 | 122 | 117·3 | 23·51 | 172 | 165·4 | 33·14 |
| 23 | 22·11 | 4·43 | 73 | 70·18 | 14·07 | 123 | 118·2 | 23·70 | 173 | 166·3 | 33·33 |
| 24 | 23·07 | 4·62 | 74 | 71·14 | 14·26 | 124 | 119·2 | 23·89 | 174 | 167·3 | 33·53 |
| 25 | 24·03 | 4·82 | 75 | 72·10 | 14·45 | 125 | 120·2 | 24·09 | 175 | 168·2 | 33·72 |
| 26 | 25·00 | 5·01 | 76 | 73·06 | 14·64 | 126 | 121·1 | 24·28 | 176 | 169·2 | 33·91 |
| 27 | 25·96 | 5·20 | 77 | 74·03 | 14·84 | 127 | 122·1 | 24·47 | 177 | 170·2 | 34·11 |
| 28 | 26·92 | 5·40 | 78 | 74·99 | 15·03 | 128 | 123·1 | 24·66 | 178 | 171·1 | 34·30 |
| 29 | 27·88 | 5·59 | 79 | 75·95 | 15·22 | 129 | 124·0 | 24·86 | 179 | 172·1 | 34·49 |
| 30 | 28·84 | 5·78 | 80 | 76·91 | 15·41 | 130 | 125·0 | 25·05 | 180 | 173·0 | 34·68 |
| 31 | 29·80 | 5·97 | 81 | 77·87 | 15·61 | 131 | 125·9 | 25·24 | 181 | 174·0 | 34·88 |
| 32 | 30·76 | 6·17 | 82 | 78·83 | 15·80 | 132 | 126·9 | 25·43 | 182 | 175·0 | 35·07 |
| 33 | 31·73 | 6·36 | 83 | 79·79 | 15·99 | 133 | 127·9 | 25·63 | 183 | 175·9 | 35·26 |
| 34 | 32·69 | 6·55 | 84 | 80·76 | 16·19 | 134 | 128·8 | 25·82 | 184 | 176·9 | 35·45 |
| 35 | 33·65 | 6·74 | 85 | 81·72 | 16·38 | 135 | 129·8 | 26·01 | 185 | 177·9 | 35·65 |
| 36 | 34·61 | 6·94 | 86 | 82·68 | 16·57 | 136 | 130·7 | 26·21 | 186 | 178·8 | 35·84 |
| 37 | 35·57 | 7·13 | 87 | 83·64 | 16·76 | 137 | 131·7 | 26·40 | 187 | 179·8 | 36·03 |
| 38 | 36·53 | 7·32 | 88 | 84·60 | 16·96 | 138 | 132·7 | 26·59 | 188 | 180·7 | 36·22 |
| 39 | 37·49 | 7·51 | 89 | 85·56 | 17·15 | 139 | 133·6 | 26·78 | 189 | 181·7 | 36·42 |
| 40 | 38·46 | 7·71 | 90 | 86·52 | 17·34 | 140 | 134·6 | 26·98 | 190 | 182·7 | 36·61 |
| 41 | 39·42 | 7·90 | 91 | 87·49 | 17·53 | 141 | 135·6 | 27·17 | 191 | 183·6 | 36·80 |
| 42 | 40·38 | 8·09 | 92 | 88·45 | 17·73 | 142 | 136·5 | 27·36 | 192 | 184·6 | 37·00 |
| 43 | 41·34 | 8·29 | 93 | 89·41 | 17·92 | 143 | 137·5 | 27·55 | 193 | 185·5 | 37·19 |
| 44 | 42·30 | 8·48 | 94 | 90·37 | 18·11 | 144 | 138·4 | 27·75 | 194 | 186·5 | 37·38 |
| 45 | 43·26 | 8·67 | 95 | 91·33 | 18·30 | 145 | 139·4 | 27·94 | 195 | 187·5 | 37·57 |
| 46 | 44·22 | 8·86 | 96 | 92·29 | 18·50 | 146 | 140·4 | 28·13 | 196 | 188·4 | 37·77 |
| 47 | 45·18 | 9·06 | 97 | 93·25 | 18·69 | 147 | 141·3 | 28·32 | 197 | 189·4 | 37·96 |
| 48 | 46·15 | 9·25 | 98 | 94·22 | 18·88 | 148 | 142·3 | 28·52 | 198 | 190·4 | 38·15 |
| 49 | 47·11 | 9·44 | 99 | 95·18 | 19·08 | 149 | 143·2 | 28·71 | 199 | 191·3 | 38·34 |
| 50 | 48·07 | 9·63 | 100 | 96·14 | 19·27 | 150 | 144·2 | 28·90 | 200 | 192·3 | 38·54 |
| 51 | 49·03 | 9·83 | 101 | 97·10 | 19·46 | 151 | 145·2 | 29·10 | 201 | 193·2 | 38·73 |
| 52 | 49·99 | 10·02 | 102 | 98·06 | 19·65 | 152 | 146·1 | 29·29 | 202 | 194·2 | 38·92 |
| 53 | 50·95 | 10·21 | 103 | 99·02 | 19·85 | 153 | 147·1 | 29·48 | 203 | 195·2 | 39·11 |
| 54 | 51·91 | 10·40 | 104 | 99·98 | 20·04 | 154 | 148·1 | 29·67 | 204 | 196·1 | 39·31 |
| 55 | 52·88 | 10·60 | 105 | 100·9 | 20·23 | 155 | 149·0 | 29·87 | 205 | 197·1 | 39·50 |
| 56 | 53·84 | 10·79 | 106 | 101·9 | 20·42 | 156 | 150·0 | 30·06 | 206 | 198·0 | 39·69 |
| 57 | 54·80 | 10·98 | 107 | 102·9 | 20·62 | 157 | 150·9 | 30·25 | 207 | 199·0 | 39·89 |
| 58 | 55·76 | 11·18 | 108 | 103·8 | 20·81 | 158 | 151·9 | 30·44 | 208 | 200·0 | 40·08 |
| 59 | 56·72 | 11·37 | 109 | 104·8 | 21·00 | 159 | 152·9 | 30·64 | 209 | 200·9 | 40·27 |
| 60 | 57·68 | 11·56 | 110 | 105·8 | 21·20 | 160 | 153·8 | 30·83 | 210 | 201·9 | 40·46 |

TABLE I

# 11° 40′

| G | D | H | G | D | H | G | D | H | G | D | H |
|---|---|---|---|---|---|---|---|---|---|---|---|
| 10 | 9·59 | 1·98 | 60 | 57·55 | 11·88 | 110 | 105·5 | 21·78 | 160 | 153·5 | 31·69 |
| 11 | 10·55 | 2·18 | 61 | 58·51 | 12·08 | 111 | 106·5 | 21·98 | 161 | 154·4 | 31·88 |
| 12 | 11·51 | 2·38 | 62 | 59·46 | 12·28 | 112 | 107·4 | 22·18 | 162 | 155·4 | 32·08 |
| 13 | 12·47 | 2·57 | 63 | 60·42 | 12·48 | 113 | 108·4 | 22·38 | 163 | 156·3 | 32·28 |
| 14 | 13·43 | 2·77 | 64 | 61·38 | 12·67 | 114 | 109·3 | 22·58 | 164 | 157·3 | 32·48 |
| 15 | 14·39 | 2·97 | 65 | 62·34 | 12·87 | 115 | 110·3 | 22·77 | 165 | 158·3 | 32·68 |
| 16 | 15·35 | 3·17 | 66 | 63·30 | 13·07 | 116 | 111·3 | 22·97 | 166 | 159·2 | 32·87 |
| 17 | 16·30 | 3·37 | 67 | 64·26 | 13·27 | 117 | 112·2 | 23·17 | 167 | 160·2 | 33·07 |
| 18 | 17·26 | 3·56 | 68 | 65·22 | 13·47 | 118 | 113·2 | 23·37 | 168 | 161·1 | 33·27 |
| 19 | 18·22 | 3·76 | 69 | 66·18 | 13·66 | 119 | 114·1 | 23·57 | 169 | 162·1 | 33·47 |
| 20 | 19·18 | 3·96 | 70 | 67·14 | 13·86 | 120 | 115·1 | 23·76 | 170 | 163·0 | 33·67 |
| 21 | 20·14 | 4·16 | 71 | 68·10 | 14·06 | 121 | 116·1 | 23·96 | 171 | 164·0 | 33·86 |
| 22 | 21·10 | 4·36 | 72 | 69·06 | 14·26 | 122 | 117·0 | 24·16 | 172 | 165·0 | 34·06 |
| 23 | 22·06 | 4·55 | 73 | 70·01 | 14·46 | 123 | 118·0 | 24·36 | 173 | 165·9 | 34·26 |
| 24 | 23·02 | 4·75 | 74 | 70·97 | 14·65 | 124 | 118·9 | 24·56 | 174 | 166·9 | 34·46 |
| 25 | 23·98 | 4·95 | 75 | 71·93 | 14·85 | 125 | 119·9 | 24·75 | 175 | 167·8 | 34·66 |
| 26 | 24·94 | 5·15 | 76 | 72·89 | 15·05 | 126 | 120·8 | 24·95 | 176 | 168·8 | 34·85 |
| 27 | 25·90 | 5·35 | 77 | 73·85 | 15·25 | 127 | 121·8 | 25·15 | 177 | 169·8 | 35·05 |
| 28 | 26·85 | 5·55 | 78 | 74·81 | 15·45 | 128 | 122·8 | 25·35 | 178 | 170·7 | 35·25 |
| 29 | 27·81 | 5·74 | 79 | 75·77 | 15·65 | 129 | 123·7 | 25·55 | 179 | 171·7 | 35·45 |
| 30 | 28·77 | 5·94 | 80 | 76·73 | 15·84 | 130 | 124·7 | 25·75 | 180 | 172·6 | 35·65 |
| 31 | 29·73 | 6·14 | 81 | 77·69 | 16·04 | 131 | 125·6 | 25·94 | 181 | 173·6 | 35·85 |
| 32 | 30·69 | 6·34 | 82 | 78·65 | 16·24 | 132 | 126·6 | 26·14 | 182 | 174·6 | 36·04 |
| 33 | 31·65 | 6·54 | 83 | 79·61 | 16·44 | 133 | 127·6 | 26·34 | 183 | 175·5 | 36·24 |
| 34 | 32·61 | 6·73 | 84 | 80·56 | 16·64 | 134 | 128·5 | 26·54 | 184 | 176·5 | 36·44 |
| 35 | 33·57 | 6·93 | 85 | 81·52 | 16·83 | 135 | 129·5 | 26·74 | 185 | 177·4 | 36·64 |
| 36 | 34·53 | 7·13 | 86 | 82·48 | 17·03 | 136 | 130·4 | 26·93 | 186 | 178·4 | 36·84 |
| 37 | 35·49 | 7·33 | 87 | 83·44 | 17·23 | 137 | 131·4 | 27·13 | 187 | 179·4 | 37·03 |
| 38 | 36·45 | 7·53 | 88 | 84·40 | 17·43 | 138 | 132·4 | 27·33 | 188 | 180·3 | 37·23 |
| 39 | 37·41 | 7·72 | 89 | 85·36 | 17·63 | 139 | 133·3 | 27·53 | 189 | 181·3 | 37·43 |
| 40 | 38·36 | 7·92 | 90 | 86·32 | 17·82 | 140 | 134·3 | 27·73 | 190 | 182·2 | 37·63 |
| 41 | 39·32 | 8·12 | 91 | 87·28 | 18·02 | 141 | 135·2 | 27·92 | 191 | 183·2 | 37·83 |
| 42 | 40·28 | 8·32 | 92 | 88·24 | 18·22 | 142 | 136·2 | 28·12 | 192 | 184·1 | 38·02 |
| 43 | 41·24 | 8·52 | 93 | 89·20 | 18·42 | 143 | 137·2 | 28·32 | 193 | 185·1 | 38·22 |
| 44 | 42·20 | 8·71 | 94 | 90·16 | 18·62 | 144 | 138·1 | 28·52 | 194 | 186·1 | 38·42 |
| 45 | 43·16 | 8·91 | 95 | 91·12 | 18·81 | 145 | 139·1 | 28·72 | 195 | 187·0 | 38·62 |
| 46 | 44·12 | 9·11 | 96 | 92·07 | 19·01 | 146 | 140·0 | 28·91 | 196 | 188·0 | 38·82 |
| 47 | 45·08 | 9·31 | 97 | 93·03 | 19·21 | 147 | 141·0 | 29·11 | 197 | 188·9 | 39·01 |
| 48 | 46·04 | 9·51 | 98 | 93·99 | 19·41 | 148 | 141·9 | 29·31 | 198 | 189·9 | 39·21 |
| 49 | 47·00 | 9·70 | 99 | 94·95 | 19·61 | 149 | 142·9 | 29·51 | 199 | 190·9 | 39·41 |
| 50 | 47·96 | 9·90 | 100 | 95·91 | 19·80 | 150 | 143·9 | 29·71 | 200 | 191·8 | 39·61 |
| 51 | 48·91 | 10·10 | 101 | 96·87 | 20·00 | 151 | 144·8 | 29·90 | 201 | 192·8 | 39·81 |
| 52 | 49·87 | 10·30 | 102 | 97·83 | 20·20 | 152 | 145·8 | 30·10 | 202 | 193·7 | 40·00 |
| 53 | 50·83 | 10·50 | 103 | 98·79 | 20·40 | 153 | 146·7 | 30·30 | 203 | 194·7 | 40·20 |
| 54 | 51·79 | 10·69 | 104 | 99·75 | 20·60 | 154 | 147·7 | 30·50 | 204 | 195·7 | 40·40 |
| 55 | 52·75 | 10·89 | 105 | 100·7 | 20·79 | 155 | 148·7 | 30·70 | 205 | 196·6 | 40·60 |
| 56 | 53·71 | 11·09 | 106 | 101·7 | 20·99 | 156 | 149·6 | 30·89 | 206 | 197·6 | 40·80 |
| 57 | 54·67 | 11·29 | 107 | 102·6 | 21·19 | 157 | 150·6 | 31·09 | 207 | 198·5 | 40·99 |
| 58 | 55·63 | 11·49 | 108 | 103·6 | 21·39 | 158 | 151·5 | 31·29 | 208 | 199·5 | 41·19 |
| 59 | 56·59 | 11·68 | 109 | 104·5 | 21·59 | 159 | 152·5 | 31·49 | 209 | 200·5 | 41·39 |
| 60 | 57·55 | 11·88 | 110 | 105·5 | 21·78 | 160 | 153·5 | 31·69 | 210 | 201·4 | 41·59 |

| G | D | H | G | D | H | G | D | H | G | D | H |
|---|---|---|---|---|---|---|---|---|---|---|---|
| 10 | 9·57 | 2·03 | 60 | 57·41 | 12·20 | 110 | 105·2 | 22·37 | 160 | 153·1 | 32·54 |
| 11 | 10·52 | 2·24 | 61 | 58·36 | 12·41 | 111 | 106·2 | 22·57 | 161 | 154·0 | 32·74 |
| 12 | 11·48 | 2·44 | 62 | 59·32 | 12·61 | 112 | 107·2 | 22·78 | 162 | 155·0 | 32·95 |
| 13 | 12·44 | 2·64 | 63 | 60·28 | 12·81 | 113 | 108·1 | 22·98 | 163 | 156·0 | 33·15 |
| 14 | 13·39 | 2·85 | 64 | 61·23 | 13·02 | 114 | 109·1 | 23·18 | 164 | 156·9 | 33·35 |
| 15 | 14·35 | 3·05 | 65 | 62·19 | 13·22 | 115 | 110·0 | 23·39 | 165 | 157·9 | 33·56 |
| 16 | 15·31 | 3·25 | 66 | 63·15 | 13·42 | 116 | 111·0 | 23·59 | 166 | 158·8 | 33·76 |
| 17 | 16·27 | 3·46 | 67 | 64·10 | 13·63 | 117 | 111·9 | 23·79 | 167 | 159·8 | 33·96 |
| 18 | 17·22 | 3·66 | 68 | 65·06 | 13·83 | 118 | 112·9 | 24·00 | 168 | 160·7 | 34·17 |
| 19 | 18·18 | 3·86 | 69 | 66·02 | 14·03 | 119 | 113·9 | 24·20 | 169 | 161·7 | 34·37 |
| 20 | 19·14 | 4·07 | 70 | 66·97 | 14·24 | 120 | 114·8 | 24·40 | 170 | 162·7 | 34·57 |
| 21 | 20·09 | 4·27 | 71 | 67·93 | 14·44 | 121 | 115·8 | 24·61 | 171 | 163·6 | 34·78 |
| 22 | 21·05 | 4·47 | 72 | 68·89 | 14·64 | 122 | 116·7 | 24·81 | 172 | 164·6 | 34·98 |
| 23 | 22·01 | 4·68 | 73 | 69·84 | 14·85 | 123 | 117·7 | 25·01 | 173 | 165·5 | 35·18 |
| 24 | 22·96 | 4·88 | 74 | 70·80 | 15·05 | 124 | 118·6 | 25·22 | 174 | 166·5 | 35·39 |
| 25 | 23·92 | 5·08 | 75 | 71·76 | 15·25 | 125 | 119·6 | 25·42 | 175 | 167·4 | 35·59 |
| 26 | 24·88 | 5·29 | 76 | 72·71 | 15·46 | 126 | 120·6 | 25·62 | 176 | 168·4 | 35·79 |
| 27 | 25·83 | 5·49 | 77 | 73·67 | 15·66 | 127 | 121·5 | 25·83 | 177 | 169·3 | 36·00 |
| 28 | 26·79 | 5·69 | 78 | 74·63 | 15·86 | 128 | 122·5 | 26·03 | 178 | 170·3 | 36·20 |
| 29 | 27·75 | 5·90 | 79 | 75·58 | 16·07 | 129 | 123·4 | 26·23 | 179 | 171·3 | 36·40 |
| 30 | 28·70 | 6·10 | 80 | 76·54 | 16·27 | 130 | 124·4 | 26·44 | 180 | 172·2 | 36·61 |
| 31 | 29·66 | 6·30 | 81 | 77·50 | 16·47 | 131 | 125·3 | 26·64 | 181 | 173·2 | 36·81 |
| 32 | 30·62 | 6·51 | 82 | 78·46 | 16·68 | 132 | 126·3 | 26·84 | 182 | 174·1 | 37·01 |
| 33 | 31·57 | 6·71 | 83 | 79·41 | 16·88 | 133 | 127·3 | 27·05 | 183 | 175·1 | 37·22 |
| 34 | 32·53 | 6·91 | 84 | 80·37 | 17·08 | 134 | 128·2 | 27·25 | 184 | 176·0 | 37·42 |
| 35 | 33·49 | 7·12 | 85 | 81·33 | 17·29 | 135 | 129·2 | 27·45 | 185 | 177·0 | 37·62 |
| 36 | 34·44 | 7·32 | 86 | 82·28 | 17·49 | 136 | 130·1 | 27·66 | 186 | 178·0 | 37·83 |
| 37 | 35·40 | 7·52 | 87 | 83·24 | 17·69 | 137 | 131·1 | 27·86 | 187 | 178·9 | 38·03 |
| 38 | 36·36 | 7·73 | 88 | 84·20 | 17·90 | 138 | 132·0 | 28·06 | 188 | 179·9 | 38·23 |
| 39 | 37·31 | 7·93 | 89 | 85·15 | 18·10 | 139 | 133·0 | 28·27 | 189 | 180·8 | 38·44 |
| 40 | 38·27 | 8·13 | 90 | 86·11 | 18·30 | 140 | 133·9 | 28·47 | 190 | 181·8 | 38·64 |
| 41 | 39·23 | 8·34 | 91 | 87·07 | 18·51 | 141 | 134·9 | 28·67 | 191 | 182·7 | 38·84 |
| 42 | 40·18 | 8·54 | 92 | 88·02 | 18·71 | 142 | 135·9 | 28·88 | 192 | 183·7 | 39·05 |
| 43 | 41·14 | 8·74 | 93 | 88·98 | 18·91 | 143 | 136·8 | 29·08 | 193 | 184·7 | 39·25 |
| 44 | 42·10 | 8·95 | 94 | 89·94 | 19·12 | 144 | 137·8 | 29·28 | 194 | 185·6 | 39·45 |
| 45 | 43·05 | 9·15 | 95 | 90·89 | 19·32 | 145 | 138·7 | 29·49 | 195 | 186·6 | 39·66 |
| 46 | 44·01 | 9·35 | 96 | 91·85 | 19·52 | 146 | 139·7 | 29·69 | 196 | 187·5 | 39·86 |
| 47 | 44·97 | 9·56 | 97 | 92·81 | 19·73 | 147 | 140·6 | 29·90 | 197 | 188·5 | 40·06 |
| 48 | 45·93 | 9·76 | 98 | 93·76 | 19·93 | 148 | 141·6 | 30·10 | 198 | 189·4 | 40·27 |
| 49 | 46·88 | 9·97 | 99 | 94·72 | 20·13 | 149 | 142·6 | 30·30 | 199 | 190·4 | 40·47 |
| 50 | 47·84 | 10·17 | 100 | 95·68 | 20·34 | 150 | 143·5 | 30·51 | 200 | 191·4 | 40·67 |
| 51 | 48·80 | 10·37 | 101 | 96·63 | 20·54 | 151 | 144·5 | 30·71 | 201 | 192·3 | 40·88 |
| 52 | 49·75 | 10·58 | 102 | 97·59 | 20·74 | 152 | 145·4 | 30·91 | 202 | 193·3 | 41·08 |
| 53 | 50·71 | 10·78 | 103 | 98·55 | 20·95 | 153 | 146·4 | 31·12 | 203 | 194·2 | 41·28 |
| 54 | 51·67 | 10·98 | 104 | 99·50 | 21·15 | 154 | 147·3 | 31·32 | 204 | 195·2 | 41·49 |
| 55 | 52·62 | 11·19 | 105 | 100·5 | 21·35 | 155 | 148·3 | 31·52 | 205 | 196·1 | 41·69 |
| 56 | 53·58 | 11·39 | 106 | 101·4 | 21·56 | 156 | 149·3 | 31·73 | 206 | 197·1 | 41·89 |
| 57 | 54·54 | 11·59 | 107 | 102·4 | 21·76 | 157 | 150·2 | 31·93 | 207 | 198·1 | 42·10 |
| 58 | 55·49 | 11·80 | 108 | 103·3 | 21·96 | 158 | 151·2 | 32·13 | 208 | 199·0 | 42·30 |
| 59 | 56·45 | 12·00 | 109 | 104·3 | 22·17 | 159 | 152·1 | 32·34 | 209 | 200·0 | 42·50 |
| 60 | 57·41 | 12·20 | 110 | 105·2 | 22·37 | 160 | 153·1 | 32·54 | 210 | 200·9 | 42·71 |

TABLE I

# 12° 20′

| G | D | H | G | D | H | G | D | H | G | D | H |
|---|---|---|---|---|---|---|---|---|---|---|---|
| 10 | 9·54 | 2·09 | 60 | 57·26 | 12·52 | 110 | 105·0 | 22·95 | 160 | 152·7 | 33·39 |
| 11 | 10·50 | 2·30 | 61 | 58·22 | 12·73 | 111 | 105·9 | 23·16 | 161 | 153·7 | 33·60 |
| 12 | 11·45 | 2·50 | 62 | 59·17 | 12·94 | 112 | 106·9 | 23·37 | 162 | 154·6 | 33·80 |
| 13 | 12·41 | 2·71 | 63 | 60·13 | 13·15 | 113 | 107·8 | 23·58 | 163 | 155·6 | 34·01 |
| 14 | 13·36 | 2·92 | 64 | 61·08 | 13·35 | 114 | 108·8 | 23·79 | 164 | 156·5 | 34·22 |
| 15 | 14·32 | 3·13 | 65 | 62·03 | 13·56 | 115 | 109·8 | 24·00 | 165 | 157·5 | 34·43 |
| 16 | 15·27 | 3·34 | 66 | 62·99 | 13·77 | 116 | 110·7 | 24·21 | 166 | 158·4 | 34·64 |
| 17 | 16·22 | 3·55 | 67 | 63·94 | 13·98 | 117 | 111·7 | 24·41 | 167 | 159·4 | 34·85 |
| 18 | 17·18 | 3·76 | 68 | 64·90 | 14·19 | 118 | 112·6 | 24·62 | 168 | 160·3 | 35·06 |
| 19 | 18·13 | 3·96 | 69 | 65·85 | 14·40 | 119 | 113·6 | 24·83 | 169 | 161·3 | 35·27 |
| 20 | 19·09 | 4·17 | 70 | 66·81 | 14·61 | 120 | 114·5 | 25·04 | 170 | 162·2 | 35·47 |
| 21 | 20·04 | 4·38 | 71 | 67·76 | 14·82 | 121 | 115·5 | 25·25 | 171 | 163·2 | 35·68 |
| 22 | 21·00 | 4·59 | 72 | 68·71 | 15·02 | 122 | 116·4 | 25·46 | 172 | 164·2 | 35·89 |
| 23 | 21·95 | 4·80 | 73 | 69·67 | 15·23 | 123 | 117·4 | 25·67 | 173 | 165·1 | 36·10 |
| 24 | 22·90 | 5·01 | 74 | 70·62 | 15·44 | 124 | 118·3 | 25·87 | 174 | 166·1 | 36·31 |
| 25 | 23·86 | 5·22 | 75 | 71·58 | 15·65 | 125 | 119·3 | 26·08 | 175 | 167·0 | 36·52 |
| 26 | 24·81 | 5·43 | 76 | 72·53 | 15·86 | 126 | 120·3 | 26·29 | 176 | 168·0 | 36·73 |
| 27 | 25·77 | 5·63 | 77 | 73·49 | 16·07 | 127 | 121·2 | 26·50 | 177 | 168·9 | 36·93 |
| 28 | 26·72 | 5·84 | 78 | 74·44 | 16·28 | 128 | 122·2 | 26·71 | 178 | 169·9 | 37·14 |
| 29 | 27·68 | 6·05 | 79 | 75·40 | 16·48 | 129 | 123·1 | 26·92 | 179 | 170·8 | 37·35 |
| 30 | 28·63 | 6·26 | 80 | 76·35 | 16·69 | 130 | 124·1 | 27·13 | 180 | 171·8 | 37·56 |
| 31 | 29·59 | 6·47 | 81 | 77·30 | 16·90 | 131 | 125·0 | 27·34 | 181 | 172·7 | 37·77 |
| 32 | 30·54 | 6·68 | 82 | 78·26 | 17·11 | 132 | 126·0 | 27·54 | 182 | 173·7 | 37·98 |
| 33 | 31·49 | 6·89 | 83 | 79·21 | 17·32 | 133 | 126·9 | 27·75 | 183 | 174·7 | 38·19 |
| 34 | 32·45 | 7·09 | 84 | 80·17 | 17·53 | 134 | 127·9 | 27·96 | 184 | 175·6 | 38·40 |
| 35 | 33·40 | 7·30 | 85 | 81·12 | 17·74 | 135 | 128·8 | 28·17 | 185 | 176·6 | 38·60 |
| 36 | 34·36 | 7·51 | 86 | 82·08 | 17·95 | 136 | 129·8 | 28·38 | 186 | 177·5 | 38·81 |
| 37 | 35·31 | 7·72 | 87 | 83·03 | 18·15 | 137 | 130·7 | 28·59 | 187 | 178·5 | 39·02 |
| 38 | 36·27 | 7·93 | 88 | 83·98 | 18·36 | 138 | 131·7 | 28·80 | 188 | 179·4 | 39·23 |
| 39 | 37·22 | 8·14 | 89 | 84·94 | 18·57 | 139 | 132·7 | 29·00 | 189 | 180·4 | 39·44 |
| 40 | 38·17 | 8·35 | 90 | 85·89 | 18·78 | 140 | 133·6 | 29·21 | 190 | 181·3 | 39·65 |
| 41 | 39·13 | 8·56 | 91 | 86·85 | 18·99 | 141 | 134·6 | 29·42 | 191 | 182·3 | 39·86 |
| 42 | 40·08 | 8·76 | 92 | 87·80 | 19·20 | 142 | 135·5 | 29·63 | 192 | 183·2 | 40·06 |
| 43 | 41·04 | 8·97 | 93 | 88·76 | 19·41 | 143 | 136·5 | 29·84 | 193 | 184·2 | 40·27 |
| 44 | 41·99 | 9·18 | 94 | 89·71 | 19·61 | 144 | 137·4 | 30·05 | 194 | 185·1 | 40·48 |
| 45 | 42·95 | 9·39 | 95 | 90·67 | 19·82 | 145 | 138·4 | 30·26 | 195 | 186·1 | 40·69 |
| 46 | 43·90 | 9·60 | 96 | 91·62 | 20·03 | 146 | 139·3 | 30·47 | 196 | 187·1 | 40·90 |
| 47 | 44·86 | 9·81 | 97 | 92·57 | 20·24 | 147 | 140·3 | 30·67 | 197 | 188·0 | 41·11 |
| 48 | 45·81 | 10·02 | 98 | 93·53 | 20·45 | 148 | 141·2 | 30·88 | 198 | 189·0 | 41·32 |
| 49 | 46·76 | 10·22 | 99 | 94·48 | 20·66 | 149 | 142·2 | 31·09 | 199 | 189·9 | 41·53 |
| 50 | 47·72 | 10·43 | 100 | 95·44 | 20·87 | 150 | 143·2 | 31·30 | 200 | 190·9 | 41·73 |
| 51 | 48·67 | 10·64 | 101 | 96·39 | 21·08 | 151 | 144·1 | 31·51 | 201 | 191·8 | 41·94 |
| 52 | 49·63 | 10·85 | 102 | 97·35 | 21·28 | 152 | 145·1 | 31·72 | 202 | 192·8 | 42·15 |
| 53 | 50·58 | 11·06 | 103 | 98·30 | 21·49 | 153 | 146·0 | 31·93 | 203 | 193·7 | 42·36 |
| 54 | 51·54 | 11·27 | 104 | 99·25 | 21·70 | 154 | 147·0 | 32·14 | 204 | 194·7 | 42·57 |
| 55 | 52·49 | 11·48 | 105 | 100·2 | 21·91 | 155 | 147·9 | 32·34 | 205 | 195·6 | 42·78 |
| 56 | 53·44 | 11·69 | 106 | 101·2 | 22·12 | 156 | 148·9 | 32·55 | 206 | 196·6 | 42·99 |
| 57 | 54·40 | 11·89 | 107 | 102·1 | 22·33 | 157 | 149·8 | 32·76 | 207 | 197·6 | 43·19 |
| 58 | 55·35 | 12·10 | 108 | 103·1 | 22·54 | 158 | 150·8 | 32·97 | 208 | 198·5 | 43·40 |
| 59 | 56·31 | 12·31 | 109 | 104·0 | 22·74 | 159 | 151·7 | 33·18 | 209 | 199·5 | 43·61 |
| 60 | 57·26 | 12·52 | 110 | 105·0 | 22·95 | 160 | 152·7 | 33·39 | 210 | 200·4 | 43·82 |

| G | D | H | G | D | H | G | D | H | G | D | H |
|---|---|---|---|---|---|---|---|---|---|---|---|
| 10 | 9·52 | 2·14 | 60 | 57·11 | 12·84 | 110 | 104·7 | 23·53 | 160 | 152·3 | 34·23 |
| 11 | 10·47 | 2·35 | 61 | 58·07 | 13·05 | 111 | 105·7 | 23·75 | 161 | 153·3 | 34·44 |
| 12 | 11·42 | 2·57 | 62 | 59·02 | 13·26 | 112 | 106·6 | 23·96 | 162 | 154·2 | 34·66 |
| 13 | 12·37 | 2·78 | 63 | 59·97 | 13·48 | 113 | 107·6 | 24·18 | 163 | 155·2 | 34·87 |
| 14 | 13·33 | 3·00 | 64 | 60·92 | 13·69 | 114 | 108·5 | 24·39 | 164 | 156·1 | 35·09 |
| 15 | 14·28 | 3·21 | 65 | 61·87 | 13·91 | 115 | 109·5 | 24·60 | 165 | 157·1 | 35·30 |
| 16 | 15·23 | 3·42 | 66 | 62·83 | 14·12 | 116 | 110·4 | 24·82 | 166 | 158·0 | 35·51 |
| 17 | 16·18 | 3·64 | 67 | 63·78 | 14·33 | 117 | 111·4 | 25·03 | 167 | 159·0 | 35·73 |
| 18 | 17·13 | 3·85 | 68 | 64·73 | 14·55 | 118 | 112·3 | 25·25 | 168 | 159·9 | 35·94 |
| 19 | 18·09 | 4·06 | 69 | 65·68 | 14·76 | 119 | 113·3 | 25·46 | 169 | 160·9 | 36·16 |
| 20 | 19·04 | 4·28 | 70 | 66·63 | 14·98 | 120 | 114·2 | 25·67 | 170 | 161·8 | 36·37 |
| 21 | 19·99 | 4·49 | 71 | 67·59 | 15·19 | 121 | 115·2 | 25·89 | 171 | 162·8 | 36·58 |
| 22 | 20·94 | 4·71 | 72 | 68·54 | 15·40 | 122 | 116·1 | 26·10 | 172 | 163·7 | 36·80 |
| 23 | 21·89 | 4·92 | 73 | 69·49 | 15·62 | 123 | 117·1 | 26·31 | 173 | 164·7 | 37·01 |
| 24 | 22·85 | 5·13 | 74 | 70·44 | 15·83 | 124 | 118·0 | 26·53 | 174 | 165·6 | 37·23 |
| 25 | 23·80 | 5·35 | 75 | 71·39 | 16·05 | 125 | 119·0 | 26·74 | 175 | 166·6 | 37·44 |
| 26 | 24·75 | 5·56 | 76 | 72·35 | 16·26 | 126 | 119·9 | 26·96 | 176 | 167·5 | 37·65 |
| 27 | 25·70 | 5·78 | 77 | 73·30 | 16·47 | 127 | 120·9 | 27·17 | 177 | 168·5 | 37·87 |
| 28 | 26·65 | 5·99 | 78 | 74·25 | 16·69 | 128 | 121·8 | 27·38 | 178 | 169·4 | 38·08 |
| 29 | 27·61 | 6·20 | 79 | 75·20 | 16·90 | 129 | 122·8 | 27·60 | 179 | 170·4 | 38·30 |
| 30 | 28·56 | 6·42 | 80 | 76·15 | 17·12 | 130 | 123·7 | 27·81 | 180 | 171·3 | 38·51 |
| 31 | 29·51 | 6·63 | 81 | 77·11 | 17·33 | 131 | 124·7 | 28·03 | 181 | 172·3 | 38·72 |
| 32 | 30·46 | 6·85 | 82 | 78·06 | 17·54 | 132 | 125·7 | 28·24 | 182 | 173·2 | 38·94 |
| 33 | 31·41 | 7·06 | 83 | 79·01 | 17·76 | 133 | 126·6 | 28·45 | 183 | 174·2 | 39·15 |
| 34 | 32·37 | 7·27 | 84 | 79·96 | 17·97 | 134 | 127·6 | 28·67 | 184 | 175·2 | 39·37 |
| 35 | 33·32 | 7·49 | 85 | 80·91 | 18·18 | 135 | 128·5 | 28·88 | 185 | 176·1 | 39·58 |
| 36 | 34·27 | 7·70 | 86 | 81·86 | 18·40 | 136 | 129·5 | 29·10 | 186 | 177·1 | 39·79 |
| 37 | 35·22 | 7·92 | 87 | 82·82 | 18·61 | 137 | 130·4 | 29·31 | 187 | 178·0 | 40·01 |
| 38 | 36·17 | 8·13 | 88 | 83·77 | 18·83 | 138 | 131·4 | 29·52 | 188 | 179·0 | 40·22 |
| 39 | 37·12 | 8·34 | 89 | 84·72 | 19·04 | 139 | 132·3 | 29·74 | 189 | 179·9 | 40·43 |
| 40 | 38·08 | 8·56 | 90 | 85·67 | 19·25 | 140 | 133·3 | 29·95 | 190 | 180·9 | 40·65 |
| 41 | 39·03 | 8·77 | 91 | 86·62 | 19·47 | 141 | 134·2 | 30·17 | 191 | 181·8 | 40·86 |
| 42 | 39·98 | 8·99 | 92 | 87·58 | 19·68 | 142 | 135·2 | 30·38 | 192 | 182·8 | 41·08 |
| 43 | 40·93 | 9·20 | 93 | 88·53 | 19·90 | 143 | 136·1 | 30·59 | 193 | 183·7 | 41·29 |
| 44 | 41·88 | 9·41 | 94 | 89·48 | 20·11 | 144 | 137·1 | 30·81 | 194 | 184·7 | 41·50 |
| 45 | 42·84 | 9·63 | 95 | 90·43 | 20·32 | 145 | 138·0 | 31·02 | 195 | 185·6 | 41·72 |
| 46 | 43·79 | 9·84 | 96 | 91·38 | 20·54 | 146 | 139·0 | 31·24 | 196 | 186·6 | 41·93 |
| 47 | 44·74 | 10·06 | 97 | 92·34 | 20·75 | 147 | 139·9 | 31·45 | 197 | 187·5 | 42·15 |
| 48 | 45·69 | 10·27 | 98 | 93·29 | 20·97 | 148 | 140·9 | 31·66 | 198 | 188·5 | 42·36 |
| 49 | 46·64 | 10·48 | 99 | 94·24 | 21·18 | 149 | 141·8 | 31·88 | 199 | 189·4 | 42·57 |
| 50 | 47·60 | 10·70 | 100 | 95·19 | 21·39 | 150 | 142·8 | 32·09 | 200 | 190·4 | 42·79 |
| 51 | 48·55 | 10·91 | 101 | 96·14 | 21·61 | 151 | 143·7 | 32·31 | 201 | 191·3 | 43·00 |
| 52 | 49·50 | 11·12 | 102 | 97·10 | 21·82 | 152 | 144·7 | 32·52 | 202 | 192·3 | 43·22 |
| 53 | 50·45 | 11·34 | 103 | 98·05 | 22·04 | 153 | 145·6 | 32·73 | 203 | 193·2 | 43·43 |
| 54 | 51·40 | 11·55 | 104 | 99·00 | 22·25 | 154 | 146·6 | 32·95 | 204 | 194·2 | 43·64 |
| 55 | 52·36 | 11·77 | 105 | 99·95 | 22·46 | 155 | 147·5 | 33·16 | 205 | 195·1 | 43·86 |
| 56 | 53·31 | 11·98 | 106 | 100·9 | 22·68 | 156 | 148·5 | 33·37 | 206 | 196·1 | 44·07 |
| 57 | 54·26 | 12·19 | 107 | 101·9 | 22·89 | 157 | 149·5 | 33·59 | 207 | 197·0 | 44·29 |
| 58 | 55·21 | 12·41 | 108 | 102·8 | 23·11 | 158 | 150·4 | 33·80 | 208 | 198·0 | 44·50 |
| 59 | 56·16 | 12·62 | 109 | 103·8 | 23·32 | 159 | 151·4 | 34·02 | 209 | 199·0 | 44·71 |
| 60 | 57·11 | 12·84 | 110 | 104·7 | 23·53 | 160 | 152·3 | 34·23 | 210 | 199·9 | 44·93 |

TABLE I

# 13° 00′

| G | D | H | G | D | H | G | D | H | G | D | H |
|---|---|---|---|---|---|---|---|---|---|---|---|
| 10 | 9·49 | 2·19 | 60 | 56·96 | 13·15 | 110 | 104·4 | 24·11 | 160 | 151·9 | 35·07 |
| 11 | 10·44 | 2·41 | 61 | 57·91 | 13·37 | 111 | 105·4 | 24·33 | 161 | 152·9 | 35·29 |
| 12 | 11·39 | 2·63 | 62 | 58·86 | 13·59 | 112 | 106·3 | 24·55 | 162 | 153·8 | 35·51 |
| 13 | 12·34 | 2·85 | 63 | 59·81 | 13·81 | 113 | 107·3 | 24·77 | 163 | 154·8 | 35·73 |
| 14 | 13·29 | 3·07 | 64 | 60·76 | 14·03 | 114 | 108·2 | 24·99 | 164 | 155·7 | 35·95 |
| 15 | 14·24 | 3·29 | 65 | 61·71 | 14·25 | 115 | 109·2 | 25·21 | 165 | 156·7 | 36·17 |
| 16 | 15·19 | 3·51 | 66 | 62·66 | 14·47 | 116 | 110·1 | 25·43 | 166 | 157·6 | 36·38 |
| 17 | 16·14 | 3·73 | 67 | 63·61 | 14·69 | 117 | 111·1 | 25·64 | 167 | 158·5 | 36·60 |
| 18 | 17·09 | 3·95 | 68 | 64·56 | 14·90 | 118 | 112·0 | 25·86 | 168 | 159·5 | 36·82 |
| 19 | 18·04 | 4·16 | 69 | 65·51 | 15·12 | 119 | 113·0 | 26·08 | 169 | 160·4 | 37·04 |
| 20 | 18·99 | 4·38 | 70 | 66·46 | 15·34 | 120 | 113·9 | 26·30 | 170 | 161·4 | 37·26 |
| 21 | 19·94 | 4·60 | 71 | 67·41 | 15·56 | 121 | 114·9 | 26·52 | 171 | 162·3 | 37·48 |
| 22 | 20·89 | 4·82 | 72 | 68·36 | 15·78 | 122 | 115·8 | 26·74 | 172 | 163·3 | 37·70 |
| 23 | 21·84 | 5·04 | 73 | 69·31 | 16·00 | 123 | 116·8 | 26·96 | 173 | 164·2 | 37·92 |
| 24 | 22·79 | 5·26 | 74 | 70·26 | 16·22 | 124 | 117·7 | 27·18 | 174 | 165·2 | 38·14 |
| 25 | 23·73 | 5·48 | 75 | 71·20 | 16·44 | 125 | 118·7 | 27·40 | 175 | 166·1 | 38·36 |
| 26 | 24·68 | 5·70 | 76 | 72·15 | 16·66 | 126 | 119·6 | 27·62 | 176 | 167·1 | 38·58 |
| 27 | 25·63 | 5·92 | 77 | 73·10 | 16·88 | 127 | 120·6 | 27·84 | 177 | 168·0 | 38·80 |
| 28 | 26·58 | 6·14 | 78 | 74·05 | 17·10 | 128 | 121·5 | 28·06 | 178 | 169·0 | 39·01 |
| 29 | 27·53 | 6·36 | 79 | 75·00 | 17·32 | 129 | 122·5 | 28·27 | 179 | 169·9 | 39·23 |
| 30 | 28·48 | 6·58 | 80 | 75·95 | 17·53 | 130 | 123·4 | 28·49 | 180 | 170·9 | 39·45 |
| 31 | 29·43 | 6·79 | 81 | 76·90 | 17·75 | 131 | 124·4 | 28·71 | 181 | 171·8 | 39·67 |
| 32 | 30·38 | 7·01 | 82 | 77·85 | 17·97 | 132 | 125·3 | 28·93 | 182 | 172·8 | 39·89 |
| 33 | 31·33 | 7·23 | 83 | 78·80 | 18·19 | 133 | 126·3 | 29·15 | 183 | 173·7 | 40·11 |
| 34 | 32·28 | 7·45 | 84 | 79·75 | 18·41 | 134 | 127·2 | 29·37 | 184 | 174·7 | 40·33 |
| 35 | 33·23 | 7·67 | 85 | 80·70 | 18·63 | 135 | 128·2 | 29·59 | 185 | 175·6 | 40·55 |
| 36 | 34·18 | 7·89 | 86 | 81·65 | 18·85 | 136 | 129·1 | 29·81 | 186 | 176·6 | 40·77 |
| 37 | 35·13 | 8·11 | 87 | 82·60 | 19·07 | 137 | 130·1 | 30·03 | 187 | 177·5 | 40·99 |
| 38 | 36·08 | 8·33 | 88 | 83·55 | 19·29 | 138 | 131·0 | 30·25 | 188 | 178·5 | 41·21 |
| 39 | 37·03 | 8·55 | 89 | 84·50 | 19·51 | 139 | 132·0 | 30·47 | 189 | 179·4 | 41·43 |
| 40 | 37·98 | 8·77 | 90 | 85·45 | 19·73 | 140 | 132·9 | 30·69 | 190 | 180·4 | 41·65 |
| 41 | 38·93 | 8·99 | 91 | 86·40 | 19·95 | 141 | 133·9 | 30·91 | 191 | 181·3 | 41·86 |
| 42 | 39·87 | 9·21 | 92 | 87·34 | 20·17 | 142 | 134·8 | 31·12 | 192 | 182·3 | 42·08 |
| 43 | 40·82 | 9·42 | 93 | 88·29 | 20·38 | 143 | 135·8 | 31·34 | 193 | 183·2 | 42·30 |
| 44 | 41·77 | 9·64 | 94 | 89·24 | 20·60 | 144 | 136·7 | 31·56 | 194 | 184·2 | 42·52 |
| 45 | 42·72 | 9·86 | 95 | 90·19 | 20·82 | 145 | 137·7 | 31·78 | 195 | 185·1 | 42·74 |
| 46 | 43·67 | 10·08 | 96 | 91·14 | 21·04 | 146 | 138·6 | 32·00 | 196 | 186·1 | 42·96 |
| 47 | 44·62 | 10·30 | 97 | 92·09 | 21·26 | 147 | 139·6 | 32·22 | 197 | 187·0 | 43·18 |
| 48 | 45·57 | 10·52 | 98 | 93·04 | 21·48 | 148 | 140·5 | 32·44 | 198 | 188·0 | 43·40 |
| 49 | 46·52 | 10·74 | 99 | 93·99 | 21·70 | 149 | 141·5 | 32·66 | 199 | 188·9 | 43·62 |
| 50 | 47·47 | 10·96 | 100 | 94·94 | 21·92 | 150 | 142·4 | 32·88 | 200 | 189·9 | 43·84 |
| 51 | 48·42 | 11·18 | 101 | 95·89 | 22·14 | 151 | 143·4 | 33·10 | 201 | 190·8 | 44·06 |
| 52 | 49·37 | 11·40 | 102 | 96·84 | 22·36 | 152 | 144·3 | 33·32 | 202 | 191·8 | 44·28 |
| 53 | 50·32 | 11·62 | 103 | 97·79 | 22·58 | 153 | 145·3 | 33·54 | 203 | 192·7 | 44·49 |
| 54 | 51·27 | 11·84 | 104 | 98·74 | 22·80 | 154 | 146·2 | 33·75 | 204 | 193·7 | 44·71 |
| 55 | 52·22 | 12·06 | 105 | 99·69 | 23·01 | 155 | 147·2 | 33·97 | 205 | 194·6 | 44·93 |
| 56 | 53·17 | 12·27 | 106 | 100·6 | 23·23 | 156 | 148·1 | 34·19 | 206 | 195·6 | 45·15 |
| 57 | 54·12 | 12·49 | 107 | 101·6 | 23·45 | 157 | 149·1 | 34·41 | 207 | 196·5 | 45·37 |
| 58 | 55·06 | 12·71 | 108 | 102·5 | 23·67 | 158 | 150·0 | 34·63 | 208 | 197·5 | 45·59 |
| 59 | 56·01 | 12·93 | 109 | 103·5 | 23·89 | 159 | 151·0 | 34·85 | 209 | 198·4 | 45·81 |
| 60 | 56·96 | 13·15 | 110 | 104·4 | 24·11 | 160 | 151·9 | 35·07 | 210 | 199·4 | 46·03 |

| G | D | H | G | D | H | G | D | H | G | D | H |
|---|---|---|---|---|---|---|---|---|---|---|---|
| 10 | 9·47 | 2·24 | 60 | 56·81 | 13·46 | 110 | 104·1 | 24·68 | 160 | 151·5 | 35·90 |
| 11 | 10·41 | 2·47 | 61 | 57·76 | 13·69 | 111 | 105·1 | 24·91 | 161 | 152·4 | 36·13 |
| 12 | 11·36 | 2·69 | 62 | 58·70 | 13·91 | 112 | 106·0 | 25·13 | 162 | 153·4 | 36·35 |
| 13 | 12·31 | 2·92 | 63 | 59·65 | 14·14 | 113 | 107·0 | 25·36 | 163 | 154·3 | 36·58 |
| 14 | 13·26 | 3·14 | 64 | 60·60 | 14·36 | 114 | 107·9 | 25·58 | 164 | 155·3 | 36·80 |
| 15 | 14·20 | 3·37 | 65 | 61·54 | 14·59 | 115 | 108·9 | 25·81 | 165 | 156·2 | 37·03 |
| 16 | 15·15 | 3·59 | 66 | 62·49 | 14·81 | 116 | 109·8 | 26·03 | 166 | 157·2 | 37·25 |
| 17 | 16·10 | 3·81 | 67 | 63·44 | 15·03 | 117 | 110·8 | 26·25 | 167 | 158·1 | 37·47 |
| 18 | 17·04 | 4·04 | 68 | 64·38 | 15·26 | 118 | 111·7 | 26·48 | 168 | 159·1 | 37·70 |
| 19 | 17·99 | 4·26 | 69 | 65·33 | 15·48 | 119 | 112·7 | 26·70 | 169 | 160·0 | 37·92 |
| 20 | 18·94 | 4·49 | 70 | 66·28 | 15·71 | 120 | 113·6 | 26·93 | 170 | 161·0 | 38·15 |
| 21 | 19·88 | 4·71 | 71 | 67·22 | 15·93 | 121 | 114·6 | 27·15 | 171 | 161·9 | 38·37 |
| 22 | 20·83 | 4·94 | 72 | 68·17 | 16·16 | 122 | 115·5 | 27·38 | 172 | 162·9 | 38·60 |
| 23 | 21·78 | 5·16 | 73 | 69·12 | 16·38 | 123 | 116·5 | 27·60 | 173 | 163·8 | 38·82 |
| 24 | 22·72 | 5·39 | 74 | 70·06 | 16·61 | 124 | 117·4 | 27·83 | 174 | 164·7 | 39·05 |
| 25 | 23·67 | 5·61 | 75 | 71·01 | 16·83 | 125 | 118·4 | 28·05 | 175 | 165·7 | 39·27 |
| 26 | 24·62 | 5·83 | 76 | 71·96 | 17·05 | 126 | 119·3 | 28·27 | 176 | 166·6 | 39·49 |
| 27 | 25·56 | 6·06 | 77 | 72·90 | 17·28 | 127 | 120·2 | 28·50 | 177 | 167·6 | 39·72 |
| 28 | 26·51 | 6·28 | 78 | 73·85 | 17·50 | 128 | 121·2 | 28·72 | 178 | 168·5 | 39·94 |
| 29 | 27·46 | 6·51 | 79 | 74·80 | 17·73 | 129 | 122·1 | 28·95 | 179 | 169·5 | 40·17 |
| 30 | 28·40 | 6·73 | 80 | 75·75 | 17·95 | 130 | 123·1 | 29·17 | 180 | 170·4 | 40·39 |
| 31 | 29·35 | 6·96 | 81 | 76·69 | 18·18 | 131 | 124·0 | 29·40 | 181 | 171·4 | 40·62 |
| 32 | 30·30 | 7·18 | 82 | 77·64 | 18·40 | 132 | 125·0 | 29·62 | 182 | 172·3 | 40·84 |
| 33 | 31·24 | 7·41 | 83 | 78·59 | 18·63 | 133 | 125·9 | 29·85 | 183 | 173·3 | 41·07 |
| 34 | 32·19 | 7·63 | 84 | 79·53 | 18·85 | 134 | 126·9 | 30·07 | 184 | 174·2 | 41·29 |
| 35 | 33·14 | 7·85 | 85 | 80·48 | 19·07 | 135 | 127·8 | 30·29 | 185 | 175·2 | 41·51 |
| 36 | 34·09 | 8·08 | 86 | 81·43 | 19·30 | 136 | 128·8 | 30·52 | 186 | 176·1 | 41·74 |
| 37 | 35·03 | 8·30 | 87 | 82·37 | 19·52 | 137 | 129·7 | 30·74 | 187 | 177·1 | 41·96 |
| 38 | 35·98 | 8·53 | 88 | 83·32 | 19·75 | 138 | 130·7 | 30·97 | 188 | 178·0 | 42·19 |
| 39 | 36·93 | 8·75 | 89 | 84·27 | 19·97 | 139 | 131·6 | 31·19 | 189 | 178·9 | 42·41 |
| 40 | 37·87 | 8·98 | 90 | 85·21 | 20·20 | 140 | 132·6 | 31·42 | 190 | 179·9 | 42·64 |
| 41 | 38·82 | 9·20 | 91 | 86·16 | 20·42 | 141 | 133·5 | 31·64 | 191 | 180·8 | 42·86 |
| 42 | 39·77 | 9·42 | 92 | 87·11 | 20·64 | 142 | 134·4 | 31·86 | 192 | 181·8 | 43·08 |
| 43 | 40·71 | 9·65 | 93 | 88·05 | 20·87 | 143 | 135·4 | 32·09 | 193 | 182·7 | 43·31 |
| 44 | 41·66 | 9·87 | 94 | 89·00 | 21·09 | 144 | 136·3 | 32·31 | 194 | 183·7 | 43·53 |
| 45 | 42·61 | 10·10 | 95 | 89·95 | 21·32 | 145 | 137·3 | 32·54 | 195 | 184·6 | 43·76 |
| 46 | 43·55 | 10·32 | 96 | 90·89 | 21·54 | 146 | 138·2 | 32·76 | 196 | 185·6 | 43·98 |
| 47 | 44·50 | 10·55 | 97 | 91·84 | 21·77 | 147 | 139·2 | 32·99 | 197 | 186·5 | 44·21 |
| 48 | 45·45 | 10·77 | 98 | 92·79 | 21·99 | 148 | 140·1 | 33·21 | 198 | 187·5 | 44·43 |
| 49 | 46·39 | 11·00 | 99 | 93·73 | 22·22 | 149 | 141·1 | 33·44 | 199 | 188·4 | 44·66 |
| 50 | 47·34 | 11·22 | 100 | 94·68 | 22·44 | 150 | 142·0 | 33·66 | 200 | 189·4 | 44·88 |
| 51 | 48·29 | 11·44 | 101 | 95·63 | 22·66 | 151 | 143·0 | 33·88 | 201 | 190·3 | 45·10 |
| 52 | 49·23 | 11·67 | 102 | 96·58 | 22·89 | 152 | 143·9 | 34·11 | 202 | 191·3 | 45·33 |
| 53 | 50·18 | 11·89 | 103 | 97·52 | 23·11 | 153 | 144·9 | 34·33 | 203 | 192·2 | 45·55 |
| 54 | 51·13 | 12·12 | 104 | 98·47 | 23·34 | 154 | 145·8 | 34·56 | 204 | 193·2 | 45·78 |
| 55 | 52·07 | 12·34 | 105 | 99·42 | 23·56 | 155 | 146·8 | 34·78 | 205 | 194·1 | 46·00 |
| 56 | 53·02 | 12·57 | 106 | 100·4 | 23·79 | 156 | 147·7 | 35·01 | 206 | 195·0 | 46·23 |
| 57 | 53·97 | 12·79 | 107 | 101·3 | 24·01 | 157 | 148·6 | 35·23 | 207 | 196·0 | 46·45 |
| 58 | 54·92 | 13·02 | 108 | 102·3 | 24·24 | 158 | 149·6 | 35·46 | 208 | 196·9 | 46·67 |
| 59 | 55·86 | 13·24 | 109 | 103·2 | 24·46 | 159 | 150·5 | 35·68 | 209 | 197·9 | 46·90 |
| 60 | 56·81 | 13·46 | 110 | 104·1 | 24·68 | 160 | 151·5 | 35·90 | 210 | 198·8 | 47·12 |

TABLE I

# 13° 40′

| G | D | H | G | D | H | G | D | H | G | D | H |
|---|---|---|---|---|---|---|---|---|---|---|---|
| 10 | 9·44 | 2·30 | 60 | 56·65 | 13·77 | 110 | 103·9 | 25·25 | 160 | 151·1 | 36·73 |
| 11 | 10·39 | 2·53 | 61 | 57·59 | 14·00 | 111 | 104·8 | 25·48 | 161 | 152·0 | 36·96 |
| 12 | 11·33 | 2·75 | 62 | 58·54 | 14·23 | 112 | 105·7 | 25·71 | 162 | 153·0 | 37·19 |
| 13 | 12·27 | 2·98 | 63 | 59·48 | 14·46 | 113 | 106·7 | 25·94 | 163 | 153·9 | 37·42 |
| 14 | 13·22 | 3·21 | 64 | 60·43 | 14·69 | 114 | 107·6 | 26·17 | 164 | 154·8 | 37·65 |
| 15 | 14·16 | 3·44 | 65 | 61·37 | 14·92 | 115 | 108·6 | 26·40 | 165 | 155·8 | 37·88 |
| 16 | 15·11 | 3·67 | 66 | 62·32 | 15·15 | 116 | 109·5 | 26·63 | 166 | 156·7 | 38·11 |
| 17 | 16·05 | 3·90 | 67 | 63·26 | 15·38 | 117 | 110·5 | 26·86 | 167 | 157·7 | 38·34 |
| 18 | 17·00 | 4·13 | 68 | 64·20 | 15·61 | 118 | 111·4 | 27·09 | 168 | 158·6 | 38·57 |
| 19 | 17·94 | 4·36 | 69 | 65·15 | 15·84 | 119 | 112·4 | 27·32 | 169 | 159·6 | 38·80 |
| 20 | 18·88 | 4·59 | 70 | 66·09 | 16·07 | 120 | 113·3 | 27·55 | 170 | 160·5 | 39·03 |
| 21 | 19·83 | 4·82 | 71 | 67·04 | 16·30 | 121 | 114·2 | 27·78 | 171 | 161·5 | 39·26 |
| 22 | 20·77 | 5·05 | 72 | 67·98 | 16·53 | 122 | 115·2 | 28·01 | 172 | 162·4 | 39·49 |
| 23 | 21·72 | 5·28 | 73 | 68·92 | 16·76 | 123 | 116·1 | 28·24 | 173 | 163·3 | 39·72 |
| 24 | 22·66 | 5·51 | 74 | 69·87 | 16·99 | 124 | 117·1 | 28·47 | 174 | 164·3 | 39·95 |
| 25 | 23·60 | 5·74 | 75 | 70·81 | 17·22 | 125 | 118·0 | 28·70 | 175 | 165·2 | 40·18 |
| 26 | 24·55 | 5·97 | 76 | 71·76 | 17·45 | 126 | 119·0 | 28·93 | 176 | 166·2 | 40·41 |
| 27 | 25·49 | 6·20 | 77 | 72·70 | 17·68 | 127 | 119·9 | 29·16 | 177 | 167·1 | 40·64 |
| 28 | 26·44 | 6·43 | 78 | 73·65 | 17·91 | 128 | 120·9 | 29·39 | 178 | 168·1 | 40·87 |
| 29 | 27·38 | 6·66 | 79 | 74·59 | 18·14 | 129 | 121·8 | 29·62 | 179 | 169·0 | 41·10 |
| 30 | 28·33 | 6·89 | 80 | 75·53 | 18·37 | 130 | 122·7 | 29·85 | 180 | 170·0 | 41·32 |
| 31 | 29·27 | 7·12 | 81 | 76·48 | 18·60 | 131 | 123·7 | 30·08 | 181 | 170·9 | 41·55 |
| 32 | 30·21 | 7·35 | 82 | 77·42 | 18·83 | 132 | 124·6 | 30·30 | 182 | 171·8 | 41·78 |
| 33 | 31·16 | 7·58 | 83 | 78·37 | 19·06 | 133 | 125·6 | 30·53 | 183 | 172·8 | 42·01 |
| 34 | 32·10 | 7·81 | 84 | 79·31 | 19·28 | 134 | 126·5 | 30·76 | 184 | 173·7 | 42·24 |
| 35 | 33·05 | 8·04 | 85 | 80·25 | 19·51 | 135 | 127·5 | 30·99 | 185 | 174·7 | 42·47 |
| 36 | 33·99 | 8·26 | 86 | 81·20 | 19·74 | 136 | 128·4 | 31·22 | 186 | 175·6 | 42·70 |
| 37 | 34·93 | 8·49 | 87 | 82·14 | 19·97 | 137 | 129·4 | 31·45 | 187 | 176·6 | 42·93 |
| 38 | 35·88 | 8·72 | 88 | 83·09 | 20·20 | 138 | 130·3 | 31·68 | 188 | 177·5 | 43·16 |
| 39 | 36·82 | 8·95 | 89 | 84·03 | 20·43 | 139 | 131·2 | 31·91 | 189 | 178·4 | 43·39 |
| 40 | 37·77 | 9·18 | 90 | 84·98 | 20·66 | 140 | 132·2 | 32·14 | 190 | 179·4 | 43·62 |
| 41 | 38·71 | 9·41 | 91 | 85·92 | 20·89 | 141 | 133·1 | 32·37 | 191 | 180·3 | 43·85 |
| 42 | 39·66 | 9·64 | 92 | 86·86 | 21·12 | 142 | 134·1 | 32·60 | 192 | 181·3 | 44·08 |
| 43 | 40·60 | 9·87 | 93 | 87·81 | 21·35 | 143 | 135·0 | 32·83 | 193 | 182·2 | 44·31 |
| 44 | 41·54 | 10·10 | 94 | 88·75 | 21·58 | 144 | 136·0 | 33·06 | 194 | 183·2 | 44·54 |
| 45 | 42·49 | 10·33 | 95 | 89·70 | 21·81 | 145 | 136·9 | 33·29 | 195 | 184·1 | 44·77 |
| 46 | 43·43 | 10·56 | 96 | 90·64 | 22·04 | 146 | 137·8 | 33·52 | 196 | 185·1 | 45·00 |
| 47 | 44·38 | 10·79 | 97 | 91·58 | 22·27 | 147 | 138·8 | 33·75 | 197 | 186·0 | 45·23 |
| 48 | 45·32 | 11·02 | 98 | 92·53 | 22·50 | 148 | 139·7 | 33·98 | 198 | 186·9 | 45·46 |
| 49 | 46·26 | 11·25 | 99 | 93·47 | 22·73 | 149 | 140·7 | 34·21 | 199 | 187·9 | 45·69 |
| 50 | 47·21 | 11·48 | 100 | 94·42 | 22·96 | 150 | 141·6 | 34·44 | 200 | 188·8 | 45·92 |
| 51 | 48·15 | 11·71 | 101 | 95·36 | 23·19 | 151 | 142·6 | 34·67 | 201 | 189·8 | 46·15 |
| 52 | 49·10 | 11·94 | 102 | 96·31 | 23·42 | 152 | 143·5 | 34·90 | 202 | 190·7 | 46·38 |
| 53 | 50·04 | 12·17 | 103 | 97·25 | 23·65 | 153 | 144·5 | 35·13 | 203 | 191·7 | 46·61 |
| 54 | 50·99 | 12·40 | 104 | 98·19 | 23·88 | 154 | 145·4 | 35·36 | 204 | 192·6 | 46·83 |
| 55 | 51·93 | 12·63 | 105 | 99·14 | 24·11 | 155 | 146·3 | 35·59 | 205 | 193·6 | 47·06 |
| 56 | 52·87 | 12·86 | 106 | 100·1 | 24·34 | 156 | 147·3 | 35·81 | 206 | 194·5 | 47·29 |
| 57 | 53·82 | 13·09 | 107 | 101·0 | 24·57 | 157 | 148·2 | 36·04 | 207 | 195·4 | 47·52 |
| 58 | 54·76 | 13·32 | 108 | 102·0 | 24·79 | 158 | 149·2 | 36·27 | 208 | 196·4 | 47·75 |
| 59 | 55·71 | 13·55 | 109 | 102·9 | 25·02 | 159 | 150·1 | 36·50 | 209 | 197·3 | 47·98 |
| 60 | 56·65 | 13·77 | 110 | 103·9 | 25·25 | 160 | 151·1 | 36·73 | 210 | 198·3 | 48·21 |

| G | D | H | G | D | H | G | D | H | G | D | H |
|---|---|---|---|---|---|---|---|---|---|---|---|
| 10 | 9·41 | 2·35 | 60 | 56·49 | 14·08 | 110 | 103·6 | 25·82 | 160 | 150·6 | 37·56 |
| 11 | 10·36 | 2·58 | 61 | 57·43 | 14·32 | 111 | 104·5 | 26·06 | 161 | 151·6 | 37·79 |
| 12 | 11·30 | 2·82 | 62 | 58·37 | 14·55 | 112 | 105·4 | 26·29 | 162 | 152·5 | 38·03 |
| 13 | 12·24 | 3·05 | 63 | 59·31 | 14·79 | 113 | 106·4 | 26·53 | 163 | 153·5 | 38·26 |
| 14 | 13·18 | 3·29 | 64 | 60·25 | 15·02 | 114 | 107·3 | 26·76 | 164 | 154·4 | 38·50 |
| 15 | 14·12 | 3·52 | 65 | 61·20 | 15·26 | 115 | 108·3 | 26·99 | 165 | 155·3 | 38·73 |
| 16 | 15·06 | 3·76 | 66 | 62·14 | 15·49 | 116 | 109·2 | 27·23 | 166 | 156·3 | 38·97 |
| 17 | 16·01 | 3·99 | 67 | 63·08 | 15·73 | 117 | 110·2 | 27·46 | 167 | 157·2 | 39·20 |
| 18 | 16·95 | 4·23 | 68 | 64·02 | 15·96 | 118 | 111·1 | 27·70 | 168 | 158·2 | 39·44 |
| 19 | 17·89 | 4·46 | 69 | 64·96 | 16·20 | 119 | 112·0 | 27·93 | 169 | 159·1 | 39·67 |
| 20 | 18·83 | 4·69 | 70 | 65·90 | 16·43 | 120 | 113·0 | 28·17 | 170 | 160·1 | 39·90 |
| 21 | 19·77 | 4·93 | 71 | 66·84 | 16·67 | 121 | 113·9 | 28·40 | 171 | 161·0 | 40·14 |
| 22 | 20·71 | 5·16 | 72 | 67·79 | 16·90 | 122 | 114·9 | 28·64 | 172 | 161·9 | 40·37 |
| 23 | 21·65 | 5·40 | 73 | 68·73 | 17·14 | 123 | 115·8 | 28·87 | 173 | 162·9 | 40·61 |
| 24 | 22·60 | 5·63 | 74 | 69·67 | 17·37 | 124 | 116·7 | 29·11 | 174 | 163·8 | 40·84 |
| 25 | 23·54 | 5·87 | 75 | 70·61 | 17·61 | 125 | 117·7 | 29·34 | 175 | 164·8 | 41·08 |
| 26 | 24·48 | 6·10 | 76 | 71·55 | 17·84 | 126 | 118·6 | 29·58 | 176 | 165·7 | 41·31 |
| 27 | 25·42 | 6·34 | 77 | 72·49 | 18·07 | 127 | 119·6 | 29·81 | 177 | 166·6 | 41·55 |
| 28 | 26·36 | 6·57 | 78 | 73·43 | 18·31 | 128 | 120·5 | 30·05 | 178 | 167·6 | 41·78 |
| 29 | 27·30 | 6·81 | 79 | 74·38 | 18·54 | 129 | 121·4 | 30·28 | 179 | 168·5 | 42·02 |
| 30 | 28·24 | 7·04 | 80 | 75·32 | 18·78 | 130 | 122·4 | 30·52 | 180 | 169·5 | 42·25 |
| 31 | 29·19 | 7·28 | 81 | 76·26 | 19·01 | 131 | 123·3 | 30·75 | 181 | 170·4 | 42·49 |
| 32 | 30·13 | 7·51 | 82 | 77·20 | 19·25 | 132 | 124·3 | 30·99 | 182 | 171·3 | 42·72 |
| 33 | 31·07 | 7·75 | 83 | 78·14 | 19·48 | 133 | 125·2 | 31·22 | 183 | 172·3 | 42·96 |
| 34 | 32·01 | 7·98 | 84 | 79·08 | 19·72 | 134 | 126·2 | 31·45 | 184 | 173·2 | 43·19 |
| 35 | 32·95 | 8·22 | 85 | 80·03 | 19·95 | 135 | 127·1 | 31·69 | 185 | 174·2 | 43·43 |
| 36 | 33·89 | 8·45 | 86 | 80·97 | 20·19 | 136 | 128·0 | 31·92 | 186 | 175·1 | 43·66 |
| 37 | 34·83 | 8·69 | 87 | 81·91 | 20·42 | 137 | 129·0 | 32·16 | 187 | 176·1 | 43·90 |
| 38 | 35·78 | 8·92 | 88 | 82·85 | 20·66 | 138 | 129·9 | 32·39 | 188 | 177·0 | 44·13 |
| 39 | 36·72 | 9·15 | 89 | 83·79 | 20·89 | 139 | 130·9 | 32·63 | 189 | 177·9 | 44·36 |
| 40 | 37·66 | 9·39 | 90 | 84·73 | 21·13 | 140 | 131·8 | 32·86 | 190 | 178·9 | 44·60 |
| 41 | 38·60 | 9·62 | 91 | 85·67 | 21·36 | 141 | 132·7 | 33·10 | 191 | 179·8 | 44·83 |
| 42 | 39·54 | 9·86 | 92 | 86·62 | 21·60 | 142 | 133·7 | 33·33 | 192 | 180·8 | 45·07 |
| 43 | 40·48 | 10·09 | 93 | 87·56 | 21·83 | 143 | 134·6 | 33·57 | 193 | 181·7 | 45·30 |
| 44 | 41·42 | 10·33 | 94 | 88·50 | 22·07 | 144 | 135·6 | 33·80 | 194 | 182·6 | 45·54 |
| 45 | 42·37 | 10·56 | 95 | 89·44 | 22·30 | 145 | 136·5 | 34·04 | 195 | 183·6 | 45·77 |
| 46 | 43·31 | 10·80 | 96 | 90·38 | 22·53 | 146 | 137·5 | 34·27 | 196 | 184·5 | 46·01 |
| 47 | 44·25 | 11·03 | 97 | 91·32 | 22·77 | 147 | 138·4 | 34·51 | 197 | 185·5 | 46·24 |
| 48 | 45·19 | 11·27 | 98 | 92·26 | 23·00 | 148 | 139·3 | 34·74 | 198 | 186·4 | 46·48 |
| 49 | 46·13 | 11·50 | 99 | 93·21 | 23·24 | 149 | 140·3 | 34·98 | 199 | 187·4 | 46·71 |
| 50 | 47·07 | 11·74 | 100 | 94·15 | 23·47 | 150 | 141·2 | 35·21 | 200 | 188·3 | 46·95 |
| 51 | 48·02 | 11·97 | 101 | 95·09 | 23·71 | 151 | 142·2 | 35·44 | 201 | 189·2 | 47·18 |
| 52 | 48·96 | 12·21 | 102 | 96·03 | 23·94 | 152 | 143·1 | 35·68 | 202 | 190·2 | 47·42 |
| 53 | 49·90 | 12·44 | 103 | 96·97 | 24·18 | 153 | 144·0 | 35·91 | 203 | 191·1 | 47·65 |
| 54 | 50·84 | 12·68 | 104 | 97·91 | 24·41 | 154 | 145·0 | 36·15 | 204 | 192·1 | 47·89 |
| 55 | 51·78 | 12·91 | 105 | 98·85 | 24·65 | 155 | 145·9 | 36·38 | 205 | 193·0 | 48·12 |
| 56 | 52·72 | 13·15 | 106 | 99·80 | 24·88 | 156 | 146·9 | 36·62 | 206 | 193·9 | 48·36 |
| 57 | 53·66 | 13·38 | 107 | 100·7 | 25·12 | 157 | 147·8 | 36·85 | 207 | 194·9 | 48·59 |
| 58 | 54·61 | 13·61 | 108 | 101·7 | 25·35 | 158 | 148·8 | 37·09 | 208 | 195·8 | 48·82 |
| 59 | 55·55 | 13·85 | 109 | 102·6 | 25·59 | 159 | 149·7 | 37·32 | 209 | 196·8 | 49·06 |
| 60 | 56·49 | 14·08 | 110 | 103·6 | 25·82 | 160 | 150·6 | 37·56 | 210 | 197·7 | 49·29 |

TABLE I

**14° 20′**

| G | D | H | G | D | H | G | D | H | G | D | H |
|---|---|---|---|---|---|---|---|---|---|---|---|
| 10 | 9·39 | 2·40 | 60 | 56·32 | 14·39 | 110 | 103·3 | 26·38 | 160 | 150·2 | 38·38 |
| 11 | 10·33 | 2·64 | 61 | 57·26 | 14·63 | 111 | 104·2 | 26·62 | 161 | 151·1 | 38·62 |
| 12 | 11·26 | 2·88 | 62 | 58·20 | 14·87 | 112 | 105·1 | 26·86 | 162 | 152·1 | 38·86 |
| 13 | 12·20 | 3·12 | 63 | 59·14 | 15·11 | 113 | 106·1 | 27·10 | 163 | 153·0 | 39·10 |
| 14 | 13·14 | 3·36 | 64 | 60·08 | 15·35 | 114 | 107·0 | 27·34 | 164 | 153·9 | 39·34 |
| 15 | 14·08 | 3·60 | 65 | 61·02 | 15·59 | 115 | 108·0 | 27·58 | 165 | 154·9 | 39·58 |
| 16 | 15·02 | 3·84 | 66 | 61·95 | 15·83 | 116 | 108·9 | 27·82 | 166 | 155·8 | 39·82 |
| 17 | 15·96 | 4·08 | 67 | 62·89 | 16·07 | 117 | 109·8 | 28·06 | 167 | 156·8 | 40·06 |
| 18 | 16·90 | 4·32 | 68 | 63·83 | 16·31 | 118 | 110·8 | 28·30 | 168 | 157·7 | 40·30 |
| 19 | 17·84 | 4·56 | 69 | 64·77 | 16·55 | 119 | 111·7 | 28·54 | 169 | 158·6 | 40·54 |
| 20 | 18·77 | 4·80 | 70 | 65·71 | 16·79 | 120 | 112·6 | 28·78 | 170 | 159·6 | 40·78 |
| 21 | 19·71 | 5·04 | 71 | 66·65 | 17·03 | 121 | 113·6 | 29·02 | 171 | 160·5 | 41·02 |
| 22 | 20·65 | 5·28 | 72 | 67·59 | 17·27 | 122 | 114·5 | 29·26 | 172 | 161·5 | 41·26 |
| 23 | 21·59 | 5·52 | 73 | 68·53 | 17·51 | 123 | 115·5 | 29·50 | 173 | 162·4 | 41·50 |
| 24 | 22·53 | 5·76 | 74 | 69·46 | 17·75 | 124 | 116·4 | 29·74 | 174 | 163·3 | 41·73 |
| 25 | 23·47 | 6·00 | 75 | 70·40 | 17·99 | 125 | 117·3 | 29·98 | 175 | 164·3 | 41·97 |
| 26 | 24·41 | 6·24 | 76 | 71·34 | 18·23 | 126 | 118·3 | 30·22 | 176 | 165·2 | 42·21 |
| 27 | 25·35 | 6·48 | 77 | 72·28 | 18·47 | 127 | 119·2 | 30·46 | 177 | 166·2 | 42·45 |
| 28 | 26·28 | 6·72 | 78 | 73·22 | 18·71 | 128 | 120·2 | 30·70 | 178 | 167·1 | 42·69 |
| 29 | 27·22 | 6·96 | 79 | 74·16 | 18·95 | 129 | 121·1 | 30·94 | 179 | 168·0 | 42·93 |
| 30 | 28·16 | 7·20 | 80 | 75·10 | 19·19 | 130 | 122·0 | 31·18 | 180 | 169·0 | 43·17 |
| 31 | 29·10 | 7·44 | 81 | 76·04 | 19·43 | 131 | 123·0 | 31·42 | 181 | 169·9 | 43·41 |
| 32 | 30·04 | 7·68 | 82 | 76·97 | 19·67 | 132 | 123·9 | 31·66 | 182 | 170·8 | 43·65 |
| 33 | 30·98 | 7·92 | 83 | 77·91 | 19·91 | 133 | 124·8 | 31·90 | 183 | 171·8 | 43·89 |
| 34 | 31·92 | 8·16 | 84 | 78·85 | 20·15 | 134 | 125·8 | 32·14 | 184 | 172·7 | 44·13 |
| 35 | 32·85 | 8·39 | 85 | 79·79 | 20·39 | 135 | 126·7 | 32·38 | 185 | 173·7 | 44·37 |
| 36 | 33·79 | 8·63 | 86 | 80·73 | 20·63 | 136 | 127·7 | 32·62 | 186 | 174·6 | 44·61 |
| 37 | 34·73 | 8·87 | 87 | 81·67 | 20·87 | 137 | 128·6 | 32·86 | 187 | 175·5 | 44·85 |
| 38 | 35·67 | 9·11 | 88 | 82·61 | 21·11 | 138 | 129·5 | 33·10 | 188 | 176·5 | 45·09 |
| 39 | 36·61 | 9·35 | 89 | 83·55 | 21·35 | 139 | 130·5 | 33·34 | 189 | 177·4 | 45·33 |
| 40 | 37·55 | 9·59 | 90 | 84·48 | 21·59 | 140 | 131·4 | 33·58 | 190 | 178·4 | 45·57 |
| 41 | 38·49 | 9·83 | 91 | 85·42 | 21·83 | 141 | 132·4 | 33·82 | 191 | 179·3 | 45·81 |
| 42 | 39·43 | 10·07 | 92 | 86·36 | 22·07 | 142 | 133·3 | 34·06 | 192 | 180·2 | 46·05 |
| 43 | 40·36 | 10·31 | 93 | 87·30 | 22·31 | 143 | 134·2 | 34·30 | 193 | 181·2 | 46·29 |
| 44 | 41·30 | 10·55 | 94 | 88·24 | 22·55 | 144 | 135·2 | 34·54 | 194 | 182·1 | 46·53 |
| 45 | 42·24 | 10·79 | 95 | 89·18 | 22·79 | 145 | 136·1 | 34·78 | 195 | 183·0 | 46·77 |
| 46 | 43·18 | 11·03 | 96 | 90·12 | 23·03 | 146 | 137·1 | 35·02 | 196 | 184·0 | 47·01 |
| 47 | 44·12 | 11·27 | 97 | 91·05 | 23·27 | 147 | 138·0 | 35·26 | 197 | 184·9 | 47·25 |
| 48 | 45·06 | 11·51 | 98 | 91·99 | 23·51 | 148 | 138·9 | 35·50 | 198 | 185·9 | 47·49 |
| 49 | 46·00 | 11·75 | 99 | 92·93 | 23·75 | 149 | 139·9 | 35·74 | 199 | 186·8 | 47·73 |
| 50 | 46·94 | 11·99 | 100 | 93·87 | 23·99 | 150 | 140·8 | 35·98 | 200 | 187·7 | 47·97 |
| 51 | 47·87 | 12·23 | 101 | 94·81 | 24·23 | 151 | 141·7 | 36·22 | 201 | 188·7 | 48·21 |
| 52 | 48·81 | 12·47 | 102 | 95·75 | 24·47 | 152 | 142·7 | 36·46 | 202 | 189·6 | 48·45 |
| 53 | 49·75 | 12·71 | 103 | 96·69 | 24·71 | 153 | 143·6 | 36·70 | 203 | 190·6 | 48·69 |
| 54 | 50·69 | 12·95 | 104 | 97·63 | 24·95 | 154 | 144·6 | 36·94 | 204 | 191·5 | 48·93 |
| 55 | 51·63 | 13·19 | 105 | 98·56 | 25·18 | 155 | 145·5 | 37·18 | 205 | 192·4 | 49·17 |
| 56 | 52·57 | 13·43 | 106 | 99·50 | 25·42 | 156 | 146·4 | 37·42 | 206 | 193·4 | 49·41 |
| 57 | 53·51 | 13·67 | 107 | 100·4 | 25·66 | 157 | 147·4 | 37·66 | 207 | 194·3 | 49·65 |
| 58 | 54·45 | 13·91 | 108 | 101·4 | 25·90 | 158 | 148·3 | 37·90 | 208 | 195·3 | 49·89 |
| 59 | 55·38 | 14·15 | 109 | 102·3 | 26·14 | 159 | 149·3 | 38·14 | 209 | 196·2 | 50·13 |
| 60 | 56·32 | 14·39 | 110 | 103·3 | 26·38 | 160 | 150·2 | 38·38 | 210 | 197·1 | 50·37 |

# 14° 40′

TABLE I

| G | D | H | G | D | H | G | D | H | G | D | H |
|---|---|---|---|---|---|---|---|---|---|---|---|
| 10 | 9·36 | 2·45 | 60 | 56·15 | 14·70 | 110 | 102·9 | 26·94 | 160 | 149·7 | 39·19 |
| 11 | 10·29 | 2·69 | 61 | 57·09 | 14·94 | 111 | 103·9 | 27·19 | 161 | 150·7 | 39·44 |
| 12 | 11·23 | 2·94 | 62 | 58·03 | 15·19 | 112 | 104·8 | 27·43 | 162 | 151·6 | 39·68 |
| 13 | 12·17 | 3·18 | 63 | 58·96 | 15·43 | 113 | 105·8 | 27·68 | 163 | 152·6 | 39·93 |
| 14 | 13·10 | 3·43 | 64 | 59·90 | 15·68 | 114 | 106·7 | 27·92 | 164 | 153·5 | 40·17 |
| 15 | 14·04 | 3·67 | 65 | 60·83 | 15·92 | 115 | 107·6 | 28·17 | 165 | 154·4 | 40·42 |
| 16 | 14·97 | 3·92 | 66 | 61·77 | 16·17 | 116 | 108·6 | 28·41 | 166 | 155·4 | 40·66 |
| 17 | 15·91 | 4·16 | 67 | 62·70 | 16·41 | 117 | 109·5 | 28·66 | 167 | 156·3 | 40·91 |
| 18 | 16·85 | 4·41 | 68 | 63·64 | 16·66 | 118 | 110·4 | 28·90 | 168 | 157·2 | 41·15 |
| 19 | 17·78 | 4·65 | 69 | 64·58 | 16·90 | 119 | 111·4 | 29·15 | 169 | 158·2 | 41·40 |
| 20 | 18·72 | 4·90 | 70 | 65·51 | 17·15 | 120 | 112·3 | 29·39 | 170 | 159·1 | 41·64 |
| 21 | 19·65 | 5·14 | 71 | 66·45 | 17·39 | 121 | 113·2 | 29·64 | 171 | 160·0 | 41·89 |
| 22 | 20·59 | 5·39 | 72 | 67·38 | 17·64 | 122 | 114·2 | 29·88 | 172 | 161·0 | 42·13 |
| 23 | 21·53 | 5·63 | 73 | 68·32 | 17·88 | 123 | 115·1 | 30·13 | 173 | 161·9 | 42·38 |
| 24 | 22·46 | 5·88 | 74 | 69·26 | 18·13 | 124 | 116·1 | 30·37 | 174 | 162·8 | 42·62 |
| 25 | 23·40 | 6·12 | 75 | 70·19 | 18·37 | 125 | 117·0 | 30·62 | 175 | 163·8 | 42·87 |
| 26 | 24·33 | 6·37 | 76 | 71·13 | 18·62 | 126 | 117·9 | 30·86 | 176 | 164·7 | 43·11 |
| 27 | 25·27 | 6·61 | 77 | 72·06 | 18·86 | 127 | 118·9 | 31·11 | 177 | 165·7 | 43·36 |
| 28 | 26·20 | 6·86 | 78 | 73·00 | 19·11 | 128 | 119·8 | 31·35 | 178 | 166·6 | 43·60 |
| 29 | 27·14 | 7·10 | 79 | 73·94 | 19·35 | 129 | 120·7 | 31·60 | 179 | 167·5 | 43·84 |
| 30 | 28·08 | 7·35 | 80 | 74·87 | 19·60 | 130 | 121·7 | 31·84 | 180 | 168·5 | 44·09 |
| 31 | 29·01 | 7·59 | 81 | 75·81 | 19·84 | 131 | 122·6 | 32·09 | 181 | 169·4 | 44·33 |
| 32 | 29·95 | 7·84 | 82 | 76·74 | 20·09 | 132 | 123·5 | 32·33 | 182 | 170·3 | 44·58 |
| 33 | 30·88 | 8·08 | 83 | 77·68 | 20·33 | 133 | 124·5 | 32·58 | 183 | 171·3 | 44·82 |
| 34 | 31·82 | 8·33 | 84 | 78·61 | 20·58 | 134 | 125·4 | 32·82 | 184 | 172·2 | 45·07 |
| 35 | 32·76 | 8·57 | 85 | 79·55 | 20·82 | 135 | 126·3 | 33·07 | 185 | 173·1 | 45·31 |
| 36 | 33·69 | 8·82 | 86 | 80·49 | 21·07 | 136 | 127·3 | 33·31 | 186 | 174·1 | 45·56 |
| 37 | 34·63 | 9·06 | 87 | 81·42 | 21·31 | 137 | 128·2 | 33·56 | 187 | 175·0 | 45·80 |
| 38 | 35·56 | 9·31 | 88 | 82·36 | 21·56 | 138 | 129·2 | 33·80 | 188 | 175·9 | 46·05 |
| 39 | 36·50 | 9·55 | 89 | 83·29 | 21·80 | 139 | 130·1 | 34·05 | 189 | 176·9 | 46·29 |
| 40 | 37·44 | 9·80 | 90 | 84·23 | 22·04 | 140 | 131·0 | 34·29 | 190 | 177·8 | 46·54 |
| 41 | 38·37 | 10·04 | 91 | 85·17 | 22·29 | 141 | 132·0 | 34·54 | 191 | 178·8 | 46·78 |
| 42 | 39·31 | 10·29 | 92 | 86·10 | 22·53 | 142 | 132·9 | 34·78 | 192 | 179·7 | 47·03 |
| 43 | 40·24 | 10·53 | 93 | 87·04 | 22·78 | 143 | 133·8 | 35·03 | 193 | 180·6 | 47·27 |
| 44 | 41·18 | 10·78 | 94 | 87·97 | 23·02 | 144 | 134·8 | 35·27 | 194 | 181·6 | 47·52 |
| 45 | 42·12 | 11·02 | 95 | 88·91 | 23·27 | 145 | 135·7 | 35·52 | 195 | 182·5 | 47·76 |
| 46 | 43·05 | 11·27 | 96 | 89·85 | 23·51 | 146 | 136·6 | 35·76 | 196 | 183·4 | 48·01 |
| 47 | 43·99 | 11·51 | 97 | 90·78 | 23·76 | 147 | 137·6 | 36·01 | 197 | 184·4 | 48·25 |
| 48 | 44·92 | 11·76 | 98 | 91·72 | 24·00 | 148 | 138·5 | 36·25 | 198 | 185·3 | 48·50 |
| 49 | 45·86 | 12·00 | 99 | 92·65 | 24·25 | 149 | 139·4 | 36·50 | 199 | 186·2 | 48·74 |
| 50 | 46·79 | 12·25 | 100 | 93·59 | 24·49 | 150 | 140·4 | 36·74 | 200 | 187·2 | 48·99 |
| 51 | 47·73 | 12·49 | 101 | 94·52 | 24·74 | 151 | 141·3 | 36·99 | 201 | 188·1 | 49·23 |
| 52 | 48·67 | 12·74 | 102 | 95·46 | 24·98 | 152 | 142·3 | 37·23 | 202 | 189·0 | 49·48 |
| 53 | 49·60 | 12·98 | 103 | 96·40 | 25·23 | 153 | 143·2 | 37·48 | 203 | 190·0 | 49·72 |
| 54 | 50·54 | 13·23 | 104 | 97·33 | 25·47 | 154 | 144·1 | 37·72 | 204 | 190·9 | 49·97 |
| 55 | 51·47 | 13·47 | 105 | 98·27 | 25·72 | 155 | 145·1 | 37·97 | 205 | 191·9 | 50·21 |
| 56 | 52·41 | 13·72 | 106 | 99·20 | 25·96 | 156 | 146·0 | 38·21 | 206 | 192·8 | 50·46 |
| 57 | 53·35 | 13·96 | 107 | 100·1 | 26·21 | 157 | 146·9 | 38·46 | 207 | 193·7 | 50·70 |
| 58 | 54·28 | 14·21 | 108 | 101·1 | 26·45 | 158 | 147·9 | 38·70 | 208 | 194·7 | 50·95 |
| 59 | 55·22 | 14·45 | 109 | 102·0 | 26·70 | 159 | 148·8 | 38·95 | 209 | 195·6 | 51·19 |
| 60 | 56·15 | 14·70 | 110 | 102·9 | 26·94 | 160 | 149·7 | 39·19 | 210 | 196·5 | 51·44 |

TABLE I

# 15° 00′

| G | D | H | G | D | H | G | D | H | G | D | H |
|---|---|---|---|---|---|---|---|---|---|---|---|
| 10 | 9·33 | 2·50 | 60 | 55·98 | 15·00 | 110 | 102·6 | 27·50 | 160 | 149·3 | 40·00 |
| 11 | 10·26 | 2·75 | 61 | 56·91 | 15·25 | 111 | 103·6 | 27·75 | 161 | 150·2 | 40·25 |
| 12 | 11·20 | 3·00 | 62 | 57·85 | 15·50 | 112 | 104·5 | 28·00 | 162 | 151·1 | 40·50 |
| 13 | 12·13 | 3·25 | 63 | 58·78 | 15·75 | 113 | 105·4 | 28·25 | 163 | 152·1 | 40·75 |
| 14 | 13·06 | 3·50 | 64 | 59·71 | 16·00 | 114 | 106·4 | 28·50 | 164 | 153·0 | 41·00 |
| 15 | 14·00 | 3·75 | 65 | 60·65 | 16·25 | 115 | 107·3 | 28·75 | 165 | 153·9 | 41·25 |
| 16 | 14·93 | 4·00 | 66 | 61·58 | 16·50 | 116 | 108·2 | 29·00 | 166 | 154·9 | 41·50 |
| 17 | 15·86 | 4·25 | 67 | 62·51 | 16·75 | 117 | 109·2 | 29·25 | 167 | 155·8 | 41·75 |
| 18 | 16·79 | 4·50 | 68 | 63·44 | 17·00 | 118 | 110·1 | 29·50 | 168 | 156·7 | 42·00 |
| 19 | 17·73 | 4·75 | 69 | 64·38 | 17·25 | 119 | 111·0 | 29·75 | 169 | 157·7 | 42·25 |
| 20 | 18·66 | 5·00 | 70 | 65·31 | 17·50 | 120 | 112·0 | 30·00 | 170 | 158·6 | 42·50 |
| 21 | 19·59 | 5·25 | 71 | 66·24 | 17·75 | 121 | 112·9 | 30·25 | 171 | 159·5 | 42·75 |
| 22 | 20·53 | 5·50 | 72 | 67·18 | 18·00 | 122 | 113·8 | 30·50 | 172 | 160·5 | 43·00 |
| 23 | 21·46 | 5·75 | 73 | 68·11 | 18·25 | 123 | 114·8 | 30·75 | 173 | 161·4 | 43·25 |
| 24 | 22·39 | 6·00 | 74 | 69·04 | 18·50 | 124 | 115·7 | 31·00 | 174 | 162·3 | 43·50 |
| 25 | 23·33 | 6·25 | 75 | 69·98 | 18·75 | 125 | 116·6 | 31·25 | 175 | 163·3 | 43·75 |
| 26 | 24·26 | 6·50 | 76 | 70·91 | 19·00 | 126 | 117·6 | 31·50 | 176 | 164·2 | 44·00 |
| 27 | 25·19 | 6·75 | 77 | 71·84 | 19·25 | 127 | 118·5 | 31·75 | 177 | 165·1 | 44·25 |
| 28 | 26·12 | 7·00 | 78 | 72·77 | 19·50 | 128 | 119·4 | 32·00 | 178 | 166·1 | 44·50 |
| 29 | 27·06 | 7·25 | 79 | 73·71 | 19·75 | 129 | 120·4 | 32·25 | 179 | 167·0 | 44·75 |
| 30 | 27·99 | 7·50 | 80 | 74·64 | 20·00 | 130 | 121·3 | 32·50 | 180 | 167·9 | 45·00 |
| 31 | 28·92 | 7·75 | 81 | 75·57 | 20·25 | 131 | 122·2 | 32·75 | 181 | 168·9 | 45·25 |
| 32 | 29·86 | 8·00 | 82 | 76·51 | 20·50 | 132 | 123·2 | 33·00 | 182 | 169·8 | 45·50 |
| 33 | 30·79 | 8·25 | 83 | 77·44 | 20·75 | 133 | 124·1 | 33·25 | 183 | 170·7 | 45·75 |
| 34 | 31·72 | 8·50 | 84 | 78·37 | 21·00 | 134 | 125·0 | 33·50 | 184 | 171·7 | 46·00 |
| 35 | 32·66 | 8·75 | 85 | 79·31 | 21·25 | 135 | 126·0 | 33·75 | 185 | 172·6 | 46·25 |
| 36 | 33·59 | 9·00 | 86 | 80·24 | 21·50 | 136 | 126·9 | 34·00 | 186 | 173·5 | 46·50 |
| 37 | 34·52 | 9·25 | 87 | 81·17 | 21·75 | 137 | 127·8 | 34·25 | 187 | 174·5 | 46·75 |
| 38 | 35·45 | 9·50 | 88 | 82·10 | 22·00 | 138 | 128·8 | 34·50 | 188 | 175·4 | 47·00 |
| 39 | 36·39 | 9·75 | 89 | 83·04 | 22·25 | 139 | 129·7 | 34·75 | 189 | 176·3 | 47·25 |
| 40 | 37·32 | 10·00 | 90 | 83·97 | 22·50 | 140 | 130·6 | 35·00 | 190 | 177·3 | 47·50 |
| 41 | 38·25 | 10·25 | 91 | 84·90 | 22·75 | 141 | 131·6 | 35·25 | 191 | 178·2 | 47·75 |
| 42 | 39·19 | 10·50 | 92 | 85·84 | 23·00 | 142 | 132·5 | 35·50 | 192 | 179·1 | 48·00 |
| 43 | 40·12 | 10·75 | 93 | 86·77 | 23·25 | 143 | 133·4 | 35·75 | 193 | 180·1 | 48·25 |
| 44 | 41·05 | 11·00 | 94 | 87·70 | 23·50 | 144 | 134·4 | 36·00 | 194 | 181·0 | 48·50 |
| 45 | 41·99 | 11·25 | 95 | 88·64 | 23·75 | 145 | 135·3 | 36·25 | 195 | 161·9 | 48·75 |
| 46 | 42·92 | 11·50 | 96 | 89·57 | 24·00 | 146 | 136·2 | 36·50 | 196 | 182·9 | 49·00 |
| 47 | 43·85 | 11·75 | 97 | 90·50 | 24·25 | 147 | 137·2 | 36·75 | 197 | 183·8 | 49·25 |
| 48 | 44·78 | 12·00 | 98 | 91·44 | 24·50 | 148 | 138·1 | 37·00 | 198 | 184·7 | 49·50 |
| 49 | 45·72 | 12·25 | 99 | 92·37 | 24·75 | 149 | 139·0 | 37·25 | 199 | 185·7 | 49·75 |
| 50 | 46·65 | 12·50 | 100 | 93·30 | 25·00 | 150 | 140·0 | 37·50 | 200 | 186·6 | 50·00 |
| 51 | 47·58 | 12·75 | 101 | 94·23 | 25·25 | 151 | 140·9 | 37·75 | 201 | 187·5 | 50·25 |
| 52 | 48·52 | 13·00 | 102 | 95·17 | 25·50 | 152 | 141·8 | 38·00 | 202 | 188·5 | 50·50 |
| 53 | 49·45 | 13·25 | 103 | 96·10 | 25·75 | 153 | 142·8 | 38·25 | 203 | 189·4 | 50·75 |
| 54 | 50·38 | 13·50 | 104 | 97·03 | 26·00 | 154 | 143·7 | 38·50 | 204 | 190·3 | 51·00 |
| 55 | 51·32 | 13·75 | 105 | 97·97 | 26·25 | 155 | 144·6 | 38·75 | 205 | 191·3 | 51·25 |
| 56 | 52·25 | 14·00 | 106 | 98·90 | 26·50 | 156 | 145·5 | 39·00 | 206 | 192·2 | 51·50 |
| 57 | 53·18 | 14·25 | 107 | 99·83 | 26·75 | 157 | 146·5 | 39·25 | 207 | 193·1 | 51·75 |
| 58 | 54·11 | 14·50 | 108 | 100·8 | 27·00 | 158 | 147·4 | 39·50 | 208 | 194·1 | 52·00 |
| 59 | 55·05 | 14·75 | 109 | 101·7 | 27·25 | 159 | 148·3 | 39·75 | 209 | 195·0 | 52·25 |
| 60 | 55·98 | 15·00 | 110 | 102·6 | 27·50 | 160 | 149·3 | 40·00 | 210 | 195·9 | 52·50 |

TABLE I

| G | D | H | G | D | H | G | D | H | G | D | H |
|---|---|---|---|---|---|---|---|---|---|---|---|
| 10 | 9.30 | 2.55 | 60 | 55.80 | 15.30 | 110 | 102.3 | 28.05 | 160 | 148.8 | 40.80 |
| 11 | 10.23 | 2.81 | 61 | 56.73 | 15.56 | 111 | 103.2 | 28.31 | 161 | 149.7 | 41.06 |
| 12 | 11.16 | 3.06 | 62 | 57.66 | 15.81 | 112 | 104.2 | 28.56 | 162 | 150.7 | 41.31 |
| 13 | 12.09 | 3.32 | 63 | 58.59 | 16.07 | 113 | 105.1 | 28.82 | 163 | 151.6 | 41.57 |
| 14 | 13.02 | 3.57 | 64 | 59.52 | 16.32 | 114 | 106.0 | 29.07 | 164 | 152.5 | 41.82 |
| 15 | 13.95 | 3.83 | 65 | 60.45 | 16.58 | 115 | 107.0 | 29.33 | 165 | 153.5 | 42.08 |
| 16 | 14.88 | 4.08 | 66 | 61.38 | 16.83 | 116 | 107.9 | 29.58 | 166 | 154.4 | 42.33 |
| 17 | 15.81 | 4.34 | 67 | 62.31 | 17.09 | 117 | 108.8 | 29.84 | 167 | 155.3 | 42.59 |
| 18 | 16.74 | 4.59 | 68 | 63.24 | 17.34 | 118 | 109.7 | 30.09 | 168 | 156.3 | 42.84 |
| 19 | 17.67 | 4.85 | 69 | 64.18 | 17.60 | 119 | 110.7 | 30.35 | 169 | 157.2 | 43.10 |
| 20 | 18.60 | 5.10 | 70 | 65.11 | 17.85 | 120 | 111.6 | 30.60 | 170 | 158.1 | 43.35 |
| 21 | 19.53 | 5.36 | 71 | 66.04 | 18.11 | 121 | 112.5 | 30.86 | 171 | 159.0 | 43.61 |
| 22 | 20.46 | 5.61 | 72 | 66.97 | 18.36 | 122 | 113.5 | 31.11 | 172 | 160.0 | 43.86 |
| 23 | 21.39 | 5.87 | 73 | 67.90 | 18.62 | 123 | 114.4 | 31.37 | 173 | 160.9 | 44.12 |
| 24 | 22.32 | 6.12 | 74 | 68.83 | 18.87 | 124 | 115.3 | 31.62 | 174 | 161.8 | 44.37 |
| 25 | 23.25 | 6.38 | 75 | 69.76 | 19.13 | 125 | 116.3 | 31.88 | 175 | 162.8 | 44.63 |
| 26 | 24.18 | 6.63 | 76 | 70.69 | 19.38 | 126 | 117.2 | 32.13 | 176 | 163.7 | 44.88 |
| 27 | 25.11 | 6.89 | 77 | 71.62 | 19.64 | 127 | 118.1 | 32.39 | 177 | 164.6 | 45.14 |
| 28 | 26.04 | 7.14 | 78 | 72.55 | 19.89 | 128 | 119.0 | 32.64 | 178 | 165.6 | 45.39 |
| 29 | 26.97 | 7.40 | 79 | 73.48 | 20.15 | 129 | 120.0 | 32.90 | 179 | 166.5 | 45.65 |
| 30 | 27.90 | 7.65 | 80 | 74.41 | 20.40 | 130 | 120.9 | 33.15 | 180 | 167.4 | 45.90 |
| 31 | 28.83 | 7.91 | 81 | 75.34 | 20.66 | 131 | 121.8 | 33.41 | 181 | 168.3 | 46.16 |
| 32 | 29.76 | 8.16 | 82 | 76.27 | 20.91 | 132 | 122.8 | 33.66 | 182 | 169.3 | 46.41 |
| 33 | 30.69 | 8.42 | 83 | 77.20 | 21.17 | 133 | 123.7 | 33.92 | 183 | 170.2 | 46.67 |
| 34 | 31.62 | 8.67 | 84 | 78.13 | 21.42 | 134 | 124.6 | 34.17 | 184 | 171.1 | 46.92 |
| 35 | 32.55 | 8.93 | 85 | 79.06 | 21.68 | 135 | 125.6 | 34.43 | 185 | 172.1 | 47.18 |
| 36 | 33.48 | 9.18 | 86 | 79.99 | 21.93 | 136 | 126.5 | 34.68 | 186 | 173.0 | 47.43 |
| 37 | 34.41 | 9.44 | 87 | 80.92 | 22.19 | 137 | 127.4 | 34.94 | 187 | 173.9 | 47.69 |
| 38 | 35.34 | 9.69 | 88 | 81.85 | 22.44 | 138 | 128.4 | 35.19 | 188 | 174.9 | 47.94 |
| 39 | 36.27 | 9.95 | 89 | 82.78 | 22.70 | 139 | 129.3 | 35.45 | 189 | 175.8 | 48.20 |
| 40 | 37.20 | 10.20 | 90 | 83.71 | 22.95 | 140 | 130.2 | 35.70 | 190 | 176.7 | 48.45 |
| 41 | 38.13 | 10.46 | 91 | 84.64 | 23.21 | 141 | 131.1 | 35.96 | 191 | 177.6 | 48.71 |
| 42 | 39.06 | 10.71 | 92 | 85.57 | 23.46 | 142 | 132.1 | 36.21 | 192 | 178.6 | 48.96 |
| 43 | 39.99 | 10.97 | 93 | 86.50 | 23.72 | 143 | 133.0 | 36.47 | 193 | 179.5 | 49.22 |
| 44 | 40.92 | 11.22 | 94 | 87.43 | 23.97 | 144 | 133.9 | 36.72 | 194 | 180.4 | 49.47 |
| 45 | 41.85 | 11.48 | 95 | 88.36 | 24.23 | 145 | 134.9 | 36.98 | 195 | 181.4 | 49.73 |
| 46 | 42.78 | 11.73 | 96 | 89.29 | 24.48 | 146 | 135.8 | 37.23 | 196 | 182.3 | 49.98 |
| 47 | 43.71 | 11.99 | 97 | 90.22 | 24.74 | 147 | 136.7 | 37.49 | 197 | 183.2 | 50.24 |
| 48 | 44.64 | 12.24 | 98 | 91.15 | 24.99 | 148 | 137.7 | 37.74 | 198 | 184.2 | 50.49 |
| 49 | 45.57 | 12.50 | 99 | 92.08 | 25.25 | 149 | 138.6 | 38.00 | 199 | 185.1 | 50.75 |
| 50 | 46.50 | 12.75 | 100 | 93.01 | 25.50 | 150 | 139.5 | 38.25 | 200 | 186.0 | 51.00 |
| 51 | 47.43 | 13.01 | 101 | 93.94 | 25.76 | 151 | 140.4 | 38.51 | 201 | 186.9 | 51.26 |
| 52 | 48.36 | 13.26 | 102 | 94.87 | 26.01 | 152 | 141.4 | 38.76 | 202 | 187.9 | 51.51 |
| 53 | 49.29 | 13.52 | 103 | 95.80 | 26.27 | 153 | 142.3 | 39.02 | 203 | 188.8 | 51.77 |
| 54 | 50.22 | 13.77 | 104 | 96.73 | 26.52 | 154 | 143.2 | 39.27 | 204 | 189.7 | 52.02 |
| 55 | 51.15 | 14.03 | 105 | 97.66 | 26.78 | 155 | 144.2 | 39.53 | 205 | 190.7 | 52.28 |
| 56 | 52.08 | 14.28 | 106 | 98.59 | 27.03 | 156 | 145.1 | 39.78 | 206 | 191.6 | 52.53 |
| 57 | 53.01 | 14.54 | 107 | 99.52 | 27.29 | 157 | 146.0 | 40.04 | 207 | 192.5 | 52.79 |
| 58 | 53.94 | 14.79 | 108 | 100.4 | 27.54 | 158 | 147.0 | 40.29 | 208 | 193.5 | 53.04 |
| 59 | 54.87 | 15.05 | 109 | 101.4 | 27.80 | 159 | 147.9 | 40.55 | 209 | 194.4 | 53.30 |
| 60 | 55.80 | 15.30 | 110 | 102.3 | 28.05 | 160 | 148.8 | 40.80 | 210 | 195.3 | 53.55 |

TABLE I

# 15° 40′

| G | D | H | G | D | H | G | D | H | G | D | H |
|---|---|---|---|---|---|---|---|---|---|---|---|
| 10 | 9·27 | 2·60 | 60 | 55·62 | 15·60 | 110 | 102·0 | 28·60 | 160 | 148·3 | 41·60 |
| 11 | 10·20 | 2·86 | 61 | 56·55 | 15·86 | 111 | 102·9 | 28·86 | 161 | 149·3 | 41·86 |
| 12 | 11·12 | 3·12 | 62 | 57·48 | 16·12 | 112 | 103·8 | 29·12 | 162 | 150·2 | 42·12 |
| 13 | 12·05 | 3·38 | 63 | 58·41 | 16·38 | 113 | 104·8 | 29·38 | 163 | 151·1 | 42·38 |
| 14 | 12·98 | 3·64 | 64 | 59·33 | 16·64 | 114 | 105·7 | 29·64 | 164 | 152·0 | 42·64 |
| 15 | 13·91 | 3·90 | 65 | 60·26 | 16·90 | 115 | 106·6 | 29·90 | 165 | 153·0 | 42·90 |
| 16 | 14·83 | 4·16 | 66 | 61·19 | 17·16 | 116 | 107·5 | 30·16 | 166 | 153·9 | 43·16 |
| 17 | 15·76 | 4·42 | 67 | 62·11 | 17·42 | 117 | 108·5 | 30·42 | 167 | 154·8 | 43·42 |
| 18 | 16·69 | 4·68 | 68 | 63·04 | 17·68 | 118 | 109·4 | 30·68 | 168 | 155·7 | 43·68 |
| 19 | 17·61 | 4·94 | 69 | 63·97 | 17·94 | 119 | 110·3 | 30·94 | 169 | 156·7 | 43·94 |
| 20 | 18·54 | 5·20 | 70 | 64·90 | 18·20 | 120 | 111·2 | 31·20 | 170 | 157·6 | 44·20 |
| 21 | 19·47 | 5·46 | 71 | 65·82 | 18·46 | 121 | 112·2 | 31·46 | 171 | 158·5 | 44·46 |
| 22 | 20·40 | 5·72 | 72 | 66·75 | 18·72 | 122 | 113·1 | 31·72 | 172 | 159·5 | 44·72 |
| 23 | 21·32 | 5·98 | 73 | 67·68 | 18·98 | 123 | 114·0 | 31·98 | 173 | 160·4 | 44·98 |
| 24 | 22·25 | 6·24 | 74 | 68·60 | 19·24 | 124 | 115·0 | 32·24 | 174 | 161·3 | 45·24 |
| 25 | 23·18 | 6·50 | 75 | 69·53 | 19·50 | 125 | 115·9 | 32·50 | 175 | 162·2 | 45·50 |
| 26 | 24·10 | 6·76 | 76 | 70·46 | 19·76 | 126 | 116·8 | 32·76 | 176 | 163·2 | 45·76 |
| 27 | 25·03 | 7·02 | 77 | 71·39 | 20·02 | 127 | 117·7 | 33·02 | 177 | 164·1 | 46·02 |
| 28 | 25·96 | 7·28 | 78 | 72·31 | 20·28 | 128 | 118·7 | 33·28 | 178 | 165·0 | 46·28 |
| 29 | 26·89 | 7·54 | 79 | 73·24 | 20·54 | 129 | 119·6 | 33·54 | 179 | 165·9 | 46·54 |
| 30 | 27·81 | 7·80 | 80 | 74·17 | 20·80 | 130 | 120·5 | 33·80 | 180 | 166·9 | 46·80 |
| 31 | 28·74 | 8·06 | 81 | 75·09 | 21·06 | 131 | 121·4 | 34·06 | 181 | 167·8 | 47·06 |
| 32 | 29·67 | 8·32 | 82 | 76·02 | 21·32 | 132 | 122·4 | 34·32 | 182 | 168·7 | 47·32 |
| 33 | 30·59 | 8·58 | 83 | 76·95 | 21·58 | 133 | 123·3 | 34·58 | 183 | 169·7 | 47·58 |
| 34 | 31·52 | 8·84 | 84 | 77·87 | 21·84 | 134 | 124·2 | 34·84 | 184 | 170·6 | 47·84 |
| 35 | 32·45 | 9·10 | 85 | 78·80 | 22·10 | 135 | 125·2 | 35·10 | 185 | 171·5 | 48·10 |
| 36 | 33·37 | 9·36 | 86 | 79·73 | 22·36 | 136 | 126·1 | 35·36 | 186 | 172·4 | 48·36 |
| 37 | 34·30 | 9·62 | 87 | 80·66 | 22·62 | 137 | 127·0 | 35·62 | 187 | 173·4 | 48·62 |
| 38 | 35·23 | 9·88 | 88 | 81·58 | 22·88 | 138 | 127·9 | 35·88 | 188 | 174·3 | 48·88 |
| 39 | 36·16 | 10·14 | 89 | 82·51 | 23·14 | 139 | 128·9 | 36·14 | 189 | 175·2 | 49·14 |
| 40 | 37·08 | 10·40 | 90 | 83·44 | 23·40 | 140 | 129·8 | 36·40 | 190 | 176·1 | 49·40 |
| 41 | 38·01 | 10·66 | 91 | 84·36 | 23·66 | 141 | 130·7 | 36·66 | 191 | 177·1 | 49·66 |
| 42 | 38·94 | 10·92 | 92 | 85·29 | 23·92 | 142 | 131·6 | 36·92 | 192 | 178·0 | 49·92 |
| 43 | 39·86 | 11·18 | 93 | 86·22 | 24·18 | 143 | 132·6 | 37·18 | 193 | 178·9 | 50·18 |
| 44 | 40·79 | 11·44 | 94 | 87·15 | 24·44 | 144 | 133·5 | 37·44 | 194 | 179·9 | 50·44 |
| 45 | 41·72 | 11·70 | 95 | 88·07 | 24·70 | 145 | 134·4 | 37·70 | 195 | 180·8 | 50·70 |
| 46 | 42·65 | 11·96 | 96 | 89·00 | 24·96 | 146 | 135·4 | 37·96 | 196 | 181·7 | 50·96 |
| 47 | 43·57 | 12·22 | 97 | 89·93 | 25·22 | 147 | 136·3 | 38·22 | 197 | 182·6 | 51·22 |
| 48 | 44·50 | 12·48 | 98 | 90·85 | 25·48 | 148 | 137·2 | 38·48 | 198 | 183·6 | 51·48 |
| 49 | 45·43 | 12·74 | 99 | 91·78 | 25·74 | 149 | 138·1 | 38·74 | 199 | 184·5 | 51·74 |
| 50 | 46·35 | 13·00 | 100 | 92·71 | 26·00 | 150 | 139·1 | 39·00 | 200 | 185·4 | 52·00 |
| 51 | 47·28 | 13·26 | 101 | 93·63 | 26·26 | 151 | 140·0 | 39·26 | 201 | 186·3 | 52·26 |
| 52 | 48·21 | 13·52 | 102 | 94·56 | 26·52 | 152 | 140·9 | 39·52 | 202 | 187·3 | 52·52 |
| 53 | 49·14 | 13·78 | 103 | 95·49 | 26·78 | 153 | 141·8 | 39·78 | 203 | 188·2 | 52·78 |
| 54 | 50·06 | 14·04 | 104 | 96·42 | 27·04 | 154 | 142·8 | 40·04 | 204 | 189·1 | 53·04 |
| 55 | 50·99 | 14·30 | 105 | 97·34 | 27·30 | 155 | 143·7 | 40·30 | 205 | 190·1 | 53·30 |
| 56 | 51·92 | 14·56 | 106 | 98·27 | 27·56 | 156 | 144·6 | 40·56 | 206 | 191·0 | 53·56 |
| 57 | 52·84 | 14·82 | 107 | 99·20 | 27·82 | 157 | 145·6 | 40·82 | 207 | 191·9 | 53·82 |
| 58 | 53·77 | 15·08 | 108 | 100·1 | 28·08 | 158 | 146·5 | 41·08 | 208 | 192·8 | 54·08 |
| 59 | 54·70 | 15·34 | 109 | 101·1 | 28·34 | 159 | 147·4 | 41·34 | 209· | 193·8 | 54·34 |
| 60 | 55·62 | 15·60 | 110 | 102·0 | 28·60 | 160 | 148·3 | 41·60 | 210 | 194·7 | 54·60 |

TABLE I

| G | D | H | G | D | H | G | D | H | G | D | H |
|---|---|---|---|---|---|---|---|---|---|---|---|
| 10 | 9·24 | 2·65 | 60 | 55·44 | 15·90 | 110 | 101·6 | 29·15 | 160 | 147·8 | 42·39 |
| 11 | 10·16 | 2·91 | 61 | 56·37 | 16·16 | 111 | 102·6 | 29·41 | 161 | 148·8 | 42·66 |
| 12 | 11·09 | 3·18 | 62 | 57·29 | 16·43 | 112 | 103·5 | 29·68 | 162 | 149·7 | 42·92 |
| 13 | 12·01 | 3·44 | 63 | 58·21 | 16·69 | 113 | 104·4 | 29·94 | 163 | 150·6 | 43·19 |
| 14 | 12·94 | 3·71 | 64 | 59·14 | 16·96 | 114 | 105·3 | 30·21 | 164 | 151·5 | 43·45 |
| 15 | 13·86 | 3·97 | 65 | 60·06 | 17·22 | 115 | 106·3 | 30·47 | 165 | 152·5 | 43·72 |
| 16 | 14·78 | 4·24 | 66 | 60·99 | 17·49 | 116 | 107·2 | 30·74 | 166 | 153·4 | 43·98 |
| 17 | 15·71 | 4·50 | 67 | 61·91 | 17·75 | 117 | 108·1 | 31·00 | 167 | 154·3 | 44·25 |
| 18 | 16·63 | 4·77 | 68 | 62·83 | 18·02 | 118 | 109·0 | 31·27 | 168 | 155·2 | 44·51 |
| 19 | 17·56 | 5·03 | 69 | 63·76 | 18·28 | 119 | 110·0 | 31·53 | 169 | 156·2 | 44·78 |
| 20 | 18·48 | 5·30 | 70 | 64·68 | 18·55 | 120 | 110·9 | 31·80 | 170 | 157·1 | 45·04 |
| 21 | 19·40 | 5·56 | 71 | 65·61 | 18·81 | 121 | 111·8 | 32·06 | 171 | 158·0 | 45·31 |
| 22 | 20·33 | 5·83 | 72 | 66·53 | 19·08 | 122 | 112·7 | 32·32 | 172 | 158·9 | 45·57 |
| 23 | 21·25 | 6·09 | 73 | 67·45 | 19·34 | 123 | 113·7 | 32·59 | 173 | 159·9 | 45·84 |
| 24 | 22·18 | 6·36 | 74 | 68·38 | 19·61 | 124 | 114·6 | 32·85 | 174 | 160·8 | 46·10 |
| 25 | 23·10 | 6·62 | 75 | 69·30 | 19·87 | 125 | 115·5 | 33·12 | 175 | 161·7 | 46·37 |
| 26 | 24·02 | 6·89 | 76 | 70·23 | 20·14 | 126 | 116·4 | 33·38 | 176 | 162·6 | 46·63 |
| 27 | 24·95 | 7·15 | 77 | 71·15 | 20·40 | 127 | 117·4 | 33·65 | 177 | 163·6 | 46·90 |
| 28 | 25·87 | 7·42 | 78 | 72·07 | 20·67 | 128 | 118·3 | 33·91 | 178 | 164·5 | 47·16 |
| 29 | 26·80 | 7·68 | 79 | 73·00 | 20·93 | 129 | 119·2 | 34·18 | 179 | 165·4 | 47·43 |
| 30 | 27·72 | 7·95 | 80 | 73·92 | 21·20 | 130 | 120·1 | 34·44 | 180 | 166·3 | 47·69 |
| 31 | 28·64 | 8·21 | 81 | 74·85 | 21·46 | 131 | 121·0 | 34·71 | 181 | 167·2 | 47·96 |
| 32 | 29·57 | 8·48 | 82 | 75·77 | 21·73 | 132 | 122·0 | 34·97 | 182 | 168·2 | 48·22 |
| 33 | 30·49 | 8·74 | 83 | 76·69 | 21·99 | 133 | 122·9 | 35·24 | 183 | 169·1 | 48·49 |
| 34 | 31·42 | 9·01 | 84 | 77·62 | 22·26 | 134 | 123·8 | 35·50 | 184 | 170·0 | 48·75 |
| 35 | 32·34 | 9·27 | 85 | 78·54 | 22·52 | 135 | 124·7 | 35·77 | 185 | 170·9 | 49·02 |
| 36 | 33·26 | 9·54 | 86 | 79·47 | 22·79 | 136 | 125·7 | 36·03 | 186 | 171·9 | 49·28 |
| 37 | 34·19 | 9·80 | 87 | 80·39 | 23·05 | 137 | 126·6 | 36·30 | 187 | 172·8 | 49·55 |
| 38 | 35·11 | 10·07 | 88 | 81·31 | 23·32 | 138 | 127·5 | 36·56 | 188 | 173·7 | 49·81 |
| 39 | 36·04 | 10·33 | 89 | 82·24 | 23·58 | 139 | 128·4 | 36·83 | 189 | 174·6 | 50·08 |
| 40 | 36·96 | 10·60 | 90 | 83·16 | 23·85 | 140 | 129·4 | 37·09 | 190 | 175·6 | 50·34 |
| 41 | 37·88 | 10·86 | 91 | 84·09 | 24·11 | 141 | 130·3 | 37·36 | 191 | 176·5 | 50·61 |
| 42 | 38·81 | 11·13 | 92 | 85·01 | 24·38 | 142 | 131·2 | 37·62 | 192 | 177·4 | 50·87 |
| 43 | 39·73 | 11·39 | 93 | 85·93 | 24·64 | 143 | 132·1 | 37·89 | 193 | 178·3 | 51·14 |
| 44 | 40·66 | 11·66 | 94 | 86·86 | 24·91 | 144 | 133·1 | 38·15 | 194 | 179·3 | 51·40 |
| 45 | 41·58 | 11·92 | 95 | 87·78 | 25·17 | 145 | 134·0 | 38·42 | 195 | 180·2 | 51·67 |
| 46 | 42·51 | 12·19 | 96 | 88·71 | 25·44 | 146 | 134·9 | 38·68 | 196 | 181·1 | 51·93 |
| 47 | 43·43 | 12·45 | 97 | 89·63 | 25·70 | 147 | 135·8 | 38·95 | 197 | 182·0 | 52·20 |
| 48 | 44·35 | 12·72 | 98 | 90·55 | 25·97 | 148 | 136·8 | 39·21 | 198 | 183·0 | 52·46 |
| 49 | 45·28 | 12·98 | 99 | 91·48 | 26·23 | 149 | 137·7 | 39·48 | 199 | 183·9 | 52·73 |
| 50 | 46·20 | 13·25 | 100 | 92·40 | 26·50 | 150 | 138·6 | 39·74 | 200 | 184·8 | 52·99 |
| 51 | 47·13 | 13·51 | 101 | 93·33 | 26·76 | 151 | 139·5 | 40·01 | 201 | 185·7 | 53·26 |
| 52 | 48·05 | 13·78 | 102 | 94·25 | 27·03 | 152 | 140·5 | 40·27 | 202 | 186·7 | 53·52 |
| 53 | 48·97 | 14·04 | 103 | 95·17 | 27·29 | 153 | 141·4 | 40·54 | 203 | 187·6 | 53·79 |
| 54 | 49·90 | 14·31 | 104 | 96·10 | 27·56 | 154 | 142·3 | 40·80 | 204 | 188·5 | 54·05 |
| 55 | 50·82 | 14·57 | 105 | 97·02 | 27·82 | 155 | 143·2 | 41·07 | 205 | 189·4 | 54·32 |
| 56 | 51·75 | 14·84 | 106 | 97·95 | 28·09 | 156 | 144·1 | 41·33 | 206 | 190·3 | 54·58 |
| 57 | 52·67 | 15·10 | 107 | 98·87 | 28·35 | 157 | 145·1 | 41·60 | 207 | 191·3 | 54·85 |
| 58 | 53·59 | 15·37 | 108 | 99·79 | 28·62 | 158 | 146·0 | 41·86 | 208 | 192·2 | 55·11 |
| 59 | 54·52 | 15·63 | 109 | 100·7 | 28·88 | 159 | 146·9 | 42·13 | 209 | 193·1 | 55·38 |
| 60 | 55·44 | 15·90 | 110 | 101·6 | 29·15 | 160 | 147·8 | 42·39 | 210 | 194·0 | 55·64 |

TABLE I

# 16° 20′

| G | D | H | G | D | H | G | D | H | G | D | H |
|---|---|---|---|---|---|---|---|---|---|---|---|
| 10 | 9·21 | 2·70 | 60 | 55·25 | 16·19 | 110 | 101·3 | 29·69 | 160 | 147·3 | 43·18 |
| 11 | 10·13 | 2·97 | 61 | 56·18 | 16·46 | 111 | 102·2 | 29·96 | 161 | 148·3 | 43·45 |
| 12 | 11·05 | 3·24 | 62 | 57·10 | 16·73 | 112 | 103·1 | 30·23 | 162 | 149·2 | 43·72 |
| 13 | 11·97 | 3·51 | 63 | 58·02 | 17·00 | 113 | 104·1 | 30·50 | 163 | 150·1 | 43·99 |
| 14 | 12·89 | 3·78 | 64 | 58·94 | 17·27 | 114 | 105·0 | 30·77 | 164 | 151·0 | 44·26 |
| 15 | 13·81 | 4·05 | 65 | 59·86 | 17·54 | 115 | 105·9 | 31·04 | 165 | 152·0 | 44·53 |
| 16 | 14·73 | 4·32 | 66 | 60·78 | 17·81 | 116 | 106·8 | 31·31 | 166 | 152·9 | 44·80 |
| 17 | 15·66 | 4·59 | 67 | 61·70 | 18·08 | 117 | 107·7 | 31·58 | 167 | 153·8 | 45·07 |
| 18 | 16·58 | 4·86 | 68 | 62·62 | 18·35 | 118 | 108·7 | 31·85 | 168 | 154·7 | 45·34 |
| 19 | 17·50 | 5·13 | 69 | 63·54 | 18·62 | 119 | 109·6 | 32·12 | 169 | 155·6 | 45·61 |
| 20 | 18·42 | 5·40 | 70 | 64·46 | 18·89 | 120 | 110·5 | 32·39 | 170 | 156·6 | 45·88 |
| 21 | 19·34 | 5·67 | 71 | 65·38 | 19·16 | 121 | 111·4 | 32·65 | 171 | 157·5 | 46·15 |
| 22 | 20·26 | 5·94 | 72 | 66·31 | 19·43 | 122 | 112·4 | 32·92 | 172 | 158·4 | 46·42 |
| 23 | 21·18 | 6·21 | 73 | 67·23 | 19·70 | 123 | 113·3 | 33·19 | 173 | 159·3 | 46·69 |
| 24 | 22·10 | 6·48 | 74 | 68·15 | 19·97 | 124 | 114·2 | 33·46 | 174 | 160·2 | 46·96 |
| 25 | 23·02 | 6·75 | 75 | 69·07 | 20·24 | 125 | 115·1 | 33·73 | 175 | 161·2 | 47·23 |
| 26 | 23·94 | 7·02 | 76 | 69·99 | 20·51 | 126 | 116·0 | 34·00 | 176 | 162·1 | 47·50 |
| 27 | 24·86 | 7·29 | 77 | 70·91 | 20·78 | 127 | 117·0 | 34·27 | 177 | 163·0 | 47·77 |
| 28 | 25·79 | 7·56 | 78 | 71·83 | 21·05 | 128 | 117·9 | 34·54 | 178 | 163·9 | 48·04 |
| 29 | 26·71 | 7·83 | 79 | 72·75 | 21·32 | 129 | 118·8 | 34·81 | 179 | 164·8 | 48·31 |
| 30 | 27·63 | 8·10 | 80 | 73·67 | 21·59 | 130 | 119·7 | 35·08 | 180 | 165·8 | 48·58 |
| 31 | 28·55 | 8·37 | 81 | 74·59 | 21·86 | 131 | 120·6 | 35·35 | 181 | 166·7 | 48·85 |
| 32 | 29·47 | 8·64 | 82 | 75·51 | 22·13 | 132 | 121·6 | 35·62 | 182 | 167·6 | 49·12 |
| 33 | 30·39 | 8·91 | 83 | 76·44 | 22·40 | 133 | 122·5 | 35·89 | 183 | 168·5 | 49·39 |
| 34 | 31·31 | 9·18 | 84 | 77·36 | 22·67 | 134 | 123·4 | 36·16 | 184 | 169·4 | 49·66 |
| 35 | 32·23 | 9·45 | 85 | 78·28 | 22·94 | 135 | 124·3 | 36·43 | 185 | 170·4 | 49·93 |
| 36 | 33·15 | 9·72 | 86 | 79·20 | 23·21 | 136 | 125·2 | 36·70 | 186 | 171·3 | 50·20 |
| 37 | 34·07 | 9·99 | 87 | 80·12 | 23·48 | 137 | 126·2 | 36·97 | 187 | 172·2 | 50·47 |
| 38 | 34·99 | 10·26 | 88 | 81·04 | 23·75 | 138 | 127·1 | 37·24 | 188 | 173·1 | 50·74 |
| 39 | 35·92 | 10·53 | 89 | 81·96 | 24·02 | 139 | 128·0 | 37·51 | 189 | 174·1 | 51·01 |
| 40 | 36·84 | 10·80 | 90 | 82·88 | 24·29 | 140 | 128·9 | 37·78 | 190 | 175·0 | 51·28 |
| 41 | 37·76 | 11·06 | 91 | 83·80 | 24·56 | 141 | 129·8 | 38·05 | 191 | 175·9 | 51·55 |
| 42 | 38·68 | 11·33 | 92 | 84·72 | 24·83 | 142 | 130·8 | 38·32 | 192 | 176·8 | 51·82 |
| 43 | 39·60 | 11·60 | 93 | 85·64 | 25·10 | 143 | 131·7 | 38·59 | 193 | 177·7 | 52·09 |
| 44 | 40·52 | 11·87 | 94 | 86·57 | 25·37 | 144 | 132·6 | 38·86 | 194 | 178·7 | 52·36 |
| 45 | 41·44 | 12·14 | 95 | 87·49 | 25·64 | 145 | 133·5 | 39·13 | 195 | 179·6 | 52·63 |
| 46 | 42·36 | 12·41 | 96 | 88·41 | 25·91 | 146 | 134·5 | 39·40 | 196 | 180·5 | 52·90 |
| 47 | 43·28 | 12·68 | 97 | 89·33 | 26·18 | 147 | 135·4 | 39·67 | 197 | 181·4 | 53·17 |
| 48 | 44·20 | 12·95 | 98 | 90·25 | 26·45 | 148 | 136·3 | 39·94 | 198 | 182·3 | 53·44 |
| 49 | 45·12 | 13·22 | 99 | 91·17 | 26·72 | 149 | 137·2 | 40·21 | 199 | 183·3 | 53·71 |
| 50 | 46·05 | 13·49 | 100 | 92·09 | 26·99 | 150 | 138·1 | 40·48 | 200 | 184·2 | 53·98 |
| 51 | 46·97 | 13·76 | 101 | 93·01 | 27·26 | 151 | 139·1 | 40·75 | 201 | 185·1 | 54·24 |
| 52 | 47·89 | 14·03 | 102 | 93·93 | 27·53 | 152 | 140·0 | 41·02 | 202 | 186·0 | 54·51 |
| 53 | 48·81 | 14·30 | 103 | 94·85 | 27·80 | 153 | 140·9 | 41·29 | 203 | 186·9 | 54·78 |
| 54 | 49·73 | 14·57 | 104 | 95·77 | 28·07 | 154 | 141·8 | 41·56 | 204 | 187·9 | 55·05 |
| 55 | 50·65 | 14·84 | 105 | 96·70 | 28·34 | 155 | 142·7 | 41·83 | 205 | 188·8 | 55·32 |
| 56 | 51·57 | 15·11 | 106 | 97·62 | 28·61 | 156 | 143·7 | 42·10 | 206 | 189·7 | 55·59 |
| 57 | 52·49 | 15·38 | 107 | 98·54 | 28·88 | 157 | 144·6 | 42·37 | 207 | 190·6 | 55·86 |
| 58 | 53·41 | 15·65 | 108 | 99·46 | 29·15 | 158 | 145·5 | 42·64 | 208 | 191·5 | 56·13 |
| 59 | 54·33 | 15·92 | 109 | 100·4 | 29·42 | 159 | 146·4 | 42·91 | 209 | 192·5 | 56·40 |
| 60 | 55·25 | 16·19 | 110 | 101·3 | 29·69 | 160 | 147·3 | 43·18 | 210 | 193·4 | 56·67 |

| G | D | H | G | D | H | G | D | H | G | D | H |
|---|---|---|---|---|---|---|---|---|---|---|---|
| 10 | 9·18 | 2·75 | 60 | 55·06 | 16·49 | 110 | 101·0 | 30·22 | 160 | 146·8 | 43·96 |
| 11 | 10·10 | 3·02 | 61 | 55·98 | 16·76 | 111 | 101·9 | 30·50 | 161 | 147·8 | 44·24 |
| 12 | 11·01 | 3·30 | 62 | 56·90 | 17·03 | 112 | 102·8 | 30·77 | 162 | 148·7 | 44·51 |
| 13 | 11·93 | 3·57 | 63 | 57·82 | 17·31 | 113 | 103·7 | 31·05 | 163 | 149·6 | 44·78 |
| 14 | 12·85 | 3·85 | 64 | 58·74 | 17·58 | 114 | 104·6 | 31·32 | 164 | 150·5 | 45·06 |
| 15 | 13·77 | 4·12 | 65 | 59·65 | 17·86 | 115 | 105·5 | 31·60 | 165 | 151·4 | 45·33 |
| 16 | 14·68 | 4·40 | 66 | 60·57 | 18·13 | 116 | 106·5 | 31·87 | 166 | 152·3 | 45·61 |
| 17 | 15·60 | 4·67 | 67 | 61·49 | 18·41 | 117 | 107·4 | 32·15 | 167 | 153·3 | 45·88 |
| 18 | 16·52 | 4·95 | 68 | 62·41 | 18·68 | 118 | 108·3 | 32·42 | 168 | 154·2 | 46·16 |
| 19 | 17·44 | 5·22 | 69 | 63·32 | 18·96 | 119 | 109·2 | 32·70 | 169 | 155·1 | 46·43 |
| 20 | 18·35 | 5·50 | 70 | 64·24 | 19·23 | 120 | 110·1 | 32·97 | 170 | 156·0 | 46·71 |
| 21 | 19·27 | 5·77 | 71 | 65·16 | 19·51 | 121 | 111·0 | 33·25 | 171 | 156·9 | 46·98 |
| 22 | 20·19 | 6·04 | 72 | 66·08 | 19·78 | 122 | 112·0 | 33·52 | 172 | 157·9 | 47·26 |
| 23 | 21·11 | 6·32 | 73 | 67·00 | 20·06 | 123 | 112·9 | 33·79 | 173 | 158·8 | 47·53 |
| 24 | 22·03 | 6·59 | 74 | 67·91 | 20·33 | 124 | 113·8 | 34·07 | 174 | 159·7 | 47·81 |
| 25 | 22·94 | 6·87 | 75 | 68·83 | 20·61 | 125 | 114·7 | 34·34 | 175 | 160·6 | 48·08 |
| 26 | 23·86 | 7·14 | 76 | 69·75 | 20·88 | 126 | 115·6 | 34·62 | 176 | 161·5 | 48·36 |
| 27 | 24·78 | 7·42 | 77 | 70·67 | 21·16 | 127 | 116·6 | 34·89 | 177 | 162·4 | 48·63 |
| 28 | 25·70 | 7·69 | 78 | 71·58 | 21·43 | 128 | 117·5 | 35·17 | 178 | 163·4 | 48·91 |
| 29 | 26·61 | 7·97 | 79 | 72·50 | 21·71 | 129 | 118·4 | 35·44 | 179 | 164·3 | 49·18 |
| 30 | 27·53 | 8·24 | 80 | 73·42 | 21·98 | 130 | 119·3 | 35·72 | 180 | 165·2 | 49·46 |
| 31 | 28·45 | 8·52 | 81 | 74·34 | 22·26 | 131 | 120·2 | 35·99 | 181 | 166·1 | 49·73 |
| 32 | 29·37 | 8·79 | 82 | 75·25 | 22·53 | 132 | 121·1 | 36·27 | 182 | 167·0 | 50·01 |
| 33 | 30·29 | 9·07 | 83 | 76·17 | 22·80 | 133 | 122·1 | 36·54 | 183 | 167·9 | 50·28 |
| 34 | 31·20 | 9·34 | 84 | 77·09 | 23·08 | 134 | 123·0 | 36·82 | 184 | 168·9 | 50·55 |
| 35 | 32·12 | 9·62 | 85 | 78·01 | 23·35 | 135 | 123·9 | 37·09 | 185 | 169·8 | 50·83 |
| 36 | 33·04 | 9·89 | 86 | 78·93 | 23·63 | 136 | 124·8 | 37·37 | 186 | 170·7 | 51·10 |
| 37 | 33·96 | 10·17 | 87 | 79·84 | 23·90 | 137 | 125·7 | 37·64 | 187 | 171·6 | 51·38 |
| 38 | 34·87 | 10·44 | 88 | 80·76 | 24·18 | 138 | 126·6 | 37·92 | 188 | 172·5 | 51·65 |
| 39 | 35·79 | 10·72 | 89 | 81·68 | 24·45 | 139 | 127·6 | 38·19 | 189 | 173·5 | 51·93 |
| '40 | 36·71 | 10·99 | 90 | 82·60 | 24·73 | 140 | 128·5 | 38·47 | 190 | 174·4 | 52·20 |
| 41 | 37·63 | 11·26 | 91 | 83·51 | 25·00 | 141 | 129·4 | 38·74 | 191 | 175·3 | 52·48 |
| 42 | 38·55 | 11·54 | 92 | 84·43 | 25·28 | 142 | 130·3 | 39·02 | 192 | 176·2 | 52·75 |
| 43 | 39·46 | 11·81 | 93 | 85·35 | 25·55 | 143 | 131·2 | 39·29 | 193 | 177·1 | 53·03 |
| 44 | 40·38 | 12·09 | 94 | 86·27 | 25·83 | 144 | 132·2 | 39·56 | 194 | 178·0 | 53·30 |
| 45 | 41·30 | 12·36 | 95 | 87·19 | 26·10 | 145 | 133·1 | 39·84 | 195 | 179·0 | 53·58 |
| 46 | 42·22 | 12·64 | 96 | 88·10 | 26·38 | 146 | 134·0 | 40·11 | 196 | 179·9 | 53·85 |
| 47 | 43·13 | 12·91 | 97 | 89·02 | 26·65 | 147 | 134·9 | 40·39 | 197 | 180·8 | 54·13 |
| 48 | 44·05 | 13·19 | 98 | 89·94 | 26·93 | 148 | 135·8 | 40·66 | 198 | 181·7 | 54·40 |
| 49 | 44·97 | 13·46 | 99 | 90·86 | 27·20 | 149 | 136·7 | 40·94 | 199 | 182·6 | 54·68 |
| 50 | 45·89 | 13·74 | 100 | 91·77 | 27·48 | 150 | 137·7 | 41·21 | 200 | 183·5 | 54·95 |
| 51 | 46·80 | 14·01 | 101 | 92·69 | 27·75 | 151 | 138·6 | 41·49 | 201 | 184·5 | 55·23 |
| 52 | 47·72 | 14·29 | 102 | 93·61 | 28·02 | 152 | 139·5 | 41·76 | 202 | 185·4 | 55·50 |
| 53 | 48·64 | 14·56 | 103 | 94·53 | 28·30 | 153 | 140·4 | 42·04 | 203 | 186·3 | 55·78 |
| 54 | 49·56 | 14·84 | 104 | 95·45 | 28·57 | 154 | 141·3 | 42·31 | 204 | 187·2 | 56·05 |
| 55 | 50·48 | 15·11 | 105 | 96·36 | 28·85 | 155 | 142·3 | 42·59 | 205 | 188·1 | 56·32 |
| 56 | 51·39 | 15·39 | 106 | 97·28 | 29·12 | 156 | 143·2 | 42·86 | 206 | 189·1 | 56·60 |
| 57 | 52·31 | 15·66 | 107 | 98·20 | 29·40 | 157 | 144·1 | 43·14 | 207 | 190·0 | 56·87 |
| 58 | 53·23 | 15·94 | 108 | 99·12 | 29·67 | 158 | 145·0 | 43·41 | 208 | 190·9 | 57·15 |
| 59 | 54·15 | 16·21 | 109 | 100·0 | 29·95 | 159 | 145·9 | 43·69 | 209 | 191·8 | 57·42 |
| 60 | 55·06 | 16·49 | 110 | 101·0 | 30·22 | 160 | 146·8 | 43·96 | 210 | 192·7 | 57·70 |

TABLE I

# 17° 00'

| G | D | H | G | D | H | G | D | H | G | D | H |
|---|---|---|---|---|---|---|---|---|---|---|---|
| 10 | 9·15 | 2·80 | 60 | 54·87 | 16·78 | 110 | 100·6 | 30·76 | 160 | 146·3 | 44·74 |
| 11 | 10·06 | 3·08 | 61 | 55·79 | 17·06 | 111 | 101·5 | 31·04 | 161 | 147·2 | 45·01 |
| 12 | 10·97 | 3·36 | 62 | 56·70 | 17·33 | 112 | 102·4 | 31·31 | 162 | 148·2 | 45·29 |
| 13 | 11·89 | 3·63 | 63 | 57·61 | 17·61 | 113 | 103·3 | 31·59 | 163 | 149·1 | 45·57 |
| 14 | 12·80 | 3·91 | 64 | 58·53 | 17·89 | 114 | 104·3 | 31·87 | 164 | 150·0 | 45·85 |
| 15 | 13·72 | 4·19 | 65 | 59·44 | 18·17 | 115 | 105·2 | 32·15 | 165 | 150·9 | 46·13 |
| 16 | 14·63 | 4·47 | 66 | 60·36 | 18·45 | 116 | 106·1 | 32·43 | 166 | 151·8 | 46·41 |
| 17 | 15·55 | 4·75 | 67 | 61·27 | 18·73 | 117 | 107·0 | 32·71 | 167 | 152·7 | 46·69 |
| 18 | 16·46 | 5·03 | 68 | 62·19 | 19·01 | 118 | 107·9 | 32·99 | 168 | 153·6 | 46·97 |
| 19 | 17·38 | 5·31 | 69 | 63·10 | 19·29 | 119 | 108·8 | 33·27 | 169 | 154·6 | 47·25 |
| 20 | 18·29 | 5·59 | 70 | 64·02 | 19·57 | 120 | 109·7 | 33·55 | 170 | 155·5 | 47·53 |
| 21 | 19·20 | 5·87 | 71 | 64·93 | 19·85 | 121 | 110·7 | 33·83 | 171 | 156·4 | 47·81 |
| 22 | 20·12 | 6·15 | 72 | 65·85 | 20·13 | 122 | 111·6 | 34·11 | 172 | 157·3 | 48·09 |
| 23 | 21·03 | 6·43 | 73 | 66·76 | 20·41 | 123 | 112·5 | 34·39 | 173 | 158·2 | 48·37 |
| 24 | 21·95 | 6·71 | 74 | 67·67 | 20·69 | 124 | 113·4 | 34·67 | 174 | 159·1 | 48·65 |
| 25 | 22·86 | 6·99 | 75 | 68·59 | 20·97 | 125 | 114·3 | 34·95 | 175 | 160·0 | 48·93 |
| 26 | 23·78 | 7·27 | 76 | 69·50 | 21·25 | 126 | 115·2 | 35·23 | 176 | 161·0 | 49·21 |
| 27 | 24·69 | 7·55 | 77 | 70·42 | 21·53 | 127 | 116·1 | 35·51 | 177 | 161·9 | 49·49 |
| 28 | 25·61 | 7·83 | 78 | 71·33 | 21·81 | 128 | 117·1 | 35·79 | 178 | 162·8 | 49·77 |
| 29 | 26·52 | 8·11 | 79 | 72·25 | 22·09 | 129 | 118·0 | 36·07 | 179 | 163·7 | 50·05 |
| 30 | 27·44 | 8·39 | 80 | 73·16 | 22·37 | 130 | 118·9 | 36·35 | 180 | 164·6 | 50·33 |
| 31 | 28·35 | 8·67 | 81 | 74·08 | 22·65 | 131 | 119·8 | 36·63 | 181 | 165·5 | 50·61 |
| 32 | 29·26 | 8·95 | 82 | 74·99 | 22·93 | 132 | 120·7 | 36·91 | 182 | 166·4 | 50·89 |
| 33 | 30·18 | 9·23 | 83 | 75·90 | 23·21 | 133 | 121·6 | 37·19 | 183 | 167·4 | 51·17 |
| 34 | 31·09 | 9·51 | 84 | 76·82 | 23·49 | 134 | 122·5 | 37·47 | 184 | 168·3 | 51·45 |
| 35 | 32·01 | 9·79 | 85 | 77·73 | 23·77 | 135 | 123·5 | 37·75 | 185 | 169·2 | 51·73 |
| 36 | 32·92 | 10·07 | 86 | 78·65 | 24·05 | 136 | 124·4 | 38·03 | 186 | 170·1 | 52·00 |
| 37 | 33·84 | 10·35 | 87 | 79·56 | 24·32 | 137 | 125·3 | 38·30 | 187 | 171·0 | 52·28 |
| 38 | 34·75 | 10·62 | 88 | 80·48 | 24·60 | 138 | 126·2 | 38·58 | 188 | 171·9 | 52·56 |
| 39 | 35·67 | 10·90 | 89 | 81·39 | 24·88 | 139 | 127·1 | 38·86 | 189 | 172·8 | 52·84 |
| 40 | 36·58 | 11·18 | 90 | 82·31 | 25·16 | 140 | 128·0 | 39·14 | 190 | 173·8 | 53·12 |
| 41 | 37·50 | 11·46 | 91 | 83·22 | 25·44 | 141 | 128·9 | 39·42 | 191 | 174·7 | 53·40 |
| 42 | 38·41 | 11·74 | 92 | 84·14 | 25·72 | 142 | 129·9 | 39·70 | 192 | 175·6 | 53·68 |
| 43 | 39·32 | 12·02 | 93 | 85·05 | 26·00 | 143 | 130·8 | 39·98 | 193 | 176·5 | 53·96 |
| 44 | 40·24 | 12·30 | 94 | 85·96 | 26·28 | 144 | 131·7 | 40·26 | 194 | 177·4 | 54·24 |
| 45 | 41·15 | 12·58 | 95 | 86·88 | 26·56 | 145 | 132·6 | 40·54 | 195 | 178·3 | 54·52 |
| 46 | 42·07 | 12·86 | 96 | 87·79 | 26·84 | 146 | 133·5 | 40·82 | 196 | 179·2 | 54·80 |
| 47 | 42·98 | 13·14 | 97 | 88·71 | 27·12 | 147 | 134·4 | 41·10 | 197 | 180·2 | 55·08 |
| 48 | 43·90 | 13·42 | 98 | 89·62 | 27·40 | 148 | 135·3 | 41·38 | 198 | 181·1 | 55·36 |
| 49 | 44·81 | 13·70 | 99 | 90·54 | 27·68 | 149 | 136·3 | 41·66 | 199 | 182·0 | 55·64 |
| 50 | 45·73 | 13·98 | 100 | 91·45 | 27·96 | 150 | 137·2 | 41·94 | 200 | 182·9 | 55·92 |
| 51 | 46·64 | 14·26 | 101 | 92·37 | 28·24 | 151 | 138·1 | 42·22 | 201 | 183·8 | 56·20 |
| 52 | 47·55 | 14·54 | 102 | 93·28 | 28·52 | 152 | 139·0 | 42·50 | 202 | 184·7 | 56·48 |
| 53 | 48·47 | 14·82 | 103 | 94·20 | 28·80 | 153 | 139·9 | 42·78 | 203 | 185·6 | 56·76 |
| 54 | 49·38 | 15·10 | 104 | 95·11 | 29·08 | 154 | 140·8 | 43·06 | 204 | 186·6 | 57·04 |
| 55 | 50·30 | 15·38 | 105 | 96·02 | 29·36 | 155 | 141·8 | 43·34 | 205 | 187·5 | 57·32 |
| 56 | 51·21 | 15·66 | 106 | 96·94 | 29·64 | 156 | 142·7 | 43·62 | 206 | 188·4 | 57·60 |
| 57 | 52·13 | 15·94 | 107 | 97·85 | 29·92 | 157 | 143·6 | 43·90 | 207 | 189·3 | 57·88 |
| 58 | 53·04 | 16·22 | 108 | 98·77 | 30·20 | 158 | 144·5 | 44·18 | 208 | 190·2 | 58·16 |
| 59 | 53·96 | 16·50 | 109 | 99·68 | 30·48 | 159 | 145·4 | 44·46 | 209 | 191·1 | 58·44 |
| 60 | 54·87 | 16·78 | 110 | 100·6 | 30·76 | 160 | 146·3 | 44·74 | 210 | 192·0 | 58·72 |

TABLE I

| G | D | H | G | D | H | G | D | H | G | D | H |
|---|---|---|---|---|---|---|---|---|---|---|---|
| 10 | 9·11 | 2·84 | 60 | 54·67 | 17·06 | 110 | 100·2 | 31·28 | 160 | 145·8 | 45·50 |
| 11 | 10·02 | 3·13 | 61 | 55·59 | 17·35 | 111 | 101·1 | 31·57 | 161 | 146·7 | 45·79 |
| 12 | 10·93 | 3·41 | 62 | 56·50 | 17·63 | 112 | 102·1 | 31·85 | 162 | 147·6 | 46·07 |
| 13 | 11·85 | 3·70 | 63 | 57·41 | 17·92 | 113 | 103·0 | 32·14 | 163 | 148·5 | 46·36 |
| 14 | 12·76 | 3·98 | 64 | 58·32 | 18·20 | 114 | 103·9 | 32·42 | 164 | 149·4 | 46·64 |
| 15 | 13·67 | 4·27 | 65 | 59·23 | 18·49 | 115 | 104·8 | 32·71 | 165 | 150·4 | 46·93 |
| 16 | 14·58 | 4·55 | 66 | 60·14 | 18·77 | 116 | 105·7 | 32·99 | 166 | 151·3 | 47·21 |
| 17 | 15·49 | 4·83 | 67 | 61·05 | 19·05 | 117 | 106·6 | 33·27 | 167 | 152·2 | 47·49 |
| 18 | 16·40 | 5·12 | 68 | 61·96 | 19·34 | 118 | 107·5 | 33·56 | 168 | 153·1 | 47·78 |
| 19 | 17·31 | 5·40 | 69 | 62·88 | 19·62 | 119 | 108·4 | 33·84 | 169 | 154·0 | 48·06 |
| 20 | 18·22 | 5·69 | 70 | 63·79 | 19·91 | 120 | 109·3 | 34·13 | 170 | 154·9 | 48·35 |
| 21 | 19·14 | 5·97 | 71 | 64·70 | 20·19 | 121 | 110·3 | 34·41 | 171 | 155·8 | 48·63 |
| 22 | 20·05 | 6·26 | 72 | 65·61 | 20·48 | 122 | 111·2 | 34·70 | 172 | 156·7 | 48·92 |
| 23 | 20·96 | 6·54 | 73 | 66·52 | 20·76 | 123 | 112·1 | 34·98 | 173 | 157·6 | 49·20 |
| 24 | 21·87 | 6·83 | 74 | 67·43 | 21·05 | 124 | 113·0 | 35·27 | 174 | 158·6 | 49·49 |
| 25 | 22·78 | 7·11 | 75 | 68·34 | 21·33 | 125 | 113·9 | 35·55 | 175 | 159·5 | 49·77 |
| 26 | 23·69 | 7·39 | 76 | 69·25 | 21·61 | 126 | 114·8 | 35·83 | 176 | 160·4 | 50·05 |
| 27 | 24·60 | 7·68 | 77 | 70·17 | 21·90 | 127 | 115·7 | 36·12 | 177 | 161·3 | 50·34 |
| 28 | 25·51 | 7·96 | 78 | 71·08 | 22·18 | 128 | 116·6 | 36·40 | 178 | 162·2 | 50·62 |
| 29 | 26·43 | 8·25 | 79 | 71·99 | 22·47 | 129 | 117·5 | 36·69 | 179 | 163·1 | 50·91 |
| 30 | 27·34 | 8·53 | 80 | 72·90 | 22·75 | 130 | 118·5 | 36·97 | 180 | 164·0 | 51·19 |
| 31 | 28·25 | 8·82 | 81 | 73·81 | 23·04 | 131 | 119·4 | 37·26 | 181 | 164·9 | 51·48 |
| 32 | 29·16 | 9·10 | 82 | 74·72 | 23·32 | 132 | 120·3 | 37·54 | 182 | 165·8 | 51·76 |
| 33 | 30·07 | 9·39 | 83 | 75·63 | 23·61 | 133 | 121·2 | 37·83 | 183 | 166·8 | 52·05 |
| 34 | 30·98 | 9·67 | 84 | 76·54 | 23·89 | 134 | 122·1 | 38·11 | 184 | 167·7 | 52·33 |
| 35 | 31·89 | 9·95 | 85 | 77·46 | 24·17 | 135 | 123·0 | 38·39 | 185 | 168·6 | 52·61 |
| 36 | 32·80 | 10·24 | 86 | 78·37 | 24·46 | 136 | 123·9 | 38·68 | 186 | 169·5 | 52·90 |
| 37 | 33·72 | 10·52 | 87 | 79·28 | 24·74 | 137 | 124·8 | 38·96 | 187 | 170·4 | 53·18 |
| 38 | 34·63 | 10·81 | 88 | 80·19 | 25·03 | 138 | 125·8 | 39·25 | 188 | 171·3 | 53·47 |
| 39 | 35·54 | 11·09 | 89 | 81·10 | 25·31 | 139 | 126·7 | 39·53 | 189 | 172·2 | 53·75 |
| 40 | 36·45 | 11·38 | 90 | 82·01 | 25·60 | 140 | 127·6 | 39·82 | 190 | 173·1 | 54·04 |
| 41 | 37·36 | 11·66 | 91 | 82·92 | 25·88 | 141 | 128·5 | 40·10 | 191 | 174·0 | 54·32 |
| 42 | 38·27 | 11·94 | 92 | 83·83 | 26·16 | 142 | 129·4 | 40·38 | 192 | 175·0 | 54·60 |
| 43 | 39·18 | 12·23 | 93 | 84·74 | 26·45 | 143 | 130·3 | 40·67 | 193 | 175·9 | 54·89 |
| 44 | 40·09 | 12·51 | 94 | 85·66 | 26·73 | 144 | 131·2 | 40·95 | 194 | 176·8 | 55·17 |
| 45 | 41·01 | 12·80 | 95 | 86·57 | 27·02 | 145 | 132·1 | 41·24 | 195 | 177·7 | 55·46 |
| 46 | 41·92 | 13·08 | 96 | 87·48 | 27·30 | 146 | 133·0 | 41·52 | 196 | 178·6 | 55·74 |
| 47 | 42·83 | 13·37 | 97 | 88·39 | 27·59 | 147 | 134·0 | 41·81 | 197 | 179·5 | 56·03 |
| 48 | 43·74 | 13·65 | 98 | 89·30 | 27·87 | 148 | 134·9 | 42·09 | 198 | 180·4 | 56·31 |
| 49 | 44·65 | 13·94 | 99 | 90·21 | 28·16 | 149 | 135·8 | 42·38 | 199 | 181·3 | 56·60 |
| 50 | 45·56 | 14·22 | 100 | 91·12 | 28·44 | 150 | 136·7 | 42·66 | 200 | 182·2 | 56·88 |
| 51 | 46·47 | 14·50 | 101 | 92·03 | 28·72 | 151 | 137·6 | 42·94 | 201 | 183·2 | 57·16 |
| 52 | 47·38 | 14·79 | 102 | 92·95 | 29·01 | 152 | 138·5 | 43·23 | 202 | 184·1 | 57·45 |
| 53 | 48·30 | 15·07 | 103 | 93·86 | 29·29 | 153 | 139·4 | 43·51 | 203 | 185·0 | 57·73 |
| 54 | 49·21 | 15·36 | 104 | 94·77 | 29·58 | 154 | 140·3 | 43·80 | 204 | 185·9 | 58·02 |
| 55 | 50·12 | 15·64 | 105 | 95·68 | 29·86 | 155 | 141·2 | 44·08 | 205 | 186·8 | 58·30 |
| 56 | 51·03 | 15·93 | 106 | 96·59 | 30·15 | 156 | 142·2 | 44·37 | 206 | 187·7 | 58·59 |
| 57 | 51·94 | 16·21 | 107 | 97·50 | 30·43 | 157 | 143·1 | 44·65 | 207 | 188·6 | 58·87 |
| 58 | 52·85 | 16·50 | 108 | 98·41 | 30·72 | 158 | 144·0 | 44·94 | 208 | 189·5 | 59·16 |
| 59 | 53·76 | 16·78 | 109 | 99·32 | 31·00 | 159 | 144·9 | 45·22 | 209 | 190·4 | 59·44 |
| 60 | 54·67 | 17·06 | 110 | 100·2 | 31·28 | 160 | 145·8 | 45·50 | 210 | 191·4 | 59·72 |

TABLE I

# 17° 40′

| G | D | H | G | D | H | G | D | H | G | D | H |
|---|---|---|---|---|---|---|---|---|---|---|---|
| 10 | 9·08 | 2·89 | 60 | 54·47 | 17·35 | 110 | 99·87 | 31·81 | 160 | 145·3 | 46·27 |
| 11 | 9·99 | 3·18 | 61 | 55·38 | 17·64 | 111 | 100·8 | 32·10 | 161 | 146·2 | 46·56 |
| 12 | 10·89 | 3·47 | 62 | 56·29 | 17·93 | 112 | 101·7 | 32·39 | 162 | 147·1 | 46·84 |
| 13 | 11·80 | 3·76 | 63 | 57·20 | 18·22 | 113 | 102·6 | 32·68 | 163 | 148·0 | 47·13 |
| 14 | 12·71 | 4·05 | 64 | 58·11 | 18·51 | 114 | 103·5 | 32·96 | 164 | 148·9 | 47·42 |
| 15 | 13·62 | 4·34 | 65 | 59·01 | 18·80 | 115 | 104·4 | 33·25 | 165 | 149·8 | 47·71 |
| 16 | 14·53 | 4·63 | 66 | 59·92 | 19·08 | 116 | 105·3 | 33·54 | 166 | 150·7 | 48·00 |
| 17 | 15·43 | 4·92 | 67 | 60·83 | 19·37 | 117 | 106·2 | 33·83 | 167 | 151·6 | 48·29 |
| 18 | 16·34 | 5·20 | 68 | 61·74 | 19·66 | 118 | 107·1 | 34·12 | 168 | 152·5 | 48·58 |
| 19 | 17·25 | 5·49 | 69 | 62·65 | 19·95 | 119 | 108·0 | 34·41 | 169 | 153·4 | 48·87 |
| | | | | | | | | | | | |
| 20 | 18·16 | 5·78 | 70 | 63·55 | 20·24 | 120 | 108·9 | 34·70 | 170 | 154·3 | 49·16 |
| 21 | 19·07 | 6·07 | 71 | 64·46 | 20·53 | 121 | 109·9 | 34·99 | 171 | 155·3 | 49·45 |
| 22 | 19·97 | 6·36 | 72 | 65·37 | 20·82 | 122 | 110·8 | 35·28 | 172 | 156·2 | 49·74 |
| 23 | 20·88 | 6·65 | 73 | 66·28 | 21·11 | 123 | 111·7 | 35·57 | 173 | 157·1 | 50·03 |
| 24 | 21·79 | 6·94 | 74 | 67·18 | 21·40 | 124 | 112·6 | 35·86 | 174 | 158·0 | 50·31 |
| 25 | 22·70 | 7·23 | 75 | 68·09 | 21·69 | 125 | 113·5 | 36·15 | 175 | 158·9 | 50·60 |
| 26 | 23·61 | 7·52 | 76 | 69·00 | 21·98 | 126 | 114·4 | 36·43 | 176 | 159·8 | 50·89 |
| 27 | 24·51 | 7·81 | 77 | 69·91 | 22·27 | 127 | 115·3 | 36·72 | 177 | 160·7 | 51·18 |
| 28 | 25·42 | 8·10 | 78 | 70·82 | 22·55 | 128 | 116·2 | 37·01 | 178 | 161·6 | 51·47 |
| 29 | 26·33 | 8·39 | 79 | 71·72 | 22·84 | 129 | 117·1 | 37·30 | 179 | 162·5 | 51·76 |
| | | | | | | | | | | | |
| 30 | 27·24 | 8·67 | 80 | 72·63 | 23·13 | 130 | 118·0 | 37·59 | 180 | 163·4 | 52·05 |
| 31 | 28·14 | 8·96 | 81 | 73·54 | 23·42 | 131 | 118·9 | 37·88 | 181 | 164·3 | 52·34 |
| 32 | 29·05 | 9·25 | 82 | 74·45 | 23·71 | 132 | 119·8 | 38·17 | 182 | 165·2 | 52·63 |
| 33 | 29·96 | 9·54 | 83 | 75·36 | 24·00 | 133 | 120·8 | 38·46 | 183 | 166·1 | 52·92 |
| 34 | 30·87 | 9·83 | 84 | 76·26 | 24·29 | 134 | 121·7 | 38·75 | 184 | 167·1 | 53·21 |
| 35 | 31·78 | 10·12 | 85 | 77·17 | 24·58 | 135 | 122·6 | 39·04 | 185 | 168·0 | 53·50 |
| 36 | 32·68 | 10·41 | 86 | 78·08 | 24·87 | 136 | 123·5 | 39·33 | 186 | 168·9 | 53·78 |
| 37 | 33·59 | 10·70 | 87 | 78·99 | 25·16 | 137 | 124·4 | 39·62 | 187 | 169·8 | 54·07 |
| 38 | 34·50 | 10·99 | 88 | 79·90 | 25·45 | 138 | 125·3 | 39·90 | 188 | 170·7 | 54·36 |
| 39 | 35·41 | 11·28 | 89 | 80·80 | 25·74 | 139 | 126·2 | 40·19 | 189 | 171·6 | 54·65 |
| | | | | | | | | | | | |
| 40 | 36·32 | 11·57 | 90 | 81·71 | 26·02 | 140 | 127·1 | 40·48 | 190 | 172·5 | 54·94 |
| 41 | 37·22 | 11·86 | 91 | 82·62 | 26·31 | 141 | 128·0 | 40·77 | 191 | 173·4 | 55·23 |
| 42 | 38·13 | 12·14 | 92 | 83·53 | 26·60 | 142 | 128·9 | 41·06 | 192 | 174·3 | 55·52 |
| 43 | 39·04 | 12·43 | 93 | 84·43 | 26·89 | 143 | 129·8 | 41·35 | 193 | 175·2 | 55·81 |
| 44 | 39·95 | 12·72 | 94 | 85·34 | 27·18 | 144 | 130·7 | 41·64 | 194 | 176·1 | 56·10 |
| 45 | 40·86 | 13·01 | 95 | 86·25 | 27·47 | 145 | 131·6 | 41·93 | 195 | 177·0 | 56·39 |
| 46 | 41·76 | 13·30 | 96 | 87·16 | 27·76 | 146 | 132·6 | 42·22 | 196 | 177·9 | 56·68 |
| 47 | 42·67 | 13·59 | 97 | 88·07 | 28·05 | 147 | 133·5 | 42·51 | 197 | 178·9 | 56·97 |
| 48 | 43·58 | 13·88 | 98 | 88·97 | 28·34 | 148 | 134·4 | 42·80 | 198 | 179·8 | 57·25 |
| 49 | 44·49 | 14·17 | 99 | 89·88 | 28·63 | 149 | 135·3 | 43·09 | 199 | 180·7 | 57·54 |
| | | | | | | | | | | | |
| 50 | 45·40 | 14·46 | 100 | 90·79 | 28·92 | 150 | 136·2 | 43·37 | 200 | 181·6 | 57·83 |
| 51 | 46·30 | 14·75 | 101 | 91·70 | 29·21 | 151 | 137·1 | 43·66 | 201 | 182·5 | 58·12 |
| 52 | 47·21 | 15·04 | 102 | 92·61 | 29·49 | 152 | 138·0 | 43·95 | 202 | 183·4 | 58·41 |
| 53 | 48·12 | 15·33 | 103 | 93·51 | 29·78 | 153 | 138·9 | 44·24 | 203 | 184·3 | 58·70 |
| 54 | 49·03 | 15·61 | 104 | 94·42 | 30·07 | 154 | 139·8 | 44·53 | 204 | 185·2 | 58·99 |
| 55 | 49·93 | 15·90 | 105 | 95·33 | 30·36 | 155 | 140·7 | 44·82 | 205 | 186·1 | 59·28 |
| 56 | 50·84 | 16·19 | 106 | 96·24 | 30·65 | 156 | 141·6 | 45·11 | 206 | 187·0 | 59·57 |
| 57 | 51·75 | 16·48 | 107 | 97·15 | 30·94 | 157 | 142·5 | 45·40 | 207 | 187·9 | 59·86 |
| 58 | 52·66 | 16·77 | 108 | 98·05 | 31·23 | 158 | 143·4 | 45·69 | 208 | 188·8 | 60·15 |
| 59 | 53·57 | 17·06 | 109 | 98·96 | 31·52 | 159 | 144·4 | 45·98 | 209 | 189·8 | 60·44 |
| | | | | | | | | | | | |
| 60 | 54·47 | 17·35 | 110 | 99·87 | 31·81 | 160 | 145·3 | 46·27 | 210 | 190·7 | 60·72 |

TABLE I

| G | D | H | G | D | H | G | D | H | G | D | H |
|---|---|---|---|---|---|---|---|---|---|---|---|
| 10 | 9·05 | 2·94 | 60 | 54·27 | 17·63 | 110 | 99·50 | 32·33 | 160 | 144·7 | 47·02 |
| 11 | 9·95 | 3·23 | 61 | 55·17 | 17·93 | 111 | 100·4 | 32·62 | 161 | 145·6 | 47·32 |
| 12 | 10·85 | 3·53 | 62 | 56·08 | 18·22 | 112 | 101·3 | 32·92 | 162 | 146·5 | 47·61 |
| 13 | 11·76 | 3·82 | 63 | 56·98 | 18·52 | 113 | 102·2 | 33·21 | 163 | 147·4 | 47·90 |
| 14 | 12·66 | 4·11 | 64 | 57·89 | 18·81 | 114 | 103·1 | 33·50 | 164 | 148·3 | 48·20 |
| 15 | 13·57 | 4·41 | 65 | 58·79 | 19·10 | 115 | 104·0 | 33·80 | 165 | 149·2 | 48·49 |
| 16 | 14·47 | 4·70 | 66 | 59·70 | 19·40 | 116 | 104·9 | 34·09 | 166 | 150·1 | 48·79 |
| 17 | 15·38 | 5·00 | 67 | 60·60 | 19·69 | 117 | 105·8 | 34·39 | 167 | 151·1 | 49·08 |
| 18 | 16·28 | 5·29 | 68 | 61·51 | 19·98 | 118 | 106·7 | 34·68 | 168 | 152·0 | 49·37 |
| 19 | 17·19 | 5·58 | 69 | 62·41 | 20·28 | 119 | 107·6 | 34·97 | 169 | 152·9 | 49·67 |
| 20 | 18·09 | 5·88 | 70 | 63·32 | 20·57 | 120 | 108·5 | 35·27 | 170 | 153·8 | 49·96 |
| 21 | 18·99 | 6·17 | 71 | 64·22 | 20·87 | 121 | 109·4 | 35·56 | 171 | 154·7 | 50·26 |
| 22 | 19·90 | 6·47 | 72 | 65·12 | 21·16 | 122 | 110·3 | 35·85 | 172 | 155·6 | 50·55 |
| 23 | 20·80 | 6·76 | 73 | 66·03 | 21·45 | 123 | 111·3 | 36·15 | 173 | 156·5 | 50·84 |
| 24 | 21·71 | 7·05 | 74 | 66·93 | 21·75 | 124 | 112·2 | 36·44 | 174 | 157·4 | 51·14 |
| 25 | 22·61 | 7·35 | 75 | 67·84 | 22·04 | 125 | 113·1 | 36·74 | 175 | 158·3 | 51·43 |
| 26 | 23·52 | 7·64 | 76 | 68·74 | 22·34 | 126 | 114·0 | 37·03 | 176 | 159·2 | 51·72 |
| 27 | 24·42 | 7·94 | 77 | 69·65 | 22·63 | 127 | 114·9 | 37·32 | 177 | 160·1 | 52·02 |
| 28 | 25·33 | 8·23 | 78 | 70·55 | 22·92 | 128 | 115·8 | 37·62 | 178 | 161·0 | 52·31 |
| 29 | 26·23 | 8·52 | 79 | 71·46 | 23·22 | 129 | 116·7 | 37·91 | 179 | 161·9 | 52·61 |
| 30 | 27·14 | 8·82 | 80 | 72·36 | 23·51 | 130 | 117·6 | 38·21 | 180 | 162·8 | 52·90 |
| 31 | 28·04 | 9·11 | 81 | 73·27 | 23·81 | 131 | 118·5 | 38·50 | 181 | 163·7 | 53·19 |
| 32 | 28·94 | 9·40 | 82 | 74·17 | 24·10 | 132 | 119·4 | 38·79 | 182 | 164·6 | 53·49 |
| 33 | 29·85 | 9·70 | 83 | 75·07 | 24·39 | 133 | 120·3 | 39·09 | 183 | 165·5 | 53·78 |
| 34 | 30·75 | 9·99 | 84 | 75·98 | 24·69 | 134 | 121·2 | 39·38 | 184 | 166·4 | 54·08 |
| 35 | 31·66 | 10·29 | 85 | 76·88 | 24·98 | 135 | 122·1 | 39·68 | 185 | 167·3 | 54·37 |
| 36 | 32·56 | 10·58 | 86 | 77·79 | 25·27 | 136 | 123·0 | 39·97 | 186 | 168·2 | 54·66 |
| 37 | 33·47 | 10·87 | 87 | 78·69 | 25·57 | 137 | 123·9 | 40·26 | 187 | 169·1 | 54·96 |
| 38 | 34·37 | 11·17 | 88 | 79·60 | 25·86 | 138 | 124·8 | 40·56 | 188 | 170·0 | 55·25 |
| 39 | 35·28 | 11·46 | 89 | 80·50 | 26·16 | 139 | 125·7 | 40·85 | 189 | 171·0 | 55·55 |
| 40 | 36·18 | 11·76 | 90 | 81·41 | 26·45 | 140 | 126·6 | 41·14 | 190 | 171·9 | 55·84 |
| 41 | 37·08 | 12·05 | 91 | 82·31 | 26·74 | 141 | 127·5 | 41·44 | 191 | 172·8 | 56·13 |
| 42 | 37·99 | 12·34 | 92 | 83·21 | 27·04 | 142 | 128·4 | 41·73 | 192 | 173·7 | 56·43 |
| 43 | 38·89 | 12·64 | 93 | 84·12 | 27·33 | 143 | 129·3 | 42·03 | 193 | 174·6 | 56·72 |
| 44 | 39·80 | 12·93 | 94 | 85·02 | 27·63 | 144 | 130·2 | 42·32 | 194 | 175·5 | 57·02 |
| 45 | 40·70 | 13·23 | 95 | 85·93 | 27·92 | 145 | 131·2 | 42·61 | 195 | 176·4 | 57·31 |
| 46 | 41·61 | 13·52 | 96 | 86·83 | 28·21 | 146 | 132·1 | 42·91 | 196 | 177·3 | 57·60 |
| 47 | 42·51 | 13·81 | 97 | 87·74 | 28·51 | 147 | 133·0 | 43·20 | 197 | 178·2 | 57·90 |
| 48 | 43·42 | 14·11 | 98 | 88·64 | 28·80 | 148 | 133·9 | 43·50 | 198 | 179·1 | 58·19 |
| 49 | 44·32 | 14·40 | 99 | 89·55 | 29·10 | 149 | 134·8 | 43·79 | 199 | 180·0 | 58·48 |
| 50 | 45·23 | 14·69 | 100 | 90·45 | 29·39 | 150 | 135·7 | 44·08 | 200 | 180·9 | 58·78 |
| 51 | 46·13 | 14·99 | 101 | 91·36 | 29·68 | 151 | 136·6 | 44·38 | 201 | 181·8 | 59·07 |
| 52 | 47·03 | 15·28 | 102 | 92·26 | 29·98 | 152 | 137·5 | 44·67 | 202 | 182·7 | 59·37 |
| 53 | 47·94 | 15·58 | 103 | 93·16 | 30·27 | 153 | 138·4 | 44·97 | 203 | 183·6 | 59·66 |
| 54 | 48·84 | 15·87 | 104 | 94·07 | 30·56 | 154 | 139·3 | 45·26 | 204 | 184·5 | 59·95 |
| 55 | 49·75 | 16·16 | 105 | 94·97 | 30·86 | 155 | 140·2 | 45·55 | 205 | 185·4 | 60·25 |
| 56 | 50·65 | 16·46 | 106 | 95·88 | 31·15 | 156 | 141·1 | 45·85 | 206 | 186·3 | 60·54 |
| 57 | 51·56 | 16·75 | 107 | 96·78 | 31·45 | 157 | 142·0 | 46·14 | 207 | 187·2 | 60·84 |
| 58 | 52·46 | 17·05 | 108 | 97·69 | 31·74 | 158 | 142·9 | 46·43 | 208 | 188·1 | 61·13 |
| 59 | 53·37 | 17·34 | 109 | 98·59 | 32·03 | 159 | 143·8 | 46·73 | 209 | 189·0 | 61·42 |
| 60 | 54·27 | 17·63 | 110 | 99·50 | 32·33 | 160 | 144·7 | 47·02 | 210 | 189·9 | 61·72 |

TABLE I

# 18° 20′

| G | D | H | G | D | H | G | D | H | G | D | H |
|---|---|---|---|---|---|---|---|---|---|---|---|
| 10 | 9·01 | 2·99 | 60 | 54·06 | 17·91 | 110 | 99·12 | 32·84 | 160 | 144·2 | 47·77 |
| 11 | 9·91 | 3·28 | 61 | 54·96 | 18·21 | 111 | 100·0 | 33·14 | 161 | 145·1 | 48·07 |
| 12 | 10·81 | 3·58 | 62 | 55·87 | 18·51 | 112 | 100·9 | 33·44 | 162 | 146·0 | 48·37 |
| 13 | 11·71 | 3·88 | 63 | 56·77 | 18·81 | 113 | 101·8 | 33·74 | 163 | 146·9 | 48·67 |
| 14 | 12·61 | 4·18 | 64 | 57·67 | 19·11 | 114 | 102·7 | 34·04 | 164 | 147·8 | 48·97 |
| 15 | 13·52 | 4·48 | 65 | 58·57 | 19·41 | 115 | 103·6 | 34·34 | 165 | 148·7 | 49·27 |
| 16 | 14·42 | 4·78 | 66 | 59·47 | 19·71 | 116 | 104·5 | 34·64 | 166 | 149·6 | 49·56 |
| 17 | 15·32 | 5·08 | 67 | 60·37 | 20·00 | 117 | 105·4 | 34·93 | 167 | 150·5 | 49·86 |
| 18 | 16·22 | 5·37 | 68 | 61·27 | 20·30 | 118 | 106·3 | 35·23 | 168 | 151·4 | 50·16 |
| 19 | 17·12 | 5·67 | 69 | 62·17 | 20·60 | 119 | 107·2 | 35·53 | 169 | 152·3 | 50·46 |
| 20 | 18·02 | 5·97 | 70 | 63·07 | 20·90 | 120 | 108·1 | 35·83 | 170 | 153·2 | 50·76 |
| 21 | 18·92 | 6·27 | 71 | 63·98 | 21·20 | 121 | 109·0 | 36·13 | 171 | 154·1 | 51·06 |
| 22 | 19·82 | 6·57 | 72 | 64·88 | 21·50 | 122 | 109·9 | 36·43 | 172 | 155·0 | 51·36 |
| 23 | 20·72 | 6·87 | 73 | 65·78 | 21·80 | 123 | 110·8 | 36·73 | 173 | 155·9 | 51·65 |
| 24 | 21·63 | 7·17 | 74 | 66·68 | 22·09 | 124 | 111·7 | 37·02 | 174 | 156·8 | 51·95 |
| 25 | 22·53 | 7·46 | 75 | 67·58 | 22·39 | 125 | 112·6 | 37·32 | 175 | 157·7 | 52·25 |
| 26 | 23·43 | 7·76 | 76 | 68·48 | 22·69 | 126 | 113·5 | 37·62 | 176 | 158·6 | 52·55 |
| 27 | 24·33 | 8·06 | 77 | 69·38 | 22·99 | 127 | 114·4 | 37·92 | 177 | 159·5 | 52·85 |
| 28 | 25·23 | 8·36 | 78 | 70·28 | 23·29 | 128 | 115·3 | 38·22 | 178 | 160·4 | 53·15 |
| 29 | 26·13 | 8·66 | 79 | 71·18 | 23·59 | 129 | 116·2 | 38·52 | 179 | 161·3 | 53·45 |
| 30 | 27·03 | 8·96 | 80 | 72·08 | 23·89 | 130 | 117·1 | 38·82 | 180 | 162·2 | 53·74 |
| 31 | 27·93 | 9·26 | 81 | 72·99 | 24·18 | 131 | 118·0 | 39·11 | 181 | 163·1 | 54·04 |
| 32 | 28·83 | 9·55 | 82 | 73·89 | 24·48 | 132 | 118·9 | 39·41 | 182 | 164·0 | 54·34 |
| 33 | 29·73 | 9·85 | 83 | 74·79 | 24·78 | 133 | 119·8 | 39·71 | 183 | 164·9 | 54·64 |
| 34 | 30·64 | 10·15 | 84 | 75·69 | 25·08 | 134 | 120·7 | 40·01 | 184 | 165·8 | 54·94 |
| 35 | 31·54 | 10·45 | 85 | 76·59 | 25·38 | 135 | 121·6 | 40·31 | 185 | 166·7 | 55·24 |
| 36 | 32·44 | 10·75 | 86 | 77·49 | 25·68 | 136 | 122·5 | 40·61 | 186 | 167·6 | 55·54 |
| 37 | 33·34 | 11·05 | 87 | 78·39 | 25·98 | 137 | 123·4 | 40·91 | 187 | 168·5 | 55·83 |
| 38 | 34·24 | 11·35 | 88 | 79·29 | 26·27 | 138 | 124·3 | 41·20 | 188 | 169·4 | 56·13 |
| 39 | 35·14 | 11·64 | 89 | 80·19 | 26·57 | 139 | 125·2 | 41·50 | 189 | 170·3 | 56·43 |
| 40 | 36·04 | 11·94 | 90 | 81·10 | 26·87 | 140 | 126·1 | 41·80 | 190 | 171·2 | 56·73 |
| 41 | 36·94 | 12·24 | 91 | 82·00 | 27·17 | 141 | 127·0 | 42·10 | 191 | 172·1 | 57·03 |
| 42 | 37·84 | 12·54 | 92 | 82·90 | 27·47 | 142 | 128·0 | 42·40 | 192 | 173·0 | 57·33 |
| 43 | 38·75 | 12·84 | 93 | 83·80 | 27·77 | 143 | 128·9 | 42·70 | 193 | 173·9 | 57·63 |
| 44 | 39·65 | 13·14 | 94 | 84·70 | 28·07 | 144 | 129·8 | 43·00 | 194 | 174·8 | 57·92 |
| 45 | 40·55 | 13·44 | 95 | 85·60 | 28·37 | 145 | 130·7 | 43·29 | 195 | 175·7 | 58·22 |
| 46 | 41·45 | 13·73 | 96 | 86·50 | 28·66 | 146 | 131·6 | 43·59 | 196 | 176·6 | 58·52 |
| 47 | 42·35 | 14·03 | 97 | 87·40 | 28·96 | 147 | 132·5 | 43·89 | 197 | 177·5 | 58·82 |
| 48 | 43·25 | 14·33 | 98 | 88·30 | 29·26 | 148 | 133·4 | 44·19 | 198 | 178·4 | 59·12 |
| 49 | 44·15 | 14·63 | 99 | 89·20 | 29·56 | 149 | 134·3 | 44·49 | 199 | 179·3 | 59·42 |
| 50 | 45·05 | 14·93 | 100 | 90·11 | 29·86 | 150 | 135·2 | 44·79 | 200 | 180·2 | 59·72 |
| 51 | 45·95 | 15·23 | 101 | 91·01 | 30·16 | 151 | 136·1 | 45·09 | 201 | 181·1 | 60·01 |
| 52 | 46·86 | 15·53 | 102 | 91·91 | 30·46 | 152 | 137·0 | 45·38 | 202 | 182·0 | 60·31 |
| 53 | 47·76 | 15·82 | 103 | 92·81 | 30·75 | 153 | 137·9 | 45·68 | 203 | 182·9 | 60·61 |
| 54 | 48·66 | 16·12 | 104 | 93·71 | 31·05 | 154 | 138·8 | 45·98 | 204 | 183·8 | 60·91 |
| 55 | 49·56 | 16·42 | 105 | 94·61 | 31·35 | 155 | 139·7 | 46·28 | 205 | 184·7 | 61·21 |
| 56 | 50·46 | 16·72 | 106 | 95·51 | 31·65 | 156 | 140·6 | 46·58 | 206 | 185·6 | 61·51 |
| 57 | 51·36 | 17·02 | 107 | 96·41 | 31·95 | 157 | 141·5 | 46·88 | 207 | 186·5 | 61·81 |
| 58 | 52·26 | 17·32 | 108 | 97·31 | 32·25 | 158 | 142·4 | 47·18 | 208 | 187·4 | 62·10 |
| 59 | 53·16 | 17·62 | 109 | 98·22 | 32·55 | 159 | 143·3 | 47·47 | 209 | 188·3 | 62·40 |
| 60 | 54·06 | 17·91 | 110 | 99·12 | 32·84 | 160 | 144·2 | 47·77 | 210 | 189·2 | 62·70 |

| G | D | H | G | D | H | G | D | H | G | D | H |
|---|---|---|---|---|---|---|---|---|---|---|---|
| 10 | 8.98 | 3.03 | 60 | 53.85 | 18.19 | 110 | 98.73 | 33.35 | 160 | 143.6 | 48.52 |
| 11 | 9.87 | 3.34 | 61 | 54.75 | 18.50 | 111 | 99.63 | 33.66 | 161 | 144.5 | 48.82 |
| 12 | 10.77 | 3.64 | 62 | 55.65 | 18.80 | 112 | 100.5 | 33.96 | 162 | 145.4 | 49.12 |
| 13 | 11.67 | 3.94 | 63 | 56.55 | 19.10 | 113 | 101.4 | 34.26 | 163 | 146.3 | 49.43 |
| 14 | 12.57 | 4.25 | 64 | 57.44 | 19.41 | 114 | 102.3 | 34.57 | 164 | 147.2 | 49.73 |
| 15 | 13.46 | 4.55 | 65 | 58.34 | 19.71 | 115 | 103.2 | 34.87 | 165 | 148.1 | 50.03 |
| 16 | 14.36 | 4.85 | 66 | 59.24 | 20.01 | 116 | 104.1 | 35.17 | 166 | 149.0 | 50.34 |
| 17 | 15.26 | 5.15 | 67 | 60.14 | 20.32 | 117 | 105.0 | 35.48 | 167 | 149.9 | 50.64 |
| 18 | 16.16 | 5.46 | 68 | 61.03 | 20.62 | 118 | 105.9 | 35.78 | 168 | 150.8 | 50.94 |
| 19 | 17.05 | 5.76 | 69 | 61.93 | 20.92 | 119 | 106.8 | 36.08 | 169 | 151.7 | 51.25 |
| 20 | 17.95 | 6.06 | 70 | 62.83 | 21.23 | 120 | 107.7 | 36.39 | 170 | 152.6 | 51.55 |
| 21 | 18.85 | 6.37 | 71 | 63.73 | 21.53 | 121 | 108.6 | 36.69 | 171 | 153.5 | 51.85 |
| 22 | 19.75 | 6.67 | 72 | 64.62 | 21.83 | 122 | 109.5 | 36.99 | 172 | 154.4 | 52.15 |
| 23 | 20.64 | 6.97 | 73 | 65.52 | 22.14 | 123 | 110.4 | 37.30 | 173 | 155.3 | 52.46 |
| 24 | 21.54 | 7.28 | 74 | 66.42 | 22.44 | 124 | 111.3 | 37.60 | 174 | 156.2 | 52.76 |
| 25 | 22.44 | 7.58 | 75 | 67.32 | 22.74 | 125 | 112.2 | 37.90 | 175 | 157.1 | 53.06 |
| 26 | 23.34 | 7.88 | 76 | 68.21 | 23.05 | 126 | 113.1 | 38.21 | 176 | 158.0 | 53.37 |
| 27 | 24.23 | 8.19 | 77 | 69.11 | 23.35 | 127 | 114.0 | 38.51 | 177 | 158.9 | 53.67 |
| 28 | 25.13 | 8.49 | 78 | 70.01 | 23.65 | 128 | 114.9 | 38.81 | 178 | 159.8 | 53.97 |
| 29 | 26.03 | 8.79 | 79 | 70.91 | 23.95 | 129 | 115.8 | 39.12 | 179 | 160.7 | 54.28 |
| 30 | 26.93 | 9.10 | 80 | 71.80 | 24.26 | 130 | 116.7 | 39.42 | 180 | 161.6 | 54.58 |
| 31 | 27.82 | 9.40 | 81 | 72.70 | 24.56 | 131 | 117.6 | 39.72 | 181 | 162.5 | 54.88 |
| 32 | 28.72 | 9.70 | 82 | 73.60 | 24.86 | 132 | 118.5 | 40.03 | 182 | 163.4 | 55.19 |
| 33 | 29.62 | 10.01 | 83 | 74.50 | 25.17 | 133 | 119.4 | 40.33 | 183 | 164.3 | 55.49 |
| 34 | 30.52 | 10.31 | 84 | 75.39 | 25.47 | 134 | 120.3 | 40.63 | 184 | 165.2 | 55.79 |
| 35 | 31.41 | 10.61 | 85 | 76.29 | 25.77 | 135 | 121.2 | 40.94 | 185 | 166.0 | 56.10 |
| 36 | 32.31 | 10.92 | 86 | 77.19 | 26.08 | 136 | 122.1 | 41.24 | 186 | 166.9 | 56.40 |
| 37 | 33.21 | 11.22 | 87 | 78.09 | 26.38 | 137 | 123.0 | 41.54 | 187 | 167.8 | 56.70 |
| 38 | 34.11 | 11.52 | 88 | 78.99 | 26.68 | 138 | 123.9 | 41.85 | 188 | 168.7 | 57.01 |
| 39 | 35.00 | 11.83 | 89 | 79.88 | 26.99 | 139 | 124.8 | 42.15 | 189 | 169.6 | 57.31 |
| 40 | 35.90 | 12.13 | 90 | 80.78 | 27.29 | 140 | 125.7 | 42.45 | 190 | 170.5 | 57.61 |
| 41 | 36.80 | 12.43 | 91 | 81.68 | 27.59 | 141 | 126.6 | 42.75 | 191 | 171.4 | 57.92 |
| 42 | 37.70 | 12.74 | 92 | 82.58 | 27.90 | 142 | 127.5 | 43.06 | 192 | 172.3 | 58.22 |
| 43 | 38.60 | 13.04 | 93 | 83.47 | 28.20 | 143 | 128.4 | 43.36 | 193 | 173.2 | 58.52 |
| 44 | 39.49 | 13.34 | 94 | 84.37 | 28.50 | 144 | 129.2 | 43.66 | 194 | 174.1 | 58.83 |
| 45 | 40.39 | 13.65 | 95 | 85.27 | 28.81 | 145 | 130.1 | 43.97 | 195 | 175.0 | 59.13 |
| 46 | 41.29 | 13.95 | 96 | 86.17 | 29.11 | 146 | 131.0 | 44.27 | 196 | 175.9 | 59.43 |
| 47 | 42.19 | 14.25 | 97 | 87.06 | 29.41 | 147 | 131.9 | 44.57 | 197 | 176.8 | 59.74 |
| 48 | 43.08 | 14.55 | 98 | 87.96 | 29.72 | 148 | 132.8 | 44.88 | 198 | 177.7 | 60.04 |
| 49 | 43.98 | 14.86 | 99 | 88.86 | 30.02 | 149 | 133.7 | 45.18 | 199 | 178.6 | 60.34 |
| 50 | 44.88 | 15.16 | 100 | 89.76 | 30.32 | 150 | 134.6 | 45.48 | 200 | 179.5 | 60.65 |
| 51 | 45.78 | 15.46 | 101 | 90.65 | 30.63 | 151 | 135.5 | 45.79 | 201 | 180.4 | 60.95 |
| 52 | 46.67 | 15.77 | 102 | 91.55 | 30.93 | 152 | 136.4 | 46.09 | 202 | 181.3 | 61.25 |
| 53 | 47.57 | 16.07 | 103 | 92.45 | 31.23 | 153 | 137.3 | 46.39 | 203 | 182.2 | 61.55 |
| 54 | 48.47 | 16.37 | 104 | 93.35 | 31.54 | 154 | 138.2 | 46.70 | 204 | 183.1 | 61.86 |
| 55 | 49.37 | 16.68 | 105 | 94.24 | 31.84 | 155 | 139.1 | 47.00 | 205 | 184.0 | 62.16 |
| 56 | 50.26 | 16.98 | 106 | 95.14 | 32.14 | 156 | 140.0 | 47.30 | 206 | 184.9 | 62.46 |
| 57 | 51.16 | 17.28 | 107 | 96.04 | 32.45 | 157 | 140.9 | 47.61 | 207 | 185.8 | 62.77 |
| 58 | 52.06 | 17.59 | 108 | 96.94 | 32.75 | 158 | 141.8 | 47.91 | 208 | 186.7 | 63.07 |
| 59 | 52.96 | 17.89 | 109 | 97.83 | 33.05 | 159 | 142.7 | 48.21 | 209 | 187.6 | 63.37 |
| 60 | 53.85 | 18.19 | 110 | 98.73 | 33.35 | 160 | 143.6 | 48.52 | 210 | 188.5 | 63.68 |

TABLE I

# 19° 00′

| G | D | H | G | D | H | G | D | H | G | D | H |
|---|---|---|---|---|---|---|---|---|---|---|---|
| 10 | 8·94 | 3·08 | 60 | 53·64 | 18·47 | 110 | 98·34 | 33·86 | 160 | 143·0 | 49·25 |
| 11 | 9·83 | 3·39 | 61 | 54·53 | 18·78 | 111 | 99·23 | 34·17 | 161 | 143·9 | 49·56 |
| 12 | 10·73 | 3·69 | 62 | 55·43 | 19·09 | 112 | 100·1 | 34·48 | 162 | 144·8 | 49·87 |
| 13 | 11·62 | 4·00 | 63 | 56·32 | 19·39 | 113 | 101·0 | 34·78 | 163 | 145·7 | 50·18 |
| 14 | 12·52 | 4·31 | 64 | 57·22 | 19·70 | 114 | 101·9 | 35·09 | 164 | 146·6 | 50·48 |
| 15 | 13·41 | 4·62 | 65 | 58·11 | 20·01 | 115 | 102·8 | 35·40 | 165 | 147·5 | 50·79 |
| 16 | 14·30 | 4·93 | 66 | 59·00 | 20·32 | 116 | 103·7 | 35·71 | 166 | 148·4 | 51·10 |
| 17 | 15·20 | 5·23 | 67 | 59·90 | 20·62 | 117 | 104·6 | 36·02 | 167 | 149·3 | 51·41 |
| 18 | 16·09 | 5·54 | 68 | 60·79 | 20·93 | 118 | 105·5 | 36·32 | 168 | 150·2 | 51·72 |
| 19 | 16·99 | 5·85 | 69 | 61·69 | 21·24 | 119 | 106·4 | 36·63 | 169 | 151·1 | 52·02 |
| 20 | 17·88 | 6·16 | 70 | 62·58 | 21·55 | 120 | 107·3 | 36·94 | 170 | 152·0 | 52·33 |
| 21 | 18·77 | 6·46 | 71 | 63·47 | 21·86 | 121 | 108·2 | 37·25 | 171 | 152·9 | 52·64 |
| 22 | 19·67 | 6·77 | 72 | 64·37 | 22·16 | 122 | 109·1 | 37·56 | 172 | 153·8 | 52·95 |
| 23 | 20·56 | 7·08 | 73 | 65·26 | 22·47 | 123 | 110·0 | 37·86 | 173 | 154·7 | 53·25 |
| 24 | 21·46 | 7·39 | 74 | 66·16 | 22·78 | 124 | 110·9 | 38·17 | 174 | 155·6 | 53·56 |
| 25 | 22·35 | 7·70 | 75 | 67·05 | 23·09 | 125 | 111·8 | 38·48 | 175 | 156·5 | 53·87 |
| 26 | 23·24 | 8·00 | 76 | 67·94 | 23·40 | 126 | 112·6 | 38·79 | 176 | 157·3 | 54·18 |
| 27 | 24·14 | 8·31 | 77 | 68·84 | 23·70 | 127 | 113·5 | 39·09 | 177 | 158·2 | 54·49 |
| 28 | 25·03 | 8·62 | 78 | 69·73 | 24·01 | 128 | 114·4 | 39·40 | 178 | 159·1 | 54·79 |
| 29 | 25·93 | 8·93 | 79 | 70·63 | 24·32 | 129 | 115·3 | 39·71 | 179 | 160·0 | 55·10 |
| 30 | 26·82 | 9·23 | 80 | 71·52 | 24·63 | 130 | 116·2 | 40·02 | 180 | 160·9 | 55·41 |
| 31 | 27·71 | 9·54 | 81 | 72·41 | 24·93 | 131 | 117·1 | 40·33 | 181 | 161·8 | 55·72 |
| 32 | 28·61 | 9·85 | 82 | 73·31 | 25·24 | 132 | 118·0 | 40·63 | 182 | 162·7 | 56·03 |
| 33 | 29·50 | 10·16 | 83 | 74·20 | 25·55 | 133 | 118·9 | 40·94 | 183 | 163·6 | 56·33 |
| 34 | 30·40 | 10·47 | 84 | 75·10 | 25·86 | 134 | 119·8 | 41·25 | 184 | 164·5 | 56·64 |
| 35 | 31·29 | 10·77 | 85 | 75·99 | 26·17 | 135 | 120·7 | 41·56 | 185 | 165·4 | 56·95 |
| 36 | 32·18 | 11·08 | 86 | 76·88 | 26·47 | 136 | 121·6 | 41·86 | 186 | 166·3 | 57·26 |
| 37 | 33·08 | 11·39 | 87 | 77·78 | 26·78 | 137 | 122·5 | 42·17 | 187 | 167·2 | 57·56 |
| 38 | 33·97 | 11·70 | 88 | 78·67 | 27·09 | 138 | 123·4 | 42·48 | 188 | 168·1 | 57·87 |
| 39 | 34·87 | 12·01 | 89 | 79·57 | 27·40 | 139 | 124·3 | 42·79 | 189 | 169·0 | 58·18 |
| 40 | 35·76 | 12·31 | 90 | 80·46 | 27·70 | 140 | 125·2 | 43·10 | 190 | 169·9 | 58·49 |
| 41 | 36·65 | 12·62 | 91 | 81·35 | 28·01 | 141 | 126·1 | 43·40 | 191 | 170·8 | 58·80 |
| 42 | 37·55 | 12·93 | 92 | 82·25 | 28·32 | 142 | 126·9 | 43·71 | 192 | 171·6 | 59·10 |
| 43 | 38·44 | 13·24 | 93 | 83·14 | 28·63 | 143 | 127·8 | 44·02 | 193 | 172·5 | 59·41 |
| 44 | 39·34 | 13·54 | 94 | 84·04 | 28·94 | 144 | 128·7 | 44·33 | 194 | 173·4 | 59·72 |
| 45 | 40·23 | 13·85 | 95 | 84·93 | 29·24 | 145 | 129·6 | 44·64 | 195 | 174·3 | 60·03 |
| 46 | 41·12 | 14·16 | 96 | 85·82 | 29·55 | 146 | 130·5 | 44·94 | 196 | 175·2 | 60·33 |
| 47 | 42·02 | 14·47 | 97 | 86·72 | 29·86 | 147 | 131·4 | 45·25 | 197 | 176·1 | 60·64 |
| 48 | 42·91 | 14·78 | 98 | 87·61 | 30·17 | 148 | 132·3 | 45·56 | 198 | 177·0 | 60·95 |
| 49 | 43·81 | 15·08 | 99 | 88·51 | 30·48 | 149 | 133·2 | 45·87 | 199 | 177·9 | 61·26 |
| 50 | 44·70 | 15·39 | 100 | 89·40 | 30·78 | 150 | 134·1 | 46·17 | 200 | 178·8 | 61·57 |
| 51 | 45·59 | 15·70 | 101 | 90·29 | 31·09 | 151 | 135·0 | 46·48 | 201 | 179·7 | 61·87 |
| 52 | 46·49 | 16·01 | 102 | 91·19 | 31·40 | 152 | 135·9 | 46·79 | 202 | 180·6 | 62·18 |
| 53 | 47·38 | 16·31 | 103 | 92·08 | 31·71 | 153 | 136·8 | 47·10 | 203 | 181·5 | 62·49 |
| 54 | 48·28 | 16·62 | 104 | 92·98 | 32·01 | 154 | 137·7 | 47·41 | 204 | 182·4 | 62·80 |
| 55 | 49·17 | 16·93 | 105 | 93·87 | 32·32 | 155 | 138·6 | 47·71 | 205 | 183·3 | 63·11 |
| 56 | 50·06 | 17·24 | 106 | 94·76 | 32·63 | 156 | 139·5 | 48·02 | 206 | 184·2 | 63·41 |
| 57 | 50·96 | 17·55 | 107 | 95·66 | 32·94 | 157 | 140·4 | 48·33 | 207 | 185·1 | 63·72 |
| 58 | 51·85 | 17·85 | 108 | 96·55 | 33·25 | 158 | 141·3 | 48·64 | 208 | 186·0 | 64·03 |
| 59 | 52·75 | 18·16 | 109 | 97·45 | 33·55 | 159 | 142·1 | 48·94 | 209 | 186·8 | 64·34 |
| 60 | 53·64 | 18·47 | 110 | 98·34 | 33·86 | 160 | 143·0 | 49·25 | 210 | 187·7 | 64·64 |

| G | D | H | G | D | H | G | D | H | G | D | H |
|---|---|---|---|---|---|---|---|---|---|---|---|
| 10 | 8·90 | 3·12 | 60 | 53·42 | 18·74 | 110 | 97·94 | 34·36 | 160 | 142·5 | 49·98 |
| 11 | 9·79 | 3·44 | 61 | 54·31 | 19·06 | 111 | 98·83 | 34·68 | 161 | 143·4 | 50·30 |
| 12 | 10·68 | 3·75 | 62 | 55·20 | 19·37 | 112 | 99·72 | 34·99 | 162 | 144·2 | 50·61 |
| 13 | 11·58 | 4·06 | 63 | 56·09 | 19·68 | 113 | 100·6 | 35·30 | 163 | 145·1 | 50·92 |
| 14 | 12·47 | 4·37 | 64 | 56·99 | 19·99 | 114 | 101·5 | 35·61 | 164 | 146·0 | 51·23 |
| 15 | 13·36 | 4·69 | 65 | 57·88 | 20·31 | 115 | 102·4 | 35·93 | 165 | 146·9 | 51·55 |
| 16 | 14·25 | 5·00 | 66 | 58·77 | 20·62 | 116 | 103·3 | 36·24 | 166 | 147·8 | 51·86 |
| 17 | 15·14 | 5·31 | 67 | 59·66 | 20·93 | 117 | 104·2 | 36·55 | 167 | 148·7 | 52·17 |
| 18 | 16·03 | 5·62 | 68 | 60·55 | 21·24 | 118 | 105·1 | 36·86 | 168 | 149·6 | 52·48 |
| 19 | 16·92 | 5·94 | 69 | 61·44 | 21·56 | 119 | 106·0 | 37·17 | 169 | 150·5 | 52·79 |
| 20 | 17·81 | 6·25 | 70 | 62·33 | 21·87 | 120 | 106·8 | 37·49 | 170 | 151·4 | 53·11 |
| 21 | 18·70 | 6·56 | 71 | 63·22 | 22·18 | 121 | 107·7 | 37·80 | 171 | 152·3 | 53·42 |
| 22 | 19·59 | 6·87 | 72 | 64·11 | 22·49 | 122 | 108·6 | 38·11 | 172 | 153·1 | 53·73 |
| 23 | 20·48 | 7·19 | 73 | 65·00 | 22·80 | 123 | 109·5 | 38·42 | 173 | 154·0 | 54·04 |
| 24 | 21·37 | 7·50 | 74 | 65·89 | 23·12 | 124 | 110·4 | 38·74 | 174 | 154·9 | 54·36 |
| 25 | 22·26 | 7·81 | 75 | 66·78 | 23·43 | 125 | 111·3 | 39·05 | 175 | 155·8 | 54·67 |
| 26 | 23·15 | 8·12 | 76 | 67·67 | 23·74 | 126 | 112·2 | 39·36 | 176 | 156·7 | 54·98 |
| 27 | 24·04 | 8·43 | 77 | 68·56 | 24·05 | 127 | 113·1 | 39·67 | 177 | 157·6 | 55·29 |
| 28 | 24·93 | 8·75 | 78 | 69·45 | 24·37 | 128 | 114·0 | 39·99 | 178 | 158·5 | 55·61 |
| 29 | 25·82 | 9·06 | 79 | 70·34 | 24·68 | 129 | 114·9 | 40·30 | 179 | 159·4 | 55·92 |
| 30 | 26·71 | 9·37 | 80 | 71·23 | 24·99 | 130 | 115·8 | 40·61 | 180 | 160·3 | 56·23 |
| 31 | 27·60 | 9·68 | 81 | 72·12 | 25·30 | 131 | 116·6 | 40·92 | 181 | 161·2 | 56·54 |
| 32 | 28·49 | 10·00 | 82 | 73·01 | 25·62 | 132 | 117·5 | 41·24 | 182 | 162·1 | 56·86 |
| 33 | 29·38 | 10·31 | 83 | 73·90 | 25·93 | 133 | 118·4 | 41·55 | 183 | 162·9 | 57·17 |
| 34 | 30·27 | 10·62 | 84 | 74·79 | 26·24 | 134 | 119·3 | 41·86 | 184 | 163·8 | 57·48 |
| 35 | 31·16 | 10·93 | 85 | 75·68 | 26·55 | 135 | 120·2 | 42·17 | 185 | 164·7 | 57·79 |
| 36 | 32·05 | 11·25 | 86 | 76·57 | 26·87 | 136 | 121·1 | 42·49 | 186 | 165·6 | 58·11 |
| 37 | 32·94 | 11·56 | 87 | 77·46 | 27·18 | 137 | 122·0 | 42·80 | 187 | 166·5 | 58·42 |
| 38 | 33·84 | 11·87 | 88 | 78·35 | 27·49 | 138 | 122·9 | 43·11 | 188 | 167·4 | 58·73 |
| 39 | 34·73 | 12·18 | 89 | 79·25 | 27·80 | 139 | 123·8 | 43·42 | 189 | 168·3 | 59·04 |
| 40 | 35·62 | 12·50 | 90 | 80·14 | 28·12 | 140 | 124·7 | 43·74 | 190 | 169·2 | 59·35 |
| 41 | 36·51 | 12·81 | 91 | 81·03 | 28·43 | 141 | 125·5 | 44·05 | 191 | 170·1 | 59·67 |
| 42 | 37·40 | 13·12 | 92 | 81·92 | 28 74 | 142 | 126·4 | 44·36 | 192 | 171·0 | 59·98 |
| 43 | 38·29 | 13·43 | 93 | 82·81 | 29·05 | 143 | 127·3 | 44·67 | 193 | 171·8 | 60·29 |
| 44 | 39·18 | 13·75 | 94 | 83·70 | 29·37 | 144 | 128·2 | 44·98 | 194 | 172·7 | 60·60 |
| 45 | 40·07 | 14·06 | 95 | 84·59 | 29·68 | 145 | 129·1 | 45·30 | 195 | 173·6 | 60·92 |
| 46 | 40·96 | 14·37 | 96 | 85·48 | 29·99 | 146 | 130·0 | 45·61 | 196 | 174·5 | 61·23 |
| 47 | 41·85 | 14·68 | 97 | 86·37 | 30·30 | 147 | 130·9 | 45·92 | 197 | 175·4 | 61·54 |
| 48 | 42·74 | 14·99 | 98 | 87·26 | 30·61 | 148 | 131·8 | 46·23 | 198 | 176·3 | 61·85 |
| 49 | 43·63 | 15·31 | 99 | 88·15 | 30·93 | 149 | 132·7 | 46·55 | 199 | 177·2 | 62·17 |
| 50 | 44·52 | 15·62 | 100 | 89·04 | 31·24 | 150 | 133·6 | 46·86 | 200 | 178·1 | 62·48 |
| 51 | 45·41 | 15·93 | 101 | 89·93 | 31·55 | 151 | 134·4 | 47·17 | 201 | 179·0 | 62·79 |
| 52 | 46·30 | 16·24 | 102 | 90·82 | 31·86 | 152 | 135·3 | 47·48 | 202 | 179·9 | 63·10 |
| 53 | 47·19 | 16·56 | 103 | 91·71 | 32·18 | 153 | 136·2 | 47·80 | 203 | 180·8 | 63·42 |
| 54 | 48·08 | 16·87 | 104 | 92·60 | 32·49 | 154 | 137·1 | 48·11 | 204 | 181·6 | 63·73 |
| 55 | 48·97 | 17·18 | 105 | 93·49 | 32·80 | 155 | 138·0 | 48·42 | 205 | 182·5 | 64·04 |
| 56 | 49·86 | 17·49 | 106 | 94·38 | 33·11 | 156 | 138·9 | 48·73 | 206 | 183·4 | 64·35 |
| 57 | 50·75 | 17·81 | 107 | 95·27 | 33·43 | 157 | 139·8 | 49·05 | 207 | 184·3 | 64·67 |
| 58 | 51·64 | 18·12 | 108 | 96·16 | 33·74 | 158 | 140·7 | 49·36 | 208 | 185·2 | 64·98 |
| 59 | 52·53 | 18·43 | 109 | 97·05 | 34·05 | 159 | 141·6 | 49·67 | 209 | 186·1 | 65·29 |
| 60 | 53·42 | 18·74 | 110 | 97·94 | 34·36 | 160 | 142·5 | 49·98 | 210 | 187·0 | 65·60 |

TABLE I

# 19° 40′

| G | D | H | G | D | H | G | D | H | G | D | H |
|---|---|---|---|---|---|---|---|---|---|---|---|
| 10 | 8·87 | 3·17 | 60 | 53·20 | 19·01 | 110 | 97·54 | 34·86 | 160 | 141·9 | 50·71 |
| 11 | 9·75 | 3·49 | 61 | 54·09 | 19·33 | 111 | 98·43 | 35·18 | 161 | 142·8 | 51·02 |
| 12 | 10·64 | 3·80 | 62 | 54·98 | 19·65 | 112 | 99·31 | 35·49 | 162 | 143·7 | 51·34 |
| 13 | 11·53 | 4·12 | 63 | 55·86 | 19·97 | 113 | 100·2 | 35·81 | 163 | 144·5 | 51·66 |
| 14 | 12·41 | 4·44 | 64 | 56·75 | 20·28 | 114 | 101·1 | 36·13 | 164 | 145·4 | 51·97 |
| 15 | 13·30 | 4·75 | 65 | 57·64 | 20·60 | 115 | 102·0 | 36·45 | 165 | 146·3 | 52·29 |
| 16 | 14·19 | 5·07 | 66 | 58·52 | 20·92 | 116 | 102·9 | 36·76 | 166 | 147·2 | 52·61 |
| 17 | 15·07 | 5·39 | 67 | 59·41 | 21·23 | 117 | 103·7 | 37·08 | 167 | 148·1 | 52·92 |
| 18 | 15·96 | 5·70 | 68 | 60·30 | 21·55 | 118 | 104·6 | 37·40 | 168 | 149·0 | 53·24 |
| 19 | 16·85 | 6·02 | 69 | 61·18 | 21·87 | 119 | 105·5 | 37·71 | 169 | 149·9 | 53·56 |
| 20 | 17·73 | 6·34 | 70 | 62·07 | 22·18 | 120 | 106·4 | 38·03 | 170 | 150·7 | 53·88 |
| 21 | 18·62 | 6·66 | 71 | 62·96 | 22·50 | 121 | 107·3 | 38·35 | 171 | 151·6 | 54·19 |
| 22 | 19·51 | 6·97 | 72 | 63·84 | 22·82 | 122 | 108·2 | 38·66 | 172 | 152·5 | 54·51 |
| 23 | 20·39 | 7·29 | 73 | 64·73 | 23·13 | 123 | 109·1 | 38·98 | 173 | 153·4 | 54·83 |
| 24 | 21·28 | 7·61 | 74 | 65·62 | 23·45 | 124 | 110·0 | 39·30 | 174 | 154·3 | 55·14 |
| 25 | 22·17 | 7·92 | 75 | 66·51 | 23·77 | 125 | 110·8 | 39·61 | 175 | 155·2 | 55·46 |
| 26 | 23·06 | 8·24 | 76 | 67·39 | 24·09 | 126 | 111·7 | 39·93 | 176 | 156·1 | 55·78 |
| 27 | 23·94 | 8·56 | 77 | 68·28 | 24·40 | 127 | 112·6 | 40·25 | 177 | 157·0 | 56·09 |
| 28 | 24·83 | 8·87 | 78 | 69·17 | 24·72 | 128 | 113·5 | 40·57 | 178 | 157·8 | 56·41 |
| 29 | 25·72 | 9·19 | 79 | 70·05 | 25·04 | 129 | 114·4 | 40·88 | 179 | 158·7 | 56·73 |
| 30 | 26·60 | 9·51 | 80 | 70·94 | 25·35 | 130 | 115·3 | 41·20 | 180 | 159·6 | 57·04 |
| 31 | 27·49 | 9·82 | 81 | 71·83 | 25·67 | 131 | 116·2 | 41·52 | 181 | 160·5 | 57·36 |
| 32 | 28·38 | 10·14 | 82 | 72·71 | 25·99 | 132 | 117·0 | 41·83 | 182 | 161·4 | 57·68 |
| 33 | 29·26 | 10·46 | 83 | 73·60 | 26·30 | 133 | 117·9 | 42·15 | 183 | 162·3 | 58·00 |
| 34 | 30·15 | 10·78 | 84 | 74·49 | 26·62 | 134 | 118·8 | 42·47 | 184 | 163·2 | 58·31 |
| 35 | 31·04 | 11·09 | 85 | 75·37 | 26·94 | 135 | 119·7 | 42·78 | 185 | 164·0 | 58·63 |
| 36 | 31·92 | 11·41 | 86 | 76·26 | 27·25 | 136 | 120·6 | 43·10 | 186 | 164·9 | 58·95 |
| 37 | 32·81 | 11·73 | 87 | 77·15 | 27·57 | 137 | 121·5 | 43·42 | 187 | 165·8 | 59·26 |
| 38 | 33·70 | 12·04 | 88 | 78·03 | 27·89 | 138 | 122·4 | 43·73 | 188 | 166·7 | 59·58 |
| 39 | 34·58 | 12·36 | 89 | 78·92 | 28·21 | 139 | 123·3 | 44·05 | 189 | 167·6 | 59·90 |
| 40 | 35·47 | 12·68 | 90 | 79·81 | 28·52 | 140 | 124·1 | 44·37 | 190 | 168·5 | 60·21 |
| 41 | 36·36 | 12·99 | 91 | 80·69 | 28·84 | 141 | 125·0 | 44·69 | 191 | 169·4 | 60·53 |
| 42 | 37·24 | 13·31 | 92 | 81·58 | 29·16 | 142 | 125·9 | 45·00 | 192 | 170·3 | 60·85 |
| 43 | 38·13 | 13·63 | 93 | 82·47 | 29·47 | 143 | 126·8 | 45·32 | 193 | 171·1 | 61·16 |
| 44 | 39·02 | 13·94 | 94 | 83·35 | 29·79 | 144 | 127·7 | 45·64 | 194 | 172·0 | 61·48 |
| 45 | 39·90 | 14·26 | 95 | 84·24 | 30·11 | 145 | 128·6 | 45·95 | 195 | 172·9 | 61·80 |
| 46 | 40·79 | 14·58 | 96 | 85·13 | 30·42 | 146 | 129·5 | 46·27 | 196 | 173·8 | 62·12 |
| 47 | 41·68 | 14·90 | 97 | 86·01 | 30·74 | 147 | 130·3 | 46·59 | 197 | 174·7 | 62·43 |
| 48 | 42·56 | 15·21 | 98 | 86·90 | 31·06 | 148 | 131·2 | 46·90 | 198 | 175·6 | 62·75 |
| 49 | 43·45 | 15·53 | 99 | 87·79 | 31·37 | 149 | 132·1 | 47·22 | 199 | 176·5 | 63·07 |
| 50 | 44·34 | 15·85 | 100 | 88·67 | 31·69 | 150 | 133·0 | 47·54 | 200 | 177·3 | 63·38 |
| 51 | 45·22 | 16·16 | 101 | 89·56 | 32·01 | 151 | 133·9 | 47·85 | 201 | 178·2 | 63·70 |
| 52 | 46·11 | 16·48 | 102 | 90·45 | 32·33 | 152 | 134·8 | 48·17 | 202 | 179·1 | 64·02 |
| 53 | 47·00 | 16·80 | 103 | 91·33 | 32·64 | 153 | 135·7 | 48·49 | 203 | 180·0 | 64·33 |
| 54 | 47·88 | 17·11 | 104 | 92·22 | 32·96 | 154 | 136·6 | 48·80 | 204 | 180·9 | 64·65 |
| 55 | 48·77 | 17·43 | 105 | 93·11 | 33·28 | 155 | 137·4 | 49·12 | 205 | 181·8 | 64·97 |
| 56 | 49·66 | 17·75 | 106 | 93·99 | 33·59 | 156 | 138·3 | 49·44 | 206 | 182·7 | 65·28 |
| 57 | 50·54 | 18·06 | 107 | 94·88 | 33·91 | 157 | 139·2 | 49·76 | 207 | 183·6 | 65·60 |
| 58 | 51·43 | 18·38 | 108 | 95·77 | 34·23 | 158 | 140·1 | 50·07 | 208 | 184·4 | 65·92 |
| 59 | 52·32 | 18·70 | 109 | 96·65 | 34·54 | 159 | 141·0 | 50·39 | 209 | 185·3 | 66·24 |
| 60 | 53·20 | 19·01 | 110 | 97·54 | 34·86 | 160 | 141·9 | 50·71 | 210 | 186·2 | 66·55 |

TABLE I

| G | D | H | G | D | H | G | D | H | G | D | H |
|---|---|---|---|---|---|---|---|---|---|---|---|
| 10 | 8·83 | 3·21 | 60 | 52·98 | 19·28 | 110 | 97·13 | 35·35 | 160 | 141·3 | 51·42 |
| 11 | 9·71 | 3·54 | 61 | 53·86 | 19·60 | 111 | 98·02 | 35·67 | 161 | 142·2 | 51·74 |
| 12 | 10·60 | 3·86 | 62 | 54·75 | 19·93 | 112 | 98·90 | 36·00 | 162 | 143·0 | 52·07 |
| 13 | 11·48 | 4·18 | 63 | 55·63 | 20·25 | 113 | 99·78 | 36·32 | 163 | 143·9 | 52·39 |
| 14 | 12·36 | 4·50 | 64 | 56·51 | 20·57 | 114 | 100·7 | 36·64 | 164 | 144·8 | 52·71 |
| 15 | 13·25 | 4·82 | 65 | 57·40 | 20·89 | 115 | 101·5 | 36·96 | 165 | 145·7 | 53·03 |
| 16 | 14·13 | 5·14 | 66 | 58·28 | 21·21 | 116 | 102·4 | 37·28 | 166 | 146·6 | 53·35 |
| 17 | 15·01 | 5·46 | 67 | 59·16 | 21·53 | 117 | 103·3 | 37·60 | 167 | 147·5 | 53·67 |
| 18 | 15·89 | 5·79 | 68 | 60·05 | 21·85 | 118 | 104·2 | 37·92 | 168 | 148·3 | 53·99 |
| 19 | 16·78 | 6·11 | 69 | 60·93 | 22·18 | 119 | 105·1 | 38·25 | 169 | 149·2 | 54·32 |
| 20 | 17·66 | 6·43 | 70 | 61·81 | 22·50 | 120 | 106·0 | 38·57 | 170 | 150·1 | 54·64 |
| 21 | 18·54 | 6·75 | 71 | 62·69 | 22·82 | 121 | 106·8 | 38·89 | 171 | 151·0 | 54·96 |
| 22 | 19·43 | 7·07 | 72 | 63·58 | 23·14 | 122 | 107·7 | 39·21 | 172 | 151·9 | 55·28 |
| 23 | 20·31 | 7·39 | 73 | 64·46 | 23·46 | 123 | 108·6 | 39·53 | 173 | 152·8 | 55·60 |
| 24 | 21·19 | 7·71 | 74 | 65·34 | 23·78 | 124 | 109·5 | 39·85 | 174 | 153·6 | 55·92 |
| 25 | 22·08 | 8·03 | 75 | 66·23 | 24·10 | 125 | 110·4 | 40·17 | 175 | 154·5 | 56·24 |
| 26 | 22·96 | 8·36 | 76 | 67·11 | 24·43 | 126 | 111·3 | 40·50 | 176 | 155·4 | 56·57 |
| 27 | 23·84 | 8·68 | 77 | 67·99 | 24·75 | 127 | 112·1 | 40·82 | 177 | 156·3 | 56·89 |
| 28 | 24·72 | 9·00 | 78 | 68·88 | 25·07 | 128 | 113·0 | 41·14 | 178 | 157·2 | 57·21 |
| 29 | 25·61 | 9·32 | 79 | 69·76 | 25·39 | 129 | 113·9 | 41·46 | 179 | 158·1 | 57·53 |
| 30 | 26·49 | 9·64 | 80 | 70·64 | 25·71 | 130 | 114·8 | 41·78 | 180 | 158·9 | 57·85 |
| 31 | 27·37 | 9·96 | 81 | 71·52 | 26·03 | 131 | 115·7 | 42·10 | 181 | 159·8 | 58·17 |
| 32 | 28·26 | 10·28 | 82 | 72·41 | 26·35 | 132 | 116·6 | 42·42 | 182 | 160·7 | 58·49 |
| 33 | 29·14 | 10·61 | 83 | 73·29 | 26·68 | 133 | 117·4 | 42·75 | 183 | 161·6 | 58·81 |
| 34 | 30·02 | 10·93 | 84 | 74·17 | 27·00 | 134 | 118·3 | 43·07 | 184 | 162·5 | 59·14 |
| 35 | 30·91 | 11·25 | 85 | 75·06 | 27·32 | 135 | 119·2 | 43·39 | 185 | 163·4 | 59·46 |
| 36 | 31·79 | 11·57 | 86 | 75·94 | 27·64 | 136 | 120·1 | 43·71 | 186 | 164·2 | 59·78 |
| 37 | 32·67 | 11·89 | 87 | 76·82 | 27·96 | 137 | 121·0 | 44·03 | 187 | 165·1 | 60·10 |
| 38 | 33·55 | 12·21 | 88 | 77·71 | 28·28 | 138 | 121·9 | 44·35 | 188 | 166·0 | 60·42 |
| 39 | 34·44 | 12·53 | 89 | 78·59 | 28·60 | 139 | 122·7 | 44·67 | 189 | 166·9 | 60·74 |
| 40 | 35·32 | 12·86 | 90 | 79·47 | 28·93 | 140 | 123·6 | 45·00 | 190 | 167·8 | 61·06 |
| 41 | 36·20 | 13·18 | 91 | 80·35 | 29·25 | 141 | 124·5 | 45·32 | 191 | 168·7 | 61·39 |
| 42 | 37·09 | 13·50 | 92 | 81·24 | 29·57 | 142 | 125·4 | 45·64 | 192 | 169·5 | 61·71 |
| 43 | 37·97 | 13·82 | 93 | 82·12 | 29·89 | 143 | 126·2 | 45·96 | 193 | 170·4 | 62·03 |
| 44 | 38·85 | 14·14 | 94 | 83·00 | 30·21 | 144 | 127·2 | 46·28 | 194 | 171·3 | 62·35 |
| 45 | 39·74 | 14·46 | 95 | 83·89 | 30·53 | 145 | 128·0 | 46·60 | 195 | 172·2 | 62·67 |
| 46 | 40·62 | 14·78 | 96 | 84·77 | 30·85 | 146 | 128·9 | 46·92 | 196 | 173·1 | 62·99 |
| 47 | 41·50 | 15·11 | 97 | 85·65 | 31·18 | 147 | 129·8 | 47·24 | 197 | 174·0 | 63·31 |
| 48 | 42·39 | 15·43 | 98 | 86·54 | 31·50 | 148 | 130·7 | 47·57 | 198 | 174·8 | 63·64 |
| 49 | 43·27 | 15·75 | 99 | 87·42 | 31·82 | 149 | 131·6 | 47·89 | 199 | 175·7 | 63·96 |
| 50 | 44·15 | 16·07 | 100 | 88·30 | 32·14 | 150 | 132·5 | 48·21 | 200 | 176·6 | 64·28 |
| 51 | 45·03 | 16·39 | 101 | 89·19 | 32·46 | 151 | 133·3 | 48·53 | 201 | 177·5 | 64·60 |
| 52 | 45·92 | 16·71 | 102 | 90·07 | 32·78 | 152 | 134·2 | 48·85 | 202 | 178·4 | 64·92 |
| 53 | 46·80 | 17·03 | 103 | 90·95 | 33·10 | 153 | 135·1 | 49·17 | 203 | 179·3 | 65·24 |
| 54 | 47·68 | 17·36 | 104 | 91·83 | 33·42 | 154 | 136·0 | 49·49 | 204 | 180·1 | 65·56 |
| 55 | 48·57 | 17·68 | 105 | 92·72 | 33·75 | 155 | 136·9 | 49·82 | 205 | 181·0 | 65·89 |
| 56 | 49·45 | 18·00 | 106 | 93·60 | 34·07 | 156 | 137·8 | 50·14 | 206 | 181·9 | 66·21 |
| 57 | 50·33 | 18·32 | 107 | 94·48 | 34·39 | 157 | 138·6 | 50·46 | 207 | 182·8 | 66·53 |
| 58 | 51·22 | 18·64 | 108 | 95·37 | 34·71 | 158 | 139·5 | 50·78 | 208 | 183·7 | 66·85 |
| 59 | 52·10 | 18·96 | 109 | 96·25 | 35·03 | 159 | 140·4 | 51·10 | 209 | 184·6 | 67·17 |
| 60 | 52·98 | 19·28 | 110 | 97·13 | 35·35 | 160 | 141·3 | 51·42 | 210 | 185·4 | 67·49 |

# TABLE II

Giving the Values of D and H
at 20′ intervals of V
from 10° 10′ to 19° 50′
and at 10′ intervals of V
from 20° 10′ to 30° 00′

TABLE II

| G | D 10° 10′ | H | D 10° 30′ | H | D 10° 50′ | H |
|---|---|---|---|---|---|---|
| 10 | 9·69 | 1·74 | 9·67 | 1·79 | 9·65 | 1·85 |
| 20 | 19·38 | 3·47 | 19·34 | 3·58 | 19·29 | 3·69 |
| 30 | 29·07 | 5·21 | 29·00 | 5·38 | 28·94 | 5·54 |
| 40 | 38·75 | 6·95 | 38·67 | 7·17 | 38·59 | 7·38 |
| 50 | 48·44 | 8·69 | 48·34 | 8·96 | 48·23 | 9·23 |
| 60 | 58·13 | 10·42 | 58·01 | 10·75 | 57·88 | 11·08 |
| 70 | 67·82 | 12·16 | 67·68 | 12·54 | 67·53 | 12·92 |
| 80 | 77·51 | 13·90 | 77·34 | 14·33 | 77·17 | 14·77 |
| 90 | 87·20 | 15·64 | 87·01 | 16·13 | 86·82 | 16·61 |
| 100 | 96·88 | 17·374 | 96·68 | 17·918 | 96·47 | 18·460 |
| | 11° 10′ | | 11° 30′ | | 11° 50′ | |
| 10 | 9·62 | 1·90 | 9·60 | 1·95 | 9·58 | 2·01 |
| 20 | 19·25 | 3·80 | 19·21 | 3·91 | 19·16 | 4·01 |
| 30 | 28·87 | 5·70 | 28·81 | 5·86 | 28·74 | 6·02 |
| 40 | 38·50 | 7·60 | 38·41 | 7·81 | 38·32 | 8·03 |
| 50 | 48·12 | 9·50 | 48·01 | 9·77 | 47·90 | 10·04 |
| 60 | 57·75 | 11·40 | 57·62 | 11·72 | 57·48 | 12·04 |
| 70 | 67·37 | 13·30 | 67·22 | 13·68 | 67·06 | 14·05 |
| 80 | 77·00 | 15·20 | 76·82 | 15·63 | 76·64 | 16·06 |
| 90 | 86·62 | 17·10 | 86·42 | 17·58 | 86·22 | 18·06 |
| 100 | 96·25 | 19·000 | 96·03 | 19·537 | 95·79 | 20·071 |
| | 12° 10′ | | 12° 30′ | | 12° 50′ | |
| 10 | 9·56 | 2·06 | 9·53 | 2·11 | 9·51 | 2·17 |
| 20 | 19·11 | 4·12 | 19·06 | 4·23 | 19·01 | 4·33 |
| 30 | 28·67 | 6·18 | 28·59 | 6·34 | 28·52 | 6·50 |
| 40 | 38·22 | 8·24 | 38·13 | 8·45 | 38·03 | 8·66 |
| 50 | 47·78 | 10·30 | 47·66 | 10·57 | 47·53 | 10·83 |
| 60 | 57·33 | 12·36 | 57·19 | 12·68 | 57·04 | 12·99 |
| 70 | 66·89 | 14·42 | 66·72 | 14·79 | 66·55 | 15·16 |
| 80 | 76·45 | 16·48 | 76·25 | 16·90 | 76·05 | 17·33 |
| 90 | 86·00 | 18·54 | 85·78 | 19·02 | 85·56 | 19·49 |
| 100 | 95·56 | 20·602 | 95·32 | 21·131 | 95·07 | 21·657 |
| | 13° 10′ | | 13° 30′ | | 13° 50′ | |
| 10 | 9·48 | 2·22 | 9·46 | 2·27 | 9·43 | 2·32 |
| 20 | 18·96 | 4·44 | 18·91 | 4·54 | 18·86 | 4·64 |
| 30 | 28·44 | 6·65 | 28·37 | 6·81 | 28·28 | 6·96 |
| 40 | 37·92 | 8·87 | 37·82 | 9·08 | 37·71 | 9·29 |
| 50 | 47·41 | 11·09 | 47·28 | 11·35 | 47·14 | 11·61 |
| 60 | 56·89 | 13·31 | 56·73 | 13·62 | 56·57 | 13·93 |
| 70 | 66·37 | 15·53 | 66·19 | 15·89 | 66·00 | 16·25 |
| 80 | 75·85 | 17·74 | 75·64 | 18·16 | 75·43 | 18·57 |
| 90 | 85·33 | 19·96 | 85·10 | 20·43 | 84·85 | 20·89 |
| 100 | 94·81 | 22·180 | 94·55 | 22·700 | 94·28 | 23·216 |
| | 14° 10′ | | 14° 30′ | | 14° 50′ | |
| 10 | 9·40 | 2·37 | 9·37 | 2·42 | 9·34 | 2·47 |
| 20 | 18·80 | 4·75 | 18·75 | 4·85 | 18·69 | 4·95 |
| 30 | 28·20 | 7·12 | 28·12 | 7·27 | 28·03 | 7·42 |
| 40 | 37·60 | 9·49 | 37·49 | 9·70 | 37·38 | 9·90 |
| 50 | 47·01 | 11·86 | 46·87 | 12·12 | 46·72 | 12·37 |
| 60 | 56·41 | 14·24 | 56·24 | 14·54 | 56·07 | 14·85 |
| 70 | 65·81 | 16·61 | 65·61 | 16·97 | 65·41 | 17·32 |
| 80 | 75·21 | 18·98 | 74·98 | 19·39 | 74·76 | 19·80 |
| 90 | 84·61 | 21·36 | 84·36 | 21·82 | 84·10 | 22·27 |
| 100 | 94·01 | 23·730 | 93·73 | 24·240 | 93·45 | 24·748 |

## TABLE II

| G | D 15° 10′ | H | D 15° 30′ | H | D 15° 50′ | H |
|---|---|---|---|---|---|---|
| 10 | 9·32 | 2·53 | 9·29 | 2·58 | 9·26 | 2·62 |
| 20 | 18·63 | 5·05 | 18·57 | 5·15 | 18·51 | 5·25 |
| 30 | 27·95 | 7·58 | 27·86 | 7·73 | 27·77 | 7·87 |
| 40 | 37·26 | 10·10 | 37·14 | 10·30 | 37·02 | 10·50 |
| 50 | 46·58 | 12·63 | 46·43 | 12·88 | 46·28 | 13·12 |
| 60 | 55·89 | 15·15 | 55·71 | 15·45 | 55·53 | 15·75 |
| 70 | 65·21 | 17·68 | 65·00 | 18·03 | 64·79 | 18·37 |
| 80 | 74·52 | 20·20 | 74·29 | 20·60 | 74·04 | 21·00 |
| 90 | 83·84 | 22·73 | 83·57 | 23·18 | 83·30 | 23·62 |
| 100 | 93·16 | 25·252 | 92·86 | 25·752 | 92·56 | 26·249 |

| G | D 16° 10′ | H | D 16° 30′ | H | D 16° 50′ | H |
|---|---|---|---|---|---|---|
| 10 | 9·22 | 2·67 | 9·19 | 2·72 | 9·16 | 2·77 |
| 20 | 18·45 | 5·35 | 18·39 | 5·45 | 18·32 | 5·54 |
| 30 | 27·67 | 8·02 | 27·58 | 8·17 | 27·48 | 8·32 |
| 40 | 36·90 | 10·70 | 36·77 | 10·89 | 36·65 | 11·09 |
| 50 | 46·12 | 13·37 | 45·97 | 13·62 | 45·81 | 13·86 |
| 60 | 55·35 | 16·05 | 55·16 | 16·34 | 54·97 | 16·63 |
| 70 | 64·57 | 18·72 | 64·35 | 19·06 | 64·13 | 19·40 |
| 80 | 73·80 | 21·39 | 73·55 | 21·79 | 73·29 | 22·17 |
| 90 | 83·02 | 24·07 | 82·74 | 24·51 | 82·45 | 24·95 |
| 100 | 92·25 | 26·742 | 91·93 | 27·232 | 91·61 | 27·718 |

| G | D 17° 10′ | H | D 17° 30′ | H | D 17° 50′ | H |
|---|---|---|---|---|---|---|
| 10 | 9·13 | 2·82 | 9·10 | 2·87 | 9·06 | 2·92 |
| 20 | 18·26 | 5·64 | 18·19 | 5·74 | 18·12 | 5·83 |
| 30 | 27·39 | 8·46 | 27·29 | 8·60 | 27·19 | 8·75 |
| 40 | 36·52 | 11·28 | 36·38 | 11·47 | 36·25 | 11·66 |
| 50 | 45·64 | 14·10 | 45·48 | 14·34 | 45·31 | 14·58 |
| 60 | 54·77 | 16·92 | 54·57 | 17·21 | 54·37 | 17·49 |
| 70 | 63·90 | 19·74 | 63·67 | 20·08 | 63·43 | 20·41 |
| 80 | 73·03 | 22·56 | 72·77 | 22·94 | 72·50 | 23·32 |
| 90 | 82·16 | 25·38 | 81·86 | 25·81 | 81·56 | 26·24 |
| 100 | 91·29 | 28·200 | 90·96 | 28·679 | 90·62 | 29·153 |

| G | D 18° 10′ | H | D 18° 30′ | H | D 18° 50′ | H |
|---|---|---|---|---|---|---|
| 10 | 9·03 | 2·96 | 8·99 | 3·01 | 8·96 | 3·06 |
| 20 | 18·06 | 5·92 | 17·99 | 6·02 | 17·92 | 6·11 |
| 30 | 27·08 | 8·89 | 26·98 | 9·03 | 26·87 | 9·17 |
| 40 | 36·11 | 11·85 | 35·97 | 12·04 | 35·83 | 12·22 |
| 50 | 45·14 | 14·81 | 44·97 | 15·05 | 44·79 | 15·28 |
| 60 | 54·17 | 17·77 | 53·96 | 18·05 | 53·75 | 18·33 |
| 70 | 63·20 | 20·74 | 62·95 | 21·06 | 62·71 | 21·39 |
| 80 | 72·22 | 23·70 | 71·95 | 24·07 | 71·66 | 24·44 |
| 90 | 81·25 | 26·66 | 80·94 | 27·08 | 80·62 | 27·50 |
| 100 | 90·28 | 29·624 | 89·93 | 30·091 | 89·58 | 30·553 |

| G | D 19° 10′ | H | D 19° 30′ | H | D 19° 50′ | H |
|---|---|---|---|---|---|---|
| 10 | 8·92 | 3·10 | 8·89 | 3·15 | 8·85 | 3·19 |
| 20 | 17·84 | 6·20 | 17·77 | 6·29 | 17·70 | 6·38 |
| 30 | 26·77 | 9·30 | 26·66 | 9·44 | 26·55 | 9·57 |
| 40 | 35·69 | 12·40 | 35·54 | 12·59 | 35·40 | 12·77 |
| 50 | 44·61 | 15·51 | 44·43 | 15·73 | 44·24 | 15·96 |
| 60 | 53·53 | 18·61 | 53·31 | 18·88 | 53·09 | 19·15 |
| 70 | 62·45 | 21·71 | 62·20 | 22·03 | 61·94 | 22·34 |
| 80 | 71·38 | 24·81 | 71·09 | 25·17 | 70·79 | 25·53 |
| 90 | 80·30 | 27·91 | 79·97 | 28·32 | 79·64 | 28·72 |
| 100 | 89·22 | 31·012 | 88·86 | 31·466 | 88·49 | 31·916 |

TABLE II

| G | D (20° 10') | H (20° 10') | D (20° 20') | H (20° 20') | D (20° 30') | H (20° 30') |
|---|---|---|---|---|---|---|
| 10 | 8·81 | 3·24 | 8·79 | 3·26 | 8·77 | 3·28 |
| 20 | 17·62 | 6·47 | 17·59 | 6·52 | 17·55 | 6·56 |
| 30 | 26·43 | 9·71 | 26·38 | 9·77 | 26·32 | 9·84 |
| 40 | 35·25 | 12·94 | 35·17 | 13·03 | 35·09 | 13·12 |
| 50 | 44·06 | 16·18 | 43·96 | 16·29 | 43·87 | 16·40 |
| 60 | 52·87 | 19·42 | 52·76 | 19·55 | 52·64 | 19·68 |
| 70 | 61·68 | 22·65 | 61·55 | 22·81 | 61·41 | 22·96 |
| 80 | 70·49 | 25·89 | 70·34 | 26·07 | 70·19 | 26·24 |
| 90 | 79·30 | 29·13 | 79·13 | 29·32 | 78·96 | 29·52 |
| 100 | 88·11 | 32·362 | 87·93 | 32·583 | 87·74 | 32·803 |

| G | D (20° 40') | H (20° 40') | D (20° 50') | H (20° 50') | D (21° 00') | H (21° 00') |
|---|---|---|---|---|---|---|
| 10 | 8·75 | 3·30 | 8·74 | 3·32 | 8·72 | 3·35 |
| 20 | 17·51 | 6·60 | 17·47 | 6·65 | 17·43 | 6·69 |
| 30 | 26·26 | 9·91 | 26·21 | 9·97 | 26·15 | 10·04 |
| 40 | 35·02 | 13·21 | 34·94 | 13·30 | 34·86 | 13·38 |
| 50 | 43·77 | 16·51 | 43·68 | 16·62 | 43·58 | 16·73 |
| 60 | 52·53 | 19·81 | 52·41 | 19·94 | 52·29 | 20·07 |
| 70 | 61·28 | 23·12 | 61·15 | 23·27 | 61·01 | 23·42 |
| 80 | 70·04 | 26·42 | 69·88 | 26·59 | 69·73 | 26·77 |
| 90 | 78·79 | 29·72 | 78·62 | 29·92 | 78·44 | 30·11 |
| 100 | 87·54 | 33·022 | 87·35 | 33·240 | 87·16 | 33·457 |

| G | D (21° 10') | H (21° 10') | D (21° 20') | H (21° 20') | D (21° 30') | H (21° 30') |
|---|---|---|---|---|---|---|
| 10 | 8·70 | 3·37 | 8·68 | 3·39 | 8·66 | 3·41 |
| 20 | 17·39 | 6·73 | 17·35 | 6·78 | 17·31 | 6·82 |
| 30 | 26·09 | 10·10 | 26·03 | 10·17 | 25·97 | 10·23 |
| 40 | 34·78 | 13·47 | 34·71 | 13·55 | 34·63 | 13·64 |
| 50 | 43·48 | 16·84 | 43·38 | 16·94 | 43·28 | 17·05 |
| 60 | 52·18 | 20·20 | 52·06 | 20·33 | 51·94 | 20·46 |
| 70 | 60·87 | 23·57 | 60·74 | 23·72 | 60·60 | 23·87 |
| 80 | 69·57 | 26·94 | 69·41 | 27·11 | 69·25 | 27·28 |
| 90 | 78·27 | 30·30 | 78·09 | 30·50 | 77·91 | 30·69 |
| 100 | 86·96 | 33·672 | 86·77 | 33·887 | 86·57 | 34·100 |

| G | D (21° 40') | H (21° 40') | D (21° 50') | H (21° 50') | D (22° 00') | H (22° 00') |
|---|---|---|---|---|---|---|
| 10 | 8·64 | 3·43 | 8·62 | 3·45 | 8·60 | 3·47 |
| 20 | 17·27 | 6·86 | 17·23 | 6·90 | 17·19 | 6·95 |
| 30 | 25·91 | 10·29 | 25·85 | 10·36 | 25·79 | 10·42 |
| 40 | 34·55 | 13·72 | 34·47 | 13·81 | 34·39 | 13·89 |
| 50 | 43·18 | 17·16 | 43·08 | 17·26 | 42·98 | 17·37 |
| 60 | 51·82 | 20·59 | 51·70 | 20·71 | 51·58 | 20·84 |
| 70 | 60·46 | 24·02 | 60·32 | 24·17 | 60·18 | 24·31 |
| 80 | 69·10 | 27·45 | 68·93 | 27·62 | 68·77 | 27·79 |
| 90 | 77·73 | 30·88 | 77·55 | 31·07 | 77·37 | 31·26 |
| 100 | 86·37 | 34·312 | 86·17 | 34·523 | 85·97 | 34·733 |

| G | D (22° 10') | H (22° 10') | D (22° 20') | H (22° 20') | D (22° 30') | H (22° 30') |
|---|---|---|---|---|---|---|
| 10 | 8·58 | 3·49 | 8·56 | 3·51 | 8·54 | 3·54 |
| 20 | 17·15 | 6·99 | 17·11 | 7·03 | 17·07 | 7·07 |
| 30 | 25·73 | 10·48 | 25·67 | 10·54 | 25·61 | 10·61 |
| 40 | 34·31 | 13·98 | 34·22 | 14·06 | 34·14 | 14·14 |
| 50 | 42·88 | 17·47 | 42·78 | 17·57 | 42·68 | 17·68 |
| 60 | 51·46 | 20·97 | 51·34 | 21·09 | 51·21 | 21·21 |
| 70 | 60·03 | 24·46 | 59·89 | 24·60 | 59·75 | 24·75 |
| 80 | 68·61 | 27·95 | 68·45 | 28·12 | 68·28 | 28·28 |
| 90 | 77·19 | 31·45 | 77·00 | 31·63 | 76·82 | 31·82 |
| 100 | 85·76 | 34·942 | 85·56 | 35·149 | 85·36 | 35·355 |

## TABLE II

| G | D 22° 40' | H | D 22° 50' | H | D 23° 00' | H |
|---|---|---|---|---|---|---|
| 10 | 8·51 | 3·56 | 8·49 | 3·58 | 8·47 | 3·60 |
| 20 | 17·03 | 7·11 | 16·99 | 7·15 | 16·95 | 7·19 |
| 30 | 25·54 | 10·67 | 25·48 | 10·73 | 25·42 | 10·79 |
| 40 | 34·06 | 14·22 | 33·98 | 14·31 | 33·89 | 14·39 |
| 50 | 42·57 | 17·78 | 42·47 | 17·88 | 42·37 | 17·98 |
| 60 | 51·09 | 21·34 | 50·97 | 21·46 | 50·84 | 21·58 |
| 70 | 59·60 | 24·89 | 59·46 | 25·03 | 59·31 | 25·18 |
| 80 | 68·12 | 28·45 | 67·95 | 28·61 | 67·79 | 28·77 |
| 90 | 76·63 | 32·00 | 76·45 | 32·19 | 76·26 | 32·37 |
| 100 | 85·15 | 35·560 | 84·94 | 35·764 | 84·73 | 35·967 |

| G | D 23° 10' | H | D 23° 20' | H | D 23° 30' | H |
|---|---|---|---|---|---|---|
| 10 | 8·45 | 3·62 | 8·43 | 3·64 | 8·41 | 3·66 |
| 20 | 16·90 | 7·23 | 16·86 | 7·27 | 16·82 | 7·31 |
| 30 | 25·36 | 10·85 | 25·29 | 10·91 | 25·23 | 10·97 |
| 40 | 33·81 | 14·47 | 33·72 | 14·55 | 33·64 | 14·63 |
| 50 | 42·26 | 18·08 | 42·16 | 18·18 | 42·05 | 18·28 |
| 60 | 50·71 | 21·70 | 50·59 | 21·82 | 50·46 | 21·94 |
| 70 | 59·17 | 25·32 | 59·02 | 25·46 | 58·87 | 25·60 |
| 80 | 67·62 | 28·93 | 67·45 | 29·10 | 67·28 | 29·25 |
| 90 | 76·07 | 32·55 | 75·88 | 32·73 | 75·69 | 32·91 |
| 100 | 84·52 | 36·168 | 84·31 | 36·369 | 84·10 | 36·568 |

| G | D 23° 40' | H | D 23° 50' | H | D 24° 00' | H |
|---|---|---|---|---|---|---|
| 10 | 8·39 | 3·68 | 8·37 | 3·70 | 8·35 | 3·72 |
| 20 | 16·78 | 7·35 | 16·73 | 7·39 | 16·69 | 7·43 |
| 30 | 25·17 | 11·03 | 25·10 | 11·09 | 25·04 | 11·15 |
| 40 | 33·55 | 14·71 | 33·47 | 14·78 | 33·38 | 14·86 |
| 50 | 41·94 | 18·38 | 41·84 | 18·48 | 41·73 | 18·58 |
| 60 | 50·33 | 22·06 | 50·20 | 22·18 | 50·07 | 22·29 |
| 70 | 58·72 | 25·74 | 58·57 | 25·87 | 58·42 | 26·01 |
| 80 | 67·11 | 29·41 | 66·94 | 29·57 | 66·77 | 29·73 |
| 90 | 75·50 | 33·09 | 75·30 | 33·27 | 75·11 | 33·44 |
| 100 | 83·89 | 36·765 | 83·67 | 36·962 | 83·46 | 37·157 |

| G | D 24° 10' | H | D 24° 20' | H | D 24° 30' | H |
|---|---|---|---|---|---|---|
| 10 | 8·32 | 3·74 | 8·30 | 3·75 | 8·28 | 3·77 |
| 20 | 16·65 | 7·47 | 16·60 | 7·51 | 16·56 | 7·55 |
| 30 | 24·97 | 11·21 | 24·91 | 11·26 | 24·84 | 11·32 |
| 40 | 33·30 | 14·94 | 33·21 | 15·02 | 33·12 | 15·09 |
| 50 | 41·62 | 18·68 | 41·51 | 18·77 | 41·40 | 18·87 |
| 60 | 49·94 | 22·41 | 49·81 | 22·53 | 49·68 | 22·64 |
| 70 | 58·27 | 26·15 | 58·12 | 26·28 | 57·96 | 26·41 |
| 80 | 66·59 | 29·88 | 66·42 | 30·04 | 66·24 | 30·19 |
| 90 | 74·92 | 33·62 | 74·72 | 33·79 | 74·52 | 33·96 |
| 100 | 83·24 | 37·351 | 83·02 | 37·544 | 82·80 | 37·735 |

| G | D 24° 40' | H | D 24° 50' | H | D 25° 00' | H |
|---|---|---|---|---|---|---|
| 10 | 8·26 | 3·79 | 8·24 | 3·81 | 8·21 | 3·83 |
| 20 | 16·52 | 7·59 | 16·47 | 7·62 | 16·43 | 7·66 |
| 30 | 24·77 | 11·38 | 24·71 | 11·43 | 24·64 | 11·49 |
| 40 | 33·03 | 15·17 | 32·94 | 15·25 | 32·86 | 15·32 |
| 50 | 41·29 | 18·96 | 41·18 | 19·06 | 41·07 | 19·15 |
| 60 | 49·55 | 22·76 | 49·42 | 22·87 | 49·28 | 22·98 |
| 70 | 57·81 | 26·55 | 57·65 | 26·68 | 57·50 | 26·81 |
| 80 | 66·07 | 30·34 | 65·89 | 30·49 | 65·71 | 30·64 |
| 90 | 74·32 | 34·13 | 74·13 | 34·30 | 73·93 | 34·47 |
| 100 | 82·58 | 37·926 | 82·36 | 38·115 | 82·14 | 38·302 |

# TABLE II

| G | D 25° 10' | H | D 25° 20' | H | D 25° 30' | H |
|---|---|---|---|---|---|---|
| 10 | 8·19 | 3·85 | 8·17 | 3·87 | 8·15 | 3·89 |
| 20 | 16·38 | 7·70 | 16·34 | 7·73 | 16·29 | 7·77 |
| 30 | 24·57 | 11·55 | 24·51 | 11·60 | 24·44 | 11·66 |
| 40 | 32·77 | 15·40 | 32·68 | 15·47 | 32·59 | 15·54 |
| 50 | 40·96 | 19·24 | 40·85 | 19·34 | 40·73 | 19·43 |
| 60 | 49·15 | 23·09 | 49·02 | 23·20 | 48·88 | 23·31 |
| 70 | 57·34 | 26·94 | 57·18 | 27·07 | 57·03 | 27·20 |
| 80 | 65·53 | 30·79 | 65·35 | 30·94 | 65·17 | 31·09 |
| 90 | 73·72 | 34·64 | 73·52 | 34·81 | 73·32 | 34·97 |
| 100 | 81·92 | 38·489 | 81·69 | 38·674 | 81·47 | 38·857 |

| G | D 25° 40' | H | D 25° 50' | H | D 26° 00' | H |
|---|---|---|---|---|---|---|
| 10 | 8·12 | 3·90 | 8·10 | 3·92 | 8·08 | 3·94 |
| 20 | 16·25 | 7·81 | 16·20 | 7·84 | 16·16 | 7·88 |
| 30 | 24·37 | 11·71 | 24·30 | 11·77 | 24·23 | 11·82 |
| 40 | 32·50 | 15·62 | 32·40 | 15·69 | 32·31 | 15·76 |
| 50 | 40·62 | 19·52 | 40·51 | 19·61 | 40·39 | 19·70 |
| 60 | 48·74 | 23·42 | 48·61 | 23·53 | 48·47 | 23·64 |
| 70 | 56·87 | 27·33 | 56·71 | 27·45 | 56·55 | 27·58 |
| 80 | 64·99 | 31·23 | 64·81 | 31·38 | 64·63 | 31·52 |
| 90 | 73·12 | 35·14 | 72·91 | 35·30 | 72·70 | 35·46 |
| 100 | 81·24 | 39·040 | 81·01 | 39·221 | 80·78 | 39·401 |

| G | D 26° 10' | H | D 26° 20' | H | D 26° 30' | H |
|---|---|---|---|---|---|---|
| 10 | 8·06 | 3·96 | 8·03 | 3·98 | 8·01 | 3·99 |
| 20 | 16·11 | 7·92 | 16·06 | 7·95 | 16·02 | 7·99 |
| 30 | 24·17 | 11·87 | 24·10 | 11·93 | 24·03 | 11·98 |
| 40 | 32·22 | 15·83 | 32·13 | 15·90 | 32·04 | 15·97 |
| 50 | 40·28 | 19·79 | 40·16 | 19·88 | 40·05 | 19·97 |
| 60 | 48·33 | 23·75 | 48·19 | 23·85 | 48·05 | 23·96 |
| 70 | 56·39 | 27·71 | 56·23 | 27·83 | 56·06 | 27·95 |
| 80 | 64·44 | 31·66 | 64·26 | 31·80 | 64·07 | 31·95 |
| 90 | 72·50 | 35·62 | 72·29 | 35·78 | 72·08 | 35·94 |
| 100 | 80·55 | 39·579 | 80·32 | 39·756 | 80·09 | 39·932 |

| G | D 26° 40' | H | D 26° 50' | H | D 27° 00' | H |
|---|---|---|---|---|---|---|
| 10 | 7·99 | 4·01 | 7·96 | 4·03 | 7·94 | 4·05 |
| 20 | 15·97 | 8·02 | 15·92 | 8·06 | 15·88 | 8·09 |
| 30 | 23·96 | 12·03 | 23·89 | 12·08 | 23·82 | 12·14 |
| 40 | 31·94 | 16·04 | 31·85 | 16·11 | 31·76 | 16·18 |
| 50 | 39·93 | 20·05 | 39·81 | 20·14 | 39·69 | 20·23 |
| 60 | 47·91 | 24·06 | 47·77 | 24·17 | 47·63 | 24·27 |
| 70 | 55·90 | 28·07 | 55·74 | 28·20 | 55·57 | 28·32 |
| 80 | 63·89 | 32·08 | 63·70 | 32·22 | 63·51 | 32·36 |
| 90 | 71·87 | 36·10 | 71·66 | 36·25 | 71·45 | 36·41 |
| 100 | 79·86 | 40·106 | 79·62 | 40·279 | 79·39 | 40·451 |

| G | D 27° 10' | H | D 27° 20' | H | D 27° 30' | H |
|---|---|---|---|---|---|---|
| 10 | 7·92 | 4·06 | 7·89 | 4·08 | 7·87 | 4·10 |
| 20 | 15·83 | 8·12 | 15·78 | 8·16 | 15·74 | 8·19 |
| 30 | 23·75 | 12·19 | 23·68 | 12·24 | 23·60 | 12·29 |
| 40 | 31·66 | 16·25 | 31·57 | 16·32 | 31·47 | 16·38 |
| 50 | 39·58 | 20·31 | 39·46 | 20·40 | 39·34 | 20·48 |
| 60 | 47·49 | 24·37 | 47·35 | 24·47 | 47·21 | 24·57 |
| 70 | 55·41 | 28·43 | 55·24 | 28·55 | 55·08 | 28·67 |
| 80 | 63·32 | 32·50 | 63·13 | 32·63 | 62·94 | 32·77 |
| 90 | 71·24 | 36·56 | 71·03 | 36·71 | 70·81 | 36·86 |
| 100 | 79·15 | 40·621 | 78·92 | 40·790 | 78·68 | 40·958 |

**TABLE II**

| G | D 27° 40' | H | D 27° 50' | H | D 28° 00' | H |
|---|---|---|---|---|---|---|
| 10 | 7·84 | 4·11 | 7·82 | 4·13 | 7·80 | 4·15 |
| 20 | 15·69 | 8·22 | 15·64 | 8·26 | 15·59 | 8·29 |
| 30 | 23·53 | 12·34 | 23·46 | 12·39 | 23·39 | 12·44 |
| 40 | 31·38 | 16·45 | 31·28 | 16·52 | 31·18 | 16·58 |
| 50 | 39·22 | 20·56 | 39·10 | 20·64 | 38·98 | 20·73 |
| 60 | 47·06 | 24·67 | 46·92 | 24·77 | 46·78 | 24·87 |
| 70 | 54·91 | 28·79 | 54·74 | 28·90 | 54·57 | 29·02 |
| 80 | 62·75 | 32·90 | 62·56 | 33·03 | 62·37 | 33·16 |
| 90 | 70·60 | 37·01 | 70·38 | 37·16 | 70·16 | 37·31 |
| 100 | 78·44 | 41·124 | 78·20 | 41·289 | 77·96 | 41·452 |

| G | D 28° 10' | H | D 28° 20' | H | D 28° 30' | H |
|---|---|---|---|---|---|---|
| 10 | 7·77 | 4·16 | 7·75 | 4·18 | 7·72 | 4·19 |
| 20 | 15·54 | 8·32 | 15·50 | 8·35 | 15·45 | 8·39 |
| 30 | 23·32 | 12·48 | 23·24 | 12·53 | 23·17 | 12·58 |
| 40 | 31·09 | 16·65 | 30·99 | 16·71 | 30·89 | 16·77 |
| 50 | 38·86 | 20·81 | 38·74 | 20·89 | 38·62 | 20·97 |
| 60 | 46·63 | 24·97 | 46·49 | 25·06 | 46·34 | 25·16 |
| 70 | 54·40 | 29·13 | 54·23 | 29·24 | 54·06 | 29·35 |
| 80 | 62·17 | 33·29 | 61·98 | 33·42 | 61·79 | 33·55 |
| 90 | 69·95 | 37·45 | 69·73 | 37·60 | 69·51 | 37·74 |
| 100 | 77·72 | 41·614 | 77·48 | 41·774 | 77·23 | 41·934 |

| G | D 28° 40' | H | D 28° 50' | H | D 29° 00' | H |
|---|---|---|---|---|---|---|
| 10 | 7·70 | 4·21 | 7·67 | 4·22 | 7·65 | 4·24 |
| 20 | 15·40 | 8·42 | 15·35 | 8·45 | 15·30 | 8·48 |
| 30 | 23·10 | 12·63 | 23·02 | 12·67 | 22·95 | 12·72 |
| 40 | 30·80 | 16·84 | 30·70 | 16·90 | 30·60 | 16·96 |
| 50 | 38·49 | 21·05 | 38·37 | 21·12 | 38·25 | 21·20 |
| 60 | 46·19 | 25·25 | 46·05 | 25·35 | 45·90 | 25·44 |
| 70 | 53·89 | 29·46 | 53·72 | 29·57 | 53·55 | 29·68 |
| 80 | 61·59 | 33·67 | 61·39 | 33·80 | 61·20 | 33·92 |
| 90 | 69·29 | 37·88 | 69·07 | 38·02 | 68·85 | 38·16 |
| 100 | 76·99 | 42·091 | 76·74 | 42·248 | 76·50 | 42·402 |

| G | D 29° 10' | H | D 29° 20' | H | D 29° 30' | H |
|---|---|---|---|---|---|---|
| 10 | 7·62 | 4·26 | 7·60 | 4·27 | 7·58 | 4·29 |
| 20 | 15·25 | 8·51 | 15·20 | 8·54 | 15·15 | 8·57 |
| 30 | 22·87 | 12·77 | 22·80 | 12·81 | 22·73 | 12·86 |
| 40 | 30·50 | 17·02 | 30·40 | 17·08 | 30·30 | 17·14 |
| 50 | 38·12 | 21·28 | 38·00 | 21·35 | 37·88 | 21·43 |
| 60 | 45·75 | 25·53 | 45·60 | 25·62 | 45·45 | 25·71 |
| 70 | 53·37 | 29·79 | 53·20 | 29·90 | 53·03 | 30·00 |
| 80 | 61·00 | 34·04 | 60·80 | 34·17 | 60·60 | 34·29 |
| 90 | 68·62 | 38·30 | 68·40 | 38·44 | 68·18 | 38·57 |
| 100 | 76·25 | 42·556 | 76·00 | 42·708 | 75·75 | 42·858 |

| G | D 29° 40' | H | D 29° 50' | H | D 30° 00' | H |
|---|---|---|---|---|---|---|
| 10 | 7·55 | 4·30 | 7·53 | 4·32 | 7·50 | 4·33 |
| 20 | 15·10 | 8·60 | 15·05 | 8·63 | 15·00 | 8·66 |
| 30 | 22·65 | 12·90 | 22·58 | 12·95 | 22·50 | 12·99 |
| 40 | 30·20 | 17·20 | 30·10 | 17·26 | 30·00 | 17·32 |
| 50 | 37·75 | 21·50 | 37·63 | 21·58 | 37·50 | 21·65 |
| 60 | 45·30 | 25·80 | 45·15 | 25·89 | 45·00 | 25·98 |
| 70 | 52·85 | 30·10 | 52·68 | 30·21 | 52·50 | 30·31 |
| 80 | 60·40 | 34·41 | 60·20 | 34·52 | 60·00 | 34·64 |
| 90 | 67·95 | 38·71 | 67·73 | 38·84 | 67·50 | 38·97 |
| 100 | 75·50 | 43·007 | 75·25 | 43·155 | 75·00 | 43·301 |